A-Level

Mathematics

for Edexcel
Decision Maths 1

CGP
~ books
like no others!

CGP

The Complete Course for Edexcel D1

Contents

Chapter 4

Critical Path Analysis

Chapter 5

Linear Programming

Chapter 6

Matchings

Reference

About this book

In this book you'll find...

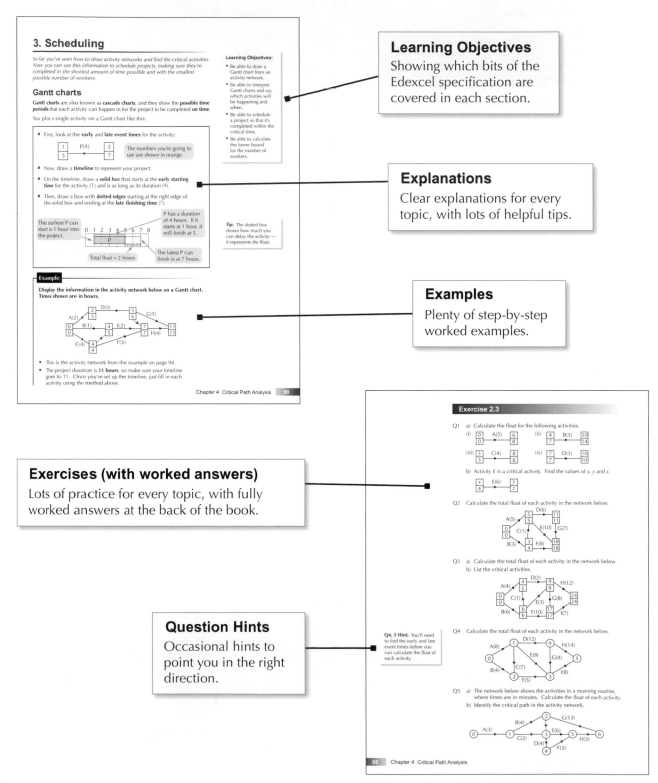

Learning Objectives
Showing which bits of the Edexcel specification are covered in each section.

Explanations
Clear explanations for every topic, with lots of helpful tips.

Examples
Plenty of step-by-step worked examples.

Exercises (with worked answers)
Lots of practice for every topic, with fully worked answers at the back of the book.

Question Hints
Occasional hints to point you in the right direction.

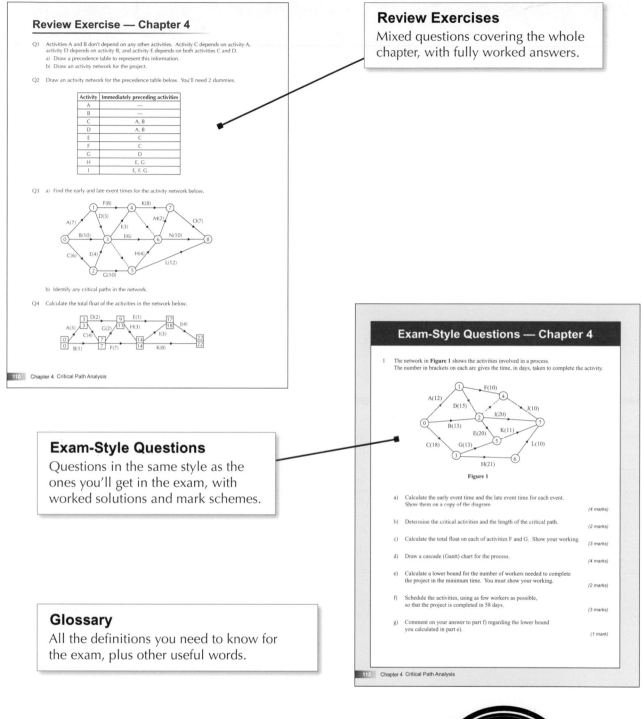

Review Exercise — Chapter 4

Q1 Activities A and B don't depend on any other activities. Activity C depends on activity A, activity D depends on activity B, and activity E depends on both activities C and D.
    a) Draw a precedence table to represent this information.
    b) Draw an activity network for the project.

Q2 Draw an activity network for the precedence table below. You'll need 2 dummies.

Activity	Immediately preceding activities
A	—
B	—
C	A, B
D	A, B
E	C
F	C
G	D
H	E, G
I	E, F, G

Q3 a) Find the early and late event times for the activity network below.

    b) Identify any critical paths in the network.

Q4 Calculate the total float of the activities in the network below.

Review Exercises
Mixed questions covering the whole chapter, with fully worked answers.

Exam-Style Questions — Chapter 4

1 The network in **Figure 1** shows the activities involved in a process.
The number in brackets on each arc gives the time, in days, taken to complete the activity.

Figure 1

    a) Calculate the early event time and the late event time for each event. Show them on a copy of the diagram
      (4 marks)

    b) Determine the critical activities and the length of the critical path.
      (2 marks)

    c) Calculate the total float on each of activities F and G. Show your working.
      (3 marks)

    d) Draw a cascade (Gantt) chart for the process.
      (4 marks)

    e) Calculate a lower bound for the number of workers needed to complete the project in the minimum time. You must show your working.
      (2 marks)

    f) Schedule the activities, using as few workers as possible, so that the project is completed in 58 days.
      (3 marks)

    g) Comment on your answer to part f) regarding the lower bound you calculated in part e).
      (1 mark)

Exam-Style Questions
Questions in the same style as the ones you'll get in the exam, with worked solutions and mark schemes.

Glossary
All the definitions you need to know for the exam, plus other useful words.

Practice Exam Papers (on CD-ROM)
Two printable exam papers, with fully worked answers and mark schemes.

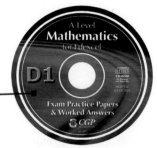

Published by CGP

Editors:
Paul Jordin, Sharon Keeley-Holden, Simon Little, Matteo Orsini Jones, Caley Simpson.

Contributors:
Peter Clegg, Claire Creasor, Paul Freeman, Dave Harding, Charlotte O'Brien, Andy Pierson, Rosemary Rogers.

ISBN: 978 1 84762 806 0

With thanks to Alastair Duncombe for the proofreading.
With thanks to Paul Garrett for the reviewing.

Groovy website: www.cgpbooks.co.uk

Printed by Elanders Ltd, Newcastle upon Tyne.
Jolly bits of clipart from CorelDRAW®

1. Algorithms

Algorithms are sets of instructions that turn inputs into outputs, or end results. There are loads of different types of algorithms and they can be presented in a number of different ways — in words, graphically, mathematically, and so on.

Algorithms in words

An **algorithm** is just a fancy mathematical name for a **set of instructions** for solving a problem. You come across lots of algorithms in everyday life — **recipes**, **directions** and **assembly instructions** are all examples of algorithms.

- Algorithms start with an **input** (e.g. in a recipe, the inputs are the raw ingredients). You carry out the algorithm on the input, following the instructions **in order**.

- Algorithms have an **end result** — something that you **achieve** by carrying out the algorithm (e.g. a cake).

- This means that algorithms will **stop** when you've reached a **solution**, or produced your **finished product**. They'll often have a **stopping condition** — an **instruction** that tells you to stop when you've reached a certain point.

- Algorithms are often written so that **computers** could follow the instructions. **Computer programming** is an important use of decision maths.

Example

Here's an example of an algorithm for making a soft-boiled egg:

- Fill a small pan with enough water to cover your egg by roughly 1 cm.

- Place the pan over heat and bring it to the boil.

- Adjust the heat so that the water is simmering at a steady rate.

- Gently lower the egg into the pan and leave it to simmer with the lid off for 1 minute.

- Remove the pan from the heat and cover it with a lid.

- Leave the pan for 6 minutes.

- Remove the now soft-boiled egg, and enjoy.

Tip: Here the inputs are water, egg, (fuel for the stove).

Tip: The end result is a soft-boiled egg.

Algorithms can be used to solve **mathematical problems** too, where the **end result** is the **solution** to the problem.

- The **input** in a mathematical algorithm is the **number** (or numbers) you start with. Your **end result** is the **final number** you end up with — this'll be the **solution** to the original problem.

- It's a good idea to **write down** the numbers each instruction produces in a **table** — sometimes the algorithm will **tell you** when to do this. This table is called a **trace table**.

Examples

An algorithm for finding out whether a number divides by 3 goes like this:

---

1 Input starting number a.

2 Add together all of the digits of a to form number b. Output b.

3 If b has 1 digit, go to step **4**. Otherwise, let $a = b$ and go back to step **2**.

4 If b is 3, 6, or 9, your starting number a is divisible by 3. If b is any other number, then a is not divisible by 3.

---

a) Use the algorithm to find if 976 836 is divisible by 3.

- Set up a trace table to record the steps of your algorithm, then just go through the algorithm and follow the instructions.

Input a	Working out	Output b
976 836	$9 + 7 + 6 + 8 + 3 + 6$	39
39	$3 + 9$	12
12	$1 + 2$	3

- The 1-digit number you end up with is 3, so 976 836 is divisible by 3.

b) Use the algorithm to find if 3 924 326 is divisible by 3.

- Just go through the steps of the algorithm exactly the same way as before.

Input a	Working out	Output b
3 924 326	$3 + 9 + 2 + 4 + 3 + 2 + 6$	29
29	$2 + 9$	11
11	$1 + 1$	2

- This time you end up with a 1-digit number that's not 3, 6 or 9, so 3 924 326 is not divisible by 3.

The Russian Peasant Algorithm

The Russian Peasant Algorithm is a well-known algorithm that **multiplies** two numbers together.

1 Write down the two numbers that you're multiplying in a table. Call them x and y.

2 Divide x by 2 and write down the result underneath x, ignoring any halves. For example if $x = 11$, when you divide it by 2 you write down 5, not 5.5.

3 Multiply y by 2 and write down the result underneath y.

4 Repeat steps **2** - **3** for the numbers in the new row. Keep going until the number in the x-column is 1.

5 Work down your table and cross out every row that has an even value for x.

6 Add up the remaining numbers in the y-column (i.e. the ones that haven't been crossed out). This is the solution $x \times y$.

Tip: Step 5 includes the very first row — so if you started with an even number, cross out the top row.

Examples

a) Use the Russian Peasant Algorithm to multiply 37 and 43.

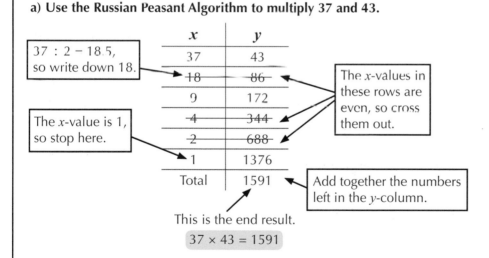

$37 : 2 = 18.5$, so write down 18.

The x-value is 1, so stop here.

x	y
37	43
~~18~~	~~86~~
9	172
~~4~~	~~344~~
~~2~~	~~688~~
1	1376
Total	1591

The x-values in these rows are even, so cross them out.

Add together the numbers left in the y-column.

This is the end result.

$37 \times 43 = 1591$

b) Use the Russian Peasant Algorithm to multiply 21 and 52.

x	y
21	52
~~10~~	~~104~~
5	208
~~2~~	~~416~~
1	832
Total	1092

Just set up the trace table as before and go through the steps of the algorithm.

This is the end result.

$21 \times 52 = 1092$

Q1 Identify the input and output for the following algorithms:
   a) Growing radishes   b) Knitting a scarf
   c) Making a cake   d) Preparing a company's accounts

Q2 Here's an algorithm that lets you convert from °C to °F:
   Step 1: Input temperature in °C.
   Step 2: Multiply by 9.
   Step 3: Divide by 5.
   Step 4: Add 32.
   Output: Temperature in °F.

   Use this algorithm to convert these temperatures from °C to °F.
   a) 0 °C   b) 20 °C   c) 100 °C   d) −35 °C

Q3 Here's an algorithm for working out an electricity bill:
   Step 1: Input units used
   Step 2: Input price per unit
   Step 3: Input standing charge
   Step 4: Multiply units used by price per unit
   Step 5: Add standing charge
   Step 6: Multiply by 1.2
   Output: Electricity bill

   Use this algorithm to work out the electricity bill when:
   a) Units used = 300, price per unit = £0.12, standing charge = £15.
   b) Units used = 460, price per unit = £0.09, standing charge = £42.
   c) Units used = 320, price per unit = £0.23, standing charge = £22.

Q4 Work through the following algorithm for parts a) to d).
   Step 1: Input n
   Step 2: Input $a = 1$
   Step 3: Calculate $b = a \times n$
   Step 4: Output b
   Step 5: If $b \geq 1000$, stop
   Step 6: Otherwise, let $a = b$ and go back to step 3
   a) $n = 5$ b) $n = 10$ c) $n = 3$ d) $n = 8$
   e) What is the algorithm in this question doing?

Q4 Hint: A good trace table to use for this question would record the variables a and b each time you go through the algorithm.

Q5 Use the algorithm on page 2 to find if these numbers will divide by 3:
   a) 18   b) 239   c) 928 741   d) 298 218 744

Q6 Use the Russian Peasant Algorithm (page 3) to find the solution to:
   a) 29 × 41   b) 102 × 87   c) 57 × 67

Flow charts

Instead of giving instructions in **words** (like in the Russian Peasant example on page 3), some algorithms are written as **flow charts**. In these cases the algorithms are carried out by working through the flow chart from start to finish.

There are three different types of boxes used in flow charts:

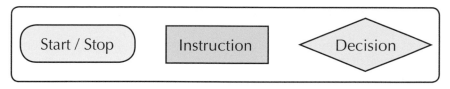

The boxes are connected with **arrows** to guide you through the flow chart. 'Decision' boxes will ask a question, and for each one you have a **choice** of arrows — one arrow for '**yes**' and one for '**no**', which will take you to another box.

Sometimes flow charts will include a loop which takes you back to an earlier stage in the chart. Loops are a way of **repeating steps** until the algorithm is **finished**.

Example

Here's the Russian Peasant Algorithm shown as a flow chart.

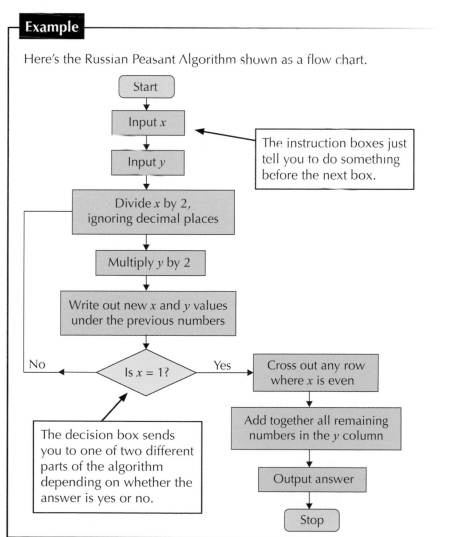

Tip: As you can see, the flow chart says the same thing as the wordy algorithm, but shows it in a way that's easier to follow. You just work your way through following the arrows and doing what each box tells you to.

It can sometimes be a bit tricky keeping track of the **results** of a flow chart, especially if you have to go round a **loop** lots of times. It's a good idea to put your results into a **trace table** — it's much easier to see the **solutions** that way.

To set up your trace table, look at the flow chart and think about what you would need to keep track of with every stage of the algorithm.

Tip: You can use a column for the inputs that don't change too, so you don't have to keep referring back to the question.

- Any input that **changes** with each loop will need its own column.

- If there are any **outputs** before the end of a loop, there should be a column to keep track of those.

- If a **decision box** affects where you go with the next loop (for example, if a 'yes' causes you to stop), then it's a good idea to give that a column too.

Tip: Some flow charts won't actually tell you what the algorithm does — you'll have to work it out yourself by looking for a pattern in the results. This is another reason trace tables can be useful when carrying out algorithms.

Examples

The flow chart shows an algorithm for finding the factors of a number a. Use it to find all of the factors of 10.

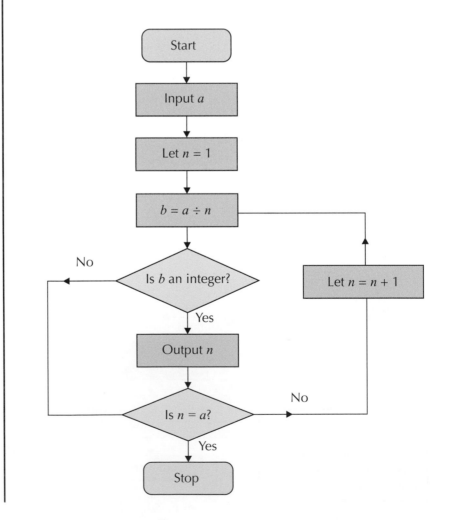

- Start by setting up a trace table for the flow chart. To do this, look down the chart and think about what you need to keep track of.

- Here the input a is constant, so leave that.

- n and b, on the other hand, change with each pass, so give those a column.

- Every time you calculate b, there's a chance of outputting n before the end, so make a column for the output.

- Finally, you'll need a column to check if you can stop (when $n = a$).

- Once your trace table is set up, just make your way through the flow chart and fill in each row with the correct numbers until you reach the stop box.

$a = 10$

n	b	Output	$n = a$?
1	10	1	No
2	5	2	No
3	$3\frac{1}{3}$		No
4	$2\frac{1}{2}$		No
5	2	5	No
6	$1\frac{2}{3}$		No
7	$1\frac{3}{7}$		No
8	$1\frac{1}{4}$		No
9	$1\frac{1}{9}$		No
10	1	10	Yes

Tip: You've reached the stopping condition, so you can stop there and output the answer(s).

- All the factors of 10 will then be shown in the output column, so the factors of 10 are 1, 2, 5 and 10.

Use the flow chart to find all of the factors of 7.

- Just set up your trace table as before and work your way through the flow chart, starting with $a = 7$.

$a = 7$

n	b	Output	$n = a$?
1	7	1	No
2	$3\frac{1}{2}$		No
3	$2\frac{1}{3}$		No
4	$1\frac{3}{4}$		No
5	$1\frac{2}{5}$		No
6	$1\frac{1}{6}$		No
7	1	7	Yes

- So the factors of 7 are 1 and 7.

Q1 a) Follow the flow chart below with the following inputs:
     (i) $a = 10$, $b = -3$
     (ii) $a = 30$, $b = -7$

    b) What does the algorithm do?

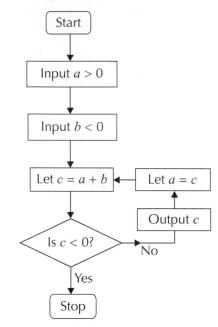

Q2 a) Follow the flow chart below with the following inputs:
     (i) $n = 6$
     (ii) $n = 13$

    b) What does the algorithm do?

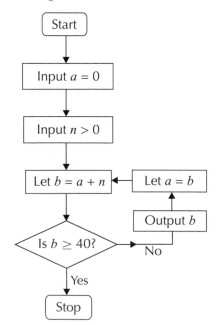

Q3 A charity provides funding for amateur theatre productions. The flow chart below shows an algorithm to calculate the maximum grant a group can apply for, where C is the capacity of the venue being used and P is the number of performances that will take place.

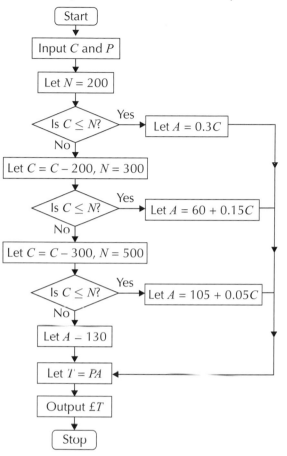

a) Complete the trace table when the flow chart is applied with $C = 800$, $P = 7$.

C	P	N	$C \leq N?$	A	T
800	7	200	no		

What is the maximum grant available in this case?

b) A group is preparing a show and will use funding from the charity to help hire the venue. They have two options: Venue A has a capacity of 350 seats and is available for 6 nights. Venue B holds 600 people but is only available for 4 nights. Calculate the maximum grant available for each venue.

Q4 Show the algorithm for finding whether a number is divisible by 3 on page 2 in the form of a flow chart.

Q4 Tip: You probably won't be asked to produce a flow chart in an exam, but it might help you to understand them better if you think about how they're made.

2. Sorting Algorithms

Learning Objectives:

- Be able to use a bubble sort to sort a list into ascending or descending order.
- Be able to calculate the maximum number of passes and comparisons required in a bubble sort.
- Be able to find the pivots to use in a quick sort.
- Be able to use a quick sort to sort a list into ascending or descending order.

Sorting things into numerical or alphabetical order might seem a bit easy for A-level maths, but you need to be able to do it using algorithms. Sorting this way is useful in computer programming.

Bubble sort

The bubble sort is an **algorithm** that **sorts** numbers or letters into order. It's pretty easy to do, but can get a bit fiddly, so take care when using it.

It's called the bubble sort because the **highest** numbers **rise** to the end of the list like bubbles. It works like this:

- Look at the **first two numbers** in your list. If they're in the right order, you don't have to do anything with them. If they're the wrong way round, **swap** them.

- Move on to the **next** pair of numbers (the first will be one of the two you've just compared) and **repeat step 1**. Keep going through the list until you've compared the **last two numbers**. This set of comparisons is called a **pass**.

- When you've finished the first pass, go back to the beginning of the list and **start again**. You won't have to compare the **last pair** of numbers, as the last number is now **in place**. Each pass has **one fewer comparison** than the one before it. When there are **no swaps** in a pass, the list is **in order**.

Tip: You might find it helpful to make note of which numbers you swap each time.

Example 1

Use bubble sort to write the list 14, 10, 6, 15, 9, 21, 17 in ascending order.

First pass:

<u>14, 10,</u> 6, 15, 9, 21, 17	14 and 10 compared and swapped
10, <u>14, 6,</u> 15, 9, 21, 17	14 and 6 compared and swapped
10, 6, <u>14, 15,</u> 9, 21, 17	14 and 15 compared, no swap
10, 6, 14, <u>15, 9,</u> 21, 17	15 and 9 compared and swapped
10, 6, 14, 9, <u>15, 21,</u> 17	15 and 21 compared, no swap
10, 6, 14, 9, 15, <u>21, 17</u>	21 and 17 compared and swapped
10, 6, 14, 9, 15, 17, 21	End of first pass

Tip: 14 and 15 are already in ascending order, so leave them as they are.

Tip: After the first pass you know 21 is in the right place now, so you can 'lock' it in place — you don't need to compare it in future passes.

At the end of the second pass the list is: 6, 10, 9, 14, 15, 17 21.

At the end of the third pass the list is: 6, 9, 10, 14, 15 17 21.

On the fourth pass there are **no swaps**, so the numbers are in **ascending order**.

You can also use the algorithm to put the numbers in **descending** order — on each comparison, just put the **highest** number **first** instead.

Example 2

Use bubble sort to write the list 14, 10, 6, 15, 9, 21, 17 in descending order.

First pass:

<u>14, 10</u>, 6, 15, 9, 21, 17	14 and 10 compared, no swap
14, <u>10, 6</u>, 15, 9, 21, 17	10 and 6 compared, no swap
14, 10, <u>6, 15</u>, 9, 21, 17	6 and 15 compared and swapped
14, 10, 15, <u>6, 9</u>, 21, 17	6 and 9 compared and swapped
14, 10, 15, 9, <u>6, 21</u>, 17	6 and 21 compared and swapped
14, 10, 15, 9, 21, <u>6, 17</u>	6 and 17 compared and swapped
14, 10, 15, 9, 21, 17, 6	End of first pass

At the end of the second pass the list is: 14, 15, 10, 21, 17, 9, 6.

At the end of the third pass the list is: 15, 14, 21, 17, 10, 9, 6.

At the end of the fourth pass the list is: 15, 21, 17, 14, 10, 9, 6.

At the end of the fifth pass the list is: 21, 17, 15, 14, 10, 9, 6.

On the sixth pass there are **no swaps**, so the numbers are in **descending order**.

Tip: Even though it's the same list as the previous example, it takes 2 more passes to organise in descending order.

Some lists need **more comparisons** to put them in order. If your list is in **reverse** order to start with, you're going to need to make the **maximum** number of **passes** and **comparisons** to put it in order.

- If there are n numbers in the list, the **maximum** number of **passes** you might have to make is n, including the **final pass** where **no swaps** are made. On each pass, you'd only get **one** number in the right place, up to the $(n - 1)^{th}$ **pass**, which swaps the **last two** numbers into the right places.

- On the **first** pass, you have to make $n - 1$ comparisons, with a **maximum** of $n - 1$ swaps. On the **second** pass, you have to make $n - 2$ comparisons, as one number is in place from the first pass. On the **third** pass, there'll be $n - 3$ comparisons, etc.

So for a bubble sort with **7 numbers**, the maximum number of comparisons (or swaps) is $6 + 5 + 4 + 3 + 2 + 1 = 21$.

Or for a bubble sort with **50 numbers**, the maximum number of comparisons (or swaps) is $\frac{1}{2} \times 49 \times 50 = 1225$.

Tip: For big lists, use the formula $S_k = \frac{1}{2}k(k + 1)$ for the sum of the first k whole numbers. Careful though — if $n = 50$, you want to put $k = 49$ into the formula.

Q1 a) Use a bubble sort to sort these numbers into ascending order:
5, 2, 7, 6, 3, 5.

   b) How many passes were needed?

Q2 a) Use a bubble sort to sort these numbers into descending order:
3, 11, 5, 0, 7, 6, 4.

   b) How many passes were needed?

Q3 a) Use a bubble sort to sort these letters into alphabetical order:
Z, W, T, S, M, L, K.

   b) What do you notice about the number of passes needed?

Q4 Use a bubble sort to sort these letters into reverse alphabetical order:
A, F, B, J, M, B, C.

Q5 Hint: The formulas for working these out are on page 11.

Q5 A list of 5 numbers is sorted using a bubble sort.

   a) What is the maximum number of passes you would need to make?

   b) What is the maximum number of comparisons you would need to make?

Q6 A list of 8 numbers is sorted using a bubble sort.

   a) What is the maximum number of passes you would need to make?

   b) What is the maximum number of swaps you would need to make?

Q7 Use a bubble sort to sort these numbers into ascending order:
6, 7, 9, 4, 5, 6, 2.

Q8 Use a bubble sort to sort these numbers into descending order:
59, 39, 89, 79, 69, 29, 39.

Q9 Use a bubble sort to sort these letters into alphabetical order:
E, L, E, P, H, A, N, T.

Q10 a) Use a bubble sort to sort these numbers into ascending order:
1, 5, 2, 3, 11, 10, 9, 3, 4, 7

   b) Use this key to form two words from the list in part a)
once the numbers are in order:

Number	1	5	2	3	11	10	9	4	7
Letter	B	E	U	B	T	R	O	L	S

Quick sort

The **quick sort algorithm** works by choosing a **pivot** (see below) which **breaks down** the list into two **smaller lists**, which are then broken down in **the same way** until the numbers are in order. To use it, follow these steps:

- Choose a **pivot**. Move any numbers that are **less** than the pivot to a new list on the **left** of it and the numbers that are **greater** to a new list on the **right**. Don't change the **order** of the numbers though.

- **Repeat the first step** for each of the smaller lists you've just made. You'll need to choose **new pivots** for the new lists.

- When **every number** has been chosen as a pivot, you can **stop**, as the list is in order.

Tip: Sometimes the smaller lists either side of the pivot will only have one number in them — you don't need to do anything with these as they're already in order.

Although the pivot can, in theory, be any item in the list, it's usually best to use the '**middle**' item (and that's what you'll be expected to do in the exam). In a list of n items:

- If n is **odd**, the middle item is the $\frac{1}{2}(n + 1)$**th** item. For $n = 7$, the pivot is the $\frac{1}{2}(7 + 1) = 4$th item in the list.

- If n is **even**, the middle item is the $\frac{1}{2}(n + 2)$**th** item. For $n = 8$, the pivot is the $\frac{1}{2}(8 + 2) = 5$th item in the list.

The 'middle' item is only in the **middle** if n is **odd**. For **even** n, the 'middle' item is the one to the **right** of the middle.

Examples

Find the pivot for the list 7, 12, 9, 16, 24.

- There's an odd number of items in the list (5) which means the pivot is the $\frac{1}{2}(n + 1)$th item.

- $\frac{1}{2}(5 + 1) = 3$, so the pivot is the 3rd item, which is 9.

Find the pivot for the list 4, 23, 5, 28, 17, 32.

- This time there's an even number of items in the list (6), so the pivot is the $\frac{1}{2}(n + 2)$th item.

- $\frac{1}{2}(6 + 2) = 4$, so the pivot is the 4th item, which is 28.

It's a good idea to **circle** or **underline** the pivots you're using at each step of the quick sort — it helps you keep track of where you're up to.

In the next example, the numbers are written in orange when they're in the correct place.

Example

Sort the numbers 54, 36, 29, 56, 45, 39, 32, 27 into ascending order using a quick sort.

- There are 8 items in the list, which means the pivot is the $\frac{1}{2}(8 + 2) = 5$th item in the list. So the pivot is **45**.

- Now go through the numbers **one by one** and place each number that's **lower** than 45 to the **left** of the pivot. After that, add all the numbers **higher** than 45 to the **right** of the pivot:

$$36 \quad 29 \quad 39 \quad 32 \quad 27 \qquad \underline{45} \qquad 54 \quad 56$$
$$\underbrace{\qquad\qquad\qquad\qquad}_{l_1} \qquad\qquad \underbrace{\qquad}_{l_2}$$

- The list has been divided into **smaller lists**, l_1 and l_2. There are **5 items** in l_1, so the **pivot** is the **3rd item** (39). There are only **2 items** in l_2, so the **pivot** is the **2nd item** (56). Rearranging around the new pivots gives:

$$36 \quad 29 \quad \underline{39} \quad 32 \quad 27 \quad 45 \quad 54 \quad \underline{56}$$
$$36 \quad 29 \quad 32 \quad 27 \quad \underline{39} \quad 45 \quad 54 \quad \underline{56}$$
$$\underbrace{\qquad\qquad\qquad}_{l_3} \qquad\qquad\qquad \underbrace{\qquad}_{l_4}$$

- The list l_4 only has **1 item** in it, so 54 is in the **correct place** (it's a pivot in a list of its own). There are now **4 items** in l_3, so the pivot is the **3rd item** (32). Rearranging again using the new pivot gives:

$$29 \quad 27 \quad \underline{32} \quad 36 \quad 39 \quad 45 \quad 54 \quad 56$$
$$\underbrace{\qquad}_{l_5} \qquad\quad \underbrace{\quad}_{l_6}$$

- The list l_6 only has **1 item** in it now, so 36 is in the **correct place**. There are **2 items** in l_5, so the pivot is the **2nd item** (27). Rearranging the list around the new pivot gives:

$$\underline{27} \quad 29 \quad 32 \quad 36 \quad 39 \quad 45 \quad 54 \quad 56$$
$$\underbrace{\quad}_{l_7}$$

- As there's only **one item** left in the final list (l_7), the list is now in the **right order**:

$$27, 29, 32, 36, 39, 45, 54, 56$$

Tip: Don't reorder the numbers, just write them down in the order they appear in the original list on the correct side of the pivot.

Tip: Once an item has been used as a pivot, it's now in the correct place (so becomes orange in this example).

Exercise 2.2

Q1 Show how you would find the pivot for a list of:
   a) 10 items   b) 43 items   c) 52 items   d) 101 items

Q2 a) Use a quick sort to sort these numbers into ascending order:
   7, 8, 3, 4, 6, 2, 9
   b) List the pivots you used.

Q3 a) Use a quick sort to sort these letters into alphabetical order:
   M, N, A, F, G, H, Q
   b) List the pivots you used.

Q4 The marks achieved in an exam were: 101, 96, 103, 94, 107, 98
   a) Use a quick sort to sort the marks into descending order.
   b) List the pivots you used.

Q4 Hint: Make sure you read each question properly before starting — this one asks for the numbers in **descending** order.

Q5 The weights of some apples, in ounces, were:
   4.4, 3.9. 3.3, 3.7, 4.1, 3.2, 4.2, 3.8
   a) Use a quick sort to sort the weights into ascending order.
   b) List the pivots you used.

Q6 Use a quick sort to sort these letters into reverse alphabetical order, listing the pivots you used: S, O, R, T, I, N, G

Q7 Times for a race are recorded as:
   13.1s, 11.0s, 11.3s, 12.3s, 11.7s, 12.9s, 12.8s
   a) Explain how you would find the first pivot.
   b) Use a quick sort to list the times in ascending order.
   c) List the pivots you used.

Q8 Some husky dogs were weighed and their weights in kg were found to be:
   14.4, 7.6, 18.0, 10.6, 15.4, 23.0
   a) Show how you would find the first pivot.
   b) Use a quick sort to list the weights in descending order.
   c) List the pivots you used.

Q9 The names of students in a class are recorded as:
   Ben, Jane, Mary, Pete, Rob, Ian, Freda, Lorna, Kim, Babatunde
   a) Show how you would find the first pivot.
   b) Use a quick sort to list the names in alphabetical order.
   c) List the pivots you used.

3. Searching Algorithms

Learning Objectives:

- Be able to use the binary search algorithm to locate an item in an ordered list.

- Be able to show that an item isn't present in an ordered list using the binary search algorithm.

In the previous section, you saw how algorithms can be used to put things in order. This will come in handy here, as you're going to use an algorithm (the binary search algorithm) to search for an item in an ordered list.

Binary search

A binary search finds the position of an item in an **ordered list**.

- The binary search algorithm works by **dividing** the list in **half** over and over again until it finds the item. At each stage, you can **get rid of** half the list to narrow the search.

- If the item you're looking for **isn't** in the list, you can use the binary search method to **show** that it isn't there.

- The list has to be **in order** (e.g. a list of names in **alphabetical order**) for the algorithm to work. You can **number** the items to show their **position** in the list.

- You need to be able to find the **'middle' item** in a list — use the same method as you did for finding the **pivot** for the quick sort (page 13).

The binary search algorithm works like this:

---

1. Find the middle item of the list. If the middle item is the item you're looking for, then you can **stop** — you've found it.

2. If not, **compare** the item you're looking for to the middle item.
   If it comes **before** the middle item in the list, you can **throw away** the **second half** of the list (**including** the middle item).
   If the item you're looking for comes **after** the middle item, you can **throw away** the **first half** of the list (**including** the middle item).

3. You'll be left with a list that's **half** (or just under half) the size of the original list. **Repeat steps 1 and 2** on this smaller list to get an even smaller one, and keep going until you find the item you're looking for.

Tip: If the list has shrunk to one item and it's not the item you're looking for, then your item isn't in the list.

Tip: If you're left with a list that doesn't start with item 1, you might find it easier to find the middle item by using the formula $\frac{1}{2}(a + l)$ and rounding up where necessary, where a is the position of the first item and l is the position of the last item.

Example

Use the binary search algorithm to locate the name Jackman in the following list:

| 1. Armitage |
| 2. Cooke |
| 3. Garcia |
| 4. Horner |
| 5. Jackman |
| 6. Marsden |
| 7. Wales |

- The middle item is the $\frac{1}{2}(7 + 1) = $ 4th item = Horner.

- Jackman ≠ Horner, and Jackman comes after Horner, so throw away the first half of the list (including Horner). This leaves a list that looks like this:

| 5. Jackman |
| 6. Marsden |
| 7. Wales |

- The middle item is the ½(3 + 1) = 2nd item. As this list starts with 5, the middle item is the 6th item = Marsden.

- Jackman ≠ Marsden, and Jackman comes before Marsden, so throw away the second half of the list (including Marsden). This leaves a list that looks like this:

5. Jackman

- There is now only one name left, and it's the name you're looking for, so the search is complete. Jackman is the 5th name in the list.

Tip: If you were looking for a name that wasn't in the list (e.g. Lewis), you'd follow the same steps, but when you were left with just Jackman, it would show that Lewis wasn't in the list.

Exercise 3.1

Q1 1. Boots   2. Coat   3. Gloves   4. Hat   5. Mittens   6. Scarf   7. Socks
Use the binary search algorithm to find:
a) Scarf   b) Gloves   c) Jacket

Q1-7 Hint: Remember, if you get to a list of one item and it's not the one you're looking for, you've shown the item is **not** in the list.

Q2 1. Biscuits   2. Coffee   3. Gateau   4. Lemonade   5. Sandwiches   6. Tea
Use the binary search algorithm to find:
a) Tea   b) Coffee   c) Orange juice

Q3 Black   Blue   Brown   Green   Grey   Orange   Red   Yellow
Use the binary search algorithm to find:
a) Red   b) Pink   c) Brown

Q4 Apple   Banana   Kiwi   Mango   Orange   Peach   Pineapple
Use the binary search algorithm to find:
a) Mango   b) Pineapple   c) Lemon   d) Kiwi

Q5 a) Use a quick sort to sort these tree species into alphabetical order:
       Beech   Cherry   Oak   Larch   Ash   Maple
    b) Use the binary search algorithm on the new list to find:
       (i) Maple   (ii) Cherry   (iii) Spruce

Q6 a) Use a bubble sort to sort these dates into chronological order:
       1066   1939   1918   1805   1642   1864
    b) Use the binary search algorithm on the new list to find:
       (i) 1918   (ii) 1864   (iii) 1815

Q7 5p   2p   1p   £2   20p   50p   £1   10p
Use the binary search algorithm to find:
a) 10p   b) £2   c) 2p

Q7 Hint: Remember, you need an ordered list to use the binary search.

4. Bin Packing

Learning Objectives:

- Be able to calculate the lower bound of a bin packing problem and say whether a solution is optimal.
- Be able to use the first-fit, first-fit decreasing and full bin packing algorithms to find solutions to bin packing problems.
- Understand the advantages and disadvantages of all the different bin packing methods.

You'll often need to do something using the least possible space, time or money, like packing suitcases or sending parcels. Bin packing lets you find solutions to these problems mathematically using 'bin packing algorithms'.

Optimal solutions

In **bin packing problems**, you have a set of items that you need to fit into the **minimum** number of **bins**.

- One of the most common examples is fitting **boxes** of **different heights** on top of each other into **bins** of a **given height**. You need to arrange the boxes to use the **fewest bins possible**.

- Other examples include things like cutting specified **lengths of wood** from **planks** of a fixed length (you want to **minimise** the number of planks used), or loading items of different **weights** into **lorries** that have a **maximum weight capacity** (again, you want to use the **smallest** number of lorries possible).

> An **optimal solution** is one that uses the **least possible number of bins**. There's often **more than one** possible optimal solution.

Example

The diagram shows boxes of the same length and width, but varying heights (shown on each box). The boxes must be packed into bins of height 4 and the same width and length as the boxes. If the boxes must fill as few bins as possible, find an optimal solution.

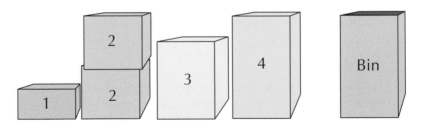

- You can see without having to use an algorithm that placing the box of height 1 on top of the box of height 3 would give 3 stacks of height 4.

- As the bins also have a height of 4, this would result in 3 full bins — as there is no space left over in any bins, **this must be an optimal solution.**

- So an optimal solution to this problem is to fill 3 bins using boxes of heights (1 and 3), (2 and 2) and (4).

Tip: If there's no space left over that means it's an optimal solution, but not all optimal solutions fill all available space — they just waste the least amount of space possible.

The **lower bound** gives a **minimum** for the **number of bins** you'll need. To work out the **lower bound**, you **add up** the height / weights etc. of the items, and **divide** the total by the **capacity** of the bins.

For the previous example, you'd add up the **heights** of all the boxes and divide by the **height** of the **bins** (the bins are all the same height).

- Always **round up** your answer — if you get a lower bound of 2.25, you'd need a **minimum** of **3 bins** (you couldn't fit the items in 2 bins).

- Just because you've worked out a lower bound, it doesn't mean you can definitely fit the items into this number of bins — you'll need **at least** this many, but possibly **more**.

- So if your solution doesn't match the lower bound, it **doesn't** necessarily mean it's **not optimal**. It might just be that the items can't be fitted into the lower bound of bins.

- But if your solution **does match** the lower bound, you know it's definitely **optimal**.

Tip: The lower bound in the previous example is $(1 + 2 + 2 + 3 + 4) \div 4 = 3$, which is the number of bins used, so the solution is optimal.

Example

Five boxes of heights 20 cm, 43 cm, 35 cm, 29 cm and 38 cm are to be packed into bins of height 60 cm. Calculate a lower bound for the number of bins.

$20 + 43 + 35 + 29 + 38 = 165$ cm

$165 \div 60 = 2.75$, so the lower bound is 3 bins.

Tip: You can't actually fit these items into 3 bins, so the optimal solution will need more bins than the lower bound.

Exercise 4.1

Q1 Sawn timber is required in lengths of 2.5 m, 3 m, 1.3 m, 3.8 m, 2.1 m, 2.2 m, 0.6 m and 1.8 m. If the timber comes in planks of length 4 m, calculate a lower bound for the number of planks needed.

Q2 Bins have a capacity of 200 litres. Calculate the lower bound for the number of bins needed if somebody needs to get rid of 6 bags containing 140 l, 190 l, 65 l, 120 l, 35 l and 70 l.

Q3 Kari wants to post some presents to her grandparents, but she can only send parcels with a maximum weight of 1200 g. The items she wants to send weigh 1000 g, 900 g, 650 g, 400 g, 250 g, 100 g and 150 g, and she packs them into 4 parcels. Is this an optimal solution?

Q3 Hint: If the solution doesn't match the lower bound, try rearranging the items and see if you can fit them into a smaller number of parcels.

Q4 Electrical wiring comes in lengths of 1 m. John wants to cut 13 pieces of wire of length 16 cm and 10 pieces of wire of length 6.5 cm. He orders 4 lengths of wire to do this. Is this an optimal solution?

Q5 Packing cases 2.8 m, 3.6 m, 5.4 m, 7.6 m, 1.8 m and 2.4 m long are to be packed into containers 9 m long. Jordan packs the cases into 3 containers. Is this solution optimal?

First-fit algorithm

The **first-fit algorithm** puts items into the **first box** they'll go in. It's quick and easy, and doesn't really involve any calculations. It works like this:

1) Take the **first item** in the list and put it in the **first bin**.

2) Move on to the next item, and put it in the **first bin** it'll **fit** into. It might fit in the first bin, or you might have to move on to **another bin**.

3) Repeat **step 2)** until **all** the items are in a bin. For each item, try the **first bin** before you move on to the next.

Example

The ad breaks in a TV programme can be no longer than 150 seconds. Use the first-fit algorithm to sort the adverts into breaks, saying how many breaks are needed and how much time is wasted.

A: 90 s   B: 75 s   C: 30 s   D: 65 s   E: 120 s   F: 45 s   G: 60 s

- Just go through each advert **one by one** and place them into the **first available** advert break that will take them, then work out the amount of **time still available** in that break. Placing the first one looks like this:

Ad break	Adverts (s)	Time left (s)
1	A (90)	60

- The second advert (B) won't fit into ad break 1, so add another row:

Ad break	Adverts (s)	Time left (s)
1	A (90)	60
2	B (75)	75

- The third advert (C) will fit into the first ad break, so put it in the first row and change the amount of time left in ad break 1:

Ad break	Adverts (s)	Time left (s)
1	A (90), C (30)	~~60~~ 30
2	B (75)	75

- Now do the same for the rest of the adverts.

Ad break	Adverts (s)	Time left (s)
1	A (90), C (30)	~~60~~ 30
2	B (75), D (65)	~~75~~ 10
3	E (120)	30
4	F (45), G (60)	~~105~~ 45

Tip: You probably won't know how many rows you'll need, so just add a new row whenever you need one.

- To find the time wasted, just add up the numbers in the third column: $30 + 10 + 30 + 45 = 115\,s$.

- So 4 advert breaks are needed, and 115 seconds are wasted.

The first-fit algorithm doesn't involve any **thinking** about which items should go into which bin — the solution depends on the **order** of the items in the list. Because of this, there's often **wasted space** and the solution often **isn't optimal**.

Example

Kate takes the train from Edinburgh to Coventry. She wants to watch 5 short films during the journey, but her video player batteries only last 100 minutes at a time. The film times, in minutes, are:

A: 50   B: 60   C: 60   D: 40   E: 50

Using the first-fit algorithm, find how many batteries she needs if she doesn't want them to run out during a film. Is this an optimal solution?

- As before, set up a trace table and work through the films:

Battery	Film	Time left on battery (mins)
1	A (50), D (40)	~~50~~ 10
2	B (60)	40
3	C (60)	40
4	E (50)	50

- So she'd use 4 batteries.

- To find if this is an optimal solution, calculate the **lower bound**:

    50 + 60 + 60 + 40 + 50 = 260
    260 ÷ 100 = 2.6, so the lower bound is 3

- This is smaller than the solution found, so you can't say from this if it's an optimal solution. However, you can tell just from looking that putting the two 50 minute films together, and the 60 and 40 minute films together means you only need 3 batteries, which is optimal.

Another way of seeing if the solution is optimal is looking at the **amount of space wasted**.

- If the amount of space (or weight, length etc.) wasted is **less than** the capacity of one bin, the solution is **optimal**.

- If the amount of space wasted is **greater than or equal to** the capacity of one bin, the solution is **not optimal** or you **don't know for sure**. It might just be that there's **no way** of arranging the items so that less space is wasted.

Exercise 4.2

Q1   a) Use the first-fit algorithm to stack blocks of height 60 cm, 35 cm, 48 cm, 15 cm, 75 cm and 40 cm into boxes 1 m high.

     b) How many boxes are needed?

Q2   a) Use the first-fit algorithm to fit crates of weight 90 kg, 45 kg, 60 kg, 58 kg, 35 kg, 10 kg and 25 kg into containers with a 100 kg capacity.

     b) How many containers are needed?

Q3 Sawn timber is supplied in 4.5 m lengths. Lengths of 2.8 m, 3.1 m, 1.2 m, 3.4 m, 2.0 m, 0.6 m and 1.8 m are required.

a) Use the first-fit algorithm to work out how many 4.5 m lengths are needed.

b) How much timber is wasted?

Q4 Bins have a capacity of 250 l. Bags containing 130 l, 185 l, 65 l, 133 l, 30 l, 65 l and 70 l are to be loaded into the bins.

a) Use the first-fit algorithm to work out how many bins are needed.

b) How much space is wasted?

Q5 Packing cases 2.7 m, 3.5 m, 5.6 m, 7.6 m, 1.3 m, 5.9 m and 2.5 m high are to be stacked into containers 9 m high.

a) Use the first-fit algorithm to work out how many containers are needed.

b) How much space is wasted?

Q6 11 cans of fruit are to be packed into bags so that each bag weighs no more than 4.5 kg. The cans weigh 1.7 kg, 0.9 kg, 2.5 kg, 1.1 kg, 0.6 kg, 3.4 kg, 2.3 kg, 1.2 kg, 0.7 kg, 2.4 kg and 1.0 kg.

a) Use the first-fit algorithm to work out how many bags are needed.

b) How much space is wasted?

Q7 Mary is sending parcels through the post. Each parcel must weigh no more than 900 g. The items she has to pack weigh 260 g, 490 g, 620 g, 800 g, 130 g, 85 g, 245 g and 350 g. Mary packs the parcels using the first-fit algorithm.

a) Calculate how many parcels Mary packs.

b) How much space is wasted?

Q7 c) Hint: Your answer to part b) will help you answer this question.

c) Is this an optimal solution? Explain your answer.

Q8 George is loading boxes onto trolleys by stacking items on top of each other. Each trolley is 1.5 m high. The items he has to load have heights 1.1 m, 0.6 m, 0.9 m, 1.4 m, 0.8 m, 0.4 m, 1.0 m and 1.3 m. George loads the boxes using the first-fit algorithm.

a) Calculate how many trolleys George loads.

b) Calculate how much space is wasted.

c) Is this solution optimal? Explain your answer.

First-fit decreasing algorithm

The **first-fit decreasing** algorithm is very **similar** to the **first-fit** algorithm except you need to put the items in **descending order** first.

- You can do this by using one of the **sorting algorithms** on pages 10-14. It doesn't matter which one you use, as long as you get an **ordered list**.

- Once you've got your ordered list, you just carry out the **first-fit algorithm** from page 20.

- The first-fit decreasing algorithm usually gives you a **better solution** than the first-fit algorithm, because it packs the **large items first**, then fits the **small items** in the **gaps**.

Examples

Ribbon comes in rolls of length 5 m. For the lengths of ribbon given below, use the first-fit decreasing algorithm to work out how the lengths can be cut from the rolls. You should also say how many rolls are needed and how much ribbon is wasted. All lengths are in metres.

2.5	1.9	2.9	3.1	2.7	2.2	1.8	2.0

- First, use a sorting algorithm to put the lengths in descending order:

3.1	2.9	2.7	2.5	2.2	2.0	1.9	1.8

- Now use the first-fit algorithm to sort the lengths into rolls:

Roll	Lengths (m)	Length of ribbon left (m)
1	3.1, 1.9	~~1.9~~ 0
2	2.9, 2.0	~~2.1~~ 0.1
3	2.7, 2.2	~~2.3~~ 0.1
4	2.5, 1.8	~~2.5~~ 0.7

- The ribbon can be cut from 4 rolls, with 0 + 0.1 + 0.1 + 0.7 = 0.9 m wasted.

Tip: If you'd used the first-fit algorithm you would have ended up using 5 rolls and wasting 5.9 m.

- The first-fit decreasing algorithm takes **a little longer** than the first-fit algorithm because there's an extra stage of sorting involved.

- However, it's **more likely** to give an **optimal solution**, so it's probably the better choice when time isn't an issue.

- Be careful though — it **doesn't always** give an optimal solution. It might be more reliable than the first-fit algorithm, but it's **not perfect**.

Ronak runs a confectionary business and has received an order for some chocolate bars. He wants to send them in as few parcels as possible, but each parcel can only hold 100 g. Use the first-fit decreasing algorithm to sort these bars into parcels. Find the lower bound for this problem and compare it to your solution.

$$60 \text{ g} \quad 40 \text{ g} \quad 30 \text{ g} \quad 20 \text{ g} \quad 20 \text{ g} \quad 60 \text{ g} \quad 50 \text{ g} \quad 20 \text{ g}$$

- Again, start by sorting the chocolate bars into descending weight order:

$$60 \text{ g} \quad 60 \text{ g} \quad 50 \text{ g} \quad 40 \text{ g} \quad 30 \text{ g} \quad 20 \text{ g} \quad 20 \text{ g} \quad 20 \text{ g}$$

- Then carry out the first-fit algorithm:

Parcel	Chocolate bars (g)	weight left (g)
1	60, 40	40̶ 0
2	60, 30	40̶ 10
3	50, 20, 20	50̶ 30̶ 10
4	20	80

- So Ronak would need 4 parcels.

- To see if this solution is optimal, calculate the lower bound:

$$60 + 60 + 50 + 40 + 30 + 20 + 20 + 20 = 300$$
$$300 \div 100 = 3$$

- 3 is smaller than your solution, so you can't say from the lower bound if it's an optimal solution. Also, the amount of space wasted (100 g) is equal to one parcel, so you might be able to find a better solution.

Tip: He could fit all of the chocolate bars into 3 parcels: [60 and 40], [60, 20 and 20], and [50, 30 and 20] — this would be an optimal solution.

Exercise 4.3

Q1 Nick needs to pack bags of clay into crates that can hold 2 tonnes. The bags weigh 1.6, 0.9, 0.6, 1.4, 1.3, 0.7, 0.8, 1.2 and 0.1 tonnes.

   a) Use a quick sort to order the bags from largest to smallest.

   b) Use the first-fit decreasing algorithm to pack the bags into crates.

Q2-10 Hint: If you're not asked to use a particular sorting algorithm, you can just sort them by eye.

Q2 Pieces of dowel are to be cut from 3.5 m lengths. The pieces are 2.3 m, 1.9 m, 0.7 m, 0.4 m, 2.0 m, 1.6 m, 0.9 m, 1.4 m and 0.3 m. Use the first-fit decreasing algorithm to fit the pieces to the 3.5 m lengths.

Q3 Boxes are to be fitted on shelves 2.5 m long. The boxes are 1.2 m, 0.9 m, 0.7 m, 1.3 m, 2.1 m, 0.4 m, 0.6 m, 1.1 m and 1.5 m long. Use the first-fit decreasing algorithm to fit the boxes onto the shelves.

Q4 Crates are to be stored on shelves, and the maximum weight each shelf can hold is 25 kg. The crates weigh: 10 kg, 13 kg, 17 kg, 6 kg, 21 kg, 3 kg, 6 kg, 12 kg, 15 kg and 4 kg. Use the first-fit decreasing algorithm to stack the crates onto the shelves.

Q5 Scrooge hoards gold coins. He has 12 sealed bags containing 30, 12, 8, 23, 27, 27, 14, 10, 25, 33, 19 and 35 coins. He keeps his gold coins in boxes under his bed. Each box holds a maximum of 50 gold coins.

    a) Using the first-fit decreasing algorithm, pack the coin bags into boxes.

    b) How many more coins could the boxes hold?

Q6 Pieces of cloth are to be cut from 10 m rolls. The lengths needed are: 5.4 m, 3.4 m, 6.2 m, 2.5 m, 4.7 m, 7.3 m, 4.8 m and 6.7 m.

    a) Calculate the lower bound for the number of rolls needed.

    b) Use the first-fit decreasing algorithm to fit the lengths to rolls of cloth.

    c) How much cloth is wasted?

Q7 Lengths of wood are to be cut from 1 m boards. The lengths needed are 0.7 m, 0.6 m, 0.3 m, 0.2 m, 0.7 m, 0.5 m, 0.4 m, 0.1 m and 0.2 m.

    a) Calculate the lower bound for the number of boards needed.

    b) Use the first-fit decreasing algorithm to fit the lengths of wood to the boards.

Q8 Cassandra is burning home videos onto DVDs. Each DVD can have 30 minutes of film on it. The video lengths are: 15 mins, 13 mins, 7 mins, 4 mins, 16 mins, 19 mins, 6 mins, 6 mins, 12 mins and 18 mins.

    a) Use the first-fit decreasing algorithm to fit the videos to the DVDs.

    b) How much space is wasted?

    c) Is this solution optimal? Explain your answer.

Q9 Bags are to be packed into bins with a capacity of 50 l each. The bags hold: 23 l, 10 l, 13 l, 19 l, 21 l, 30 l, 28 l, 17 l, 25 l and 15 l.

    a) Calculate a lower bound for the number of bins needed.

    b) Use the first-fit decreasing algorithm to fit the bags into the bins.

    c) Is this solution optimal? Explain your answer.

Q10 Sam is packing items into bags for posting. The maximum weight in each bag is 800 g, and the items weigh 230 g, 500 g, 330 g, 140 g, 520 g, 370 g, 610 g, 180 g and 160 g.

    a) Calculate the lower bound for the number of bags needed.

    b) Use the first-fit decreasing algorithm to fit the items into the bags.

    c) Is this solution optimal? Explain your answer.

Full-bin packing algorithm

The **full-bin packing algorithm** needs a bit more work than the other two, but it's more likely to produce an **optimal solution**. However, it can be quite hard to do if you've got a lot of items.

- In the full-bin packing algorithm, first you need to **look** at the items and find items that will **add up** to give a **full bin**. You just have to do this **by eye**, so it can get a bit tricky. It's also easy to make **mistakes**, so be careful when adding up the items in each bin.

- Once you've **filled** as many bins as you can, you use the **first-fit algorithm** (see page 20) to fit the **remaining items** into bins.

Example

Boxes of the same length and width need to be packed in bins of height 2.5 m. Use the full-bin packing algorithm to pack the boxes, and say how many bins are used, how much space is wasted and whether the solution is optimal. The heights of the boxes (in metres) are:

| 0.7 | 1.1 | 1.2 | 2.3 | 0.8 | 1.4 | 0.9 | 1.0 | 2.5 |

- Start by looking at the heights and see if you can find any that add up to 2.5 exactly:

$$1.1 + 1.4 = 2.5, \quad 0.7 + 0.8 + 1.0 = 2.5, \quad 2.5 = 2.5$$

- Then you just carry out a first-fit algorithm on the remaining 3 boxes.

Bin	Boxes (m)	Space left (m)
1	1.1, 1.4	0
2	0.7, 0.8, 1.0	0
3	2.5	0
4	1.2, 0.9	~~1.3~~ 0.4
5	2.3	0.2

- The boxes are packed into 5 bins, with 0.4 + 0.2 = 0.6 m wasted space.

- To see if the solution is optimal, compare the amount of space wasted to the height of one bin.

- The amount of wasted space is less than 1 bin, so the solution is optimal.

Tip: It might help to cross out the boxes you've already used from the original list.

Tip: You could also see if this was an optimal solution by working out the lower bound for the number of bins. It turns out to be 5, which is the number you've used, so it's an optimal solution.

Q1   Boxes are to be fitted onto shelves 2 m long. The box sizes are 1.1 m, 0.6 m, 0.5 m, 0.8 m, 1.2 m, 0.4 m, 0.7 m, 1.0 m, 0.9 m and 0.3 m. Use the full-bin packing algorithm to fit the boxes on to the shelves.

Q2   Bags are to be fitted into containers of capacity 500 l. The bags contain 350 l, 230 l, 180 l, 430 l, 60 l, 80 l, 120 l, 150 l, 180 l and 150 l. Use the full-bin packing algorithm to fit the bags into the containers.

Q3   A company produces chopsticks by cutting them from sticks 1 m long. They've received an order for pairs of chopsticks of length 20 cm, 25 cm, 15 cm, 30 cm, and 22 cm. Use the full-bin packing algorithm to find how many 1 m sticks are needed.

Q3 Hint: Chopsticks come in pairs, so you'll need 2 of each length.

Q4   Cathryn is packing parcels. The maximum weight of a parcel is 250 g, and the items to go in the parcels weigh 20 g, 55 g, 95 g, 130 g, 70 g, 35 g, 150 g, 50 g, 100 g and 30 g.

  a) Calculate the lower bound for the number of parcels.

  b) Use the full-bin packing algorithm to fit the items into parcels.

Q5   Hamish is fitting kitchens. Kitchen worktops come in 4 m lengths, and he needs the following lengths of worktop for the kitchens he's fitting: 2.3 m, 1.7 m, 1.5 m, 1.5 m, 2.4 m, 3.5 m, 0.7 m, 2.3 m, 1.8 m and 2.2 m.

  a) Calculate the lower bound for the number of 4 m lengths of worktop.

  b) Use the full-bin packing algorithm to fit the lengths on to the lengths of worktop.

Q6   Packing cases are to be loaded into shipping containers 9 m long. The 12 cases are the same width and height as the shipping containers and have lengths 1.3 m, 5.5 m, 3.4 m, 2.8 m, 4.6 m, 5.1 m, 5.0 m, 1.6 m, 1.2 m, 1.4 m, 2.6 m and 1.0 m.

  a) Use the full-bin packing algorithm to sort the cases into the containers.

  b) Use the first-fit algorithm to sort the cases into the containers.

  c) Is either of these solutions optimal? Give reasons for your answer.

  d) Suggest a reason why the shipping company might prefer to use:

    (i)   the full-bin packing algorithm

    (ii)   the first-fit algorithm

Q6 a) Hint: Start by filling one container with cases of length 5.1 m, 2.6 m and 1.3 m.

Q7   Pat is loading boxes onto trolleys. The maximum weight a trolley can carry is 100 kg, and the boxes weigh: 26 kg, 48 kg, 29 kg, 61 kg, 10 kg, 19 kg, 75 kg, 8 kg, 35 kg, 17 kg and 65 kg.

  a) Use the full-bin packing algorithm to stack the boxes onto trolleys.

  b) Use the first-fit algorithm to stack the boxes onto trolleys.

  c) Is either of these solutions optimal? Explain your answer.

  d) Why might Pat prefer to use the first-fit algorithm to stack the trolleys?

Review Exercise — Chapter 1

Q1   For each of the following sets of instructions, identify the input and output.

    a) a recipe for vegetable soup

    b) directions from Leicester Square to the Albert Hall

    c) flat-pack instructions for building a TV cabinet

Q2   Use the Russian Peasant Algorithm on page 3 to multiply 17 and 56.

Q3   Use the flow chart on page 6 to work out the factors of 16.

Q4   Use a bubble sort to write the numbers 72, 57, 64, 54, 68, 71 in ascending order.
How many passes do you need to make?

Q5   If you had to put a list of 12 numbers in order using a bubble sort,
what is the maximum number of comparisons you'd need to make?

Q6   Ten students took part in an egg and spoon race. Their times, in seconds, were recorded as:

    23   29   17   23   24   30   19   252   28   23

    a) Show how you would find the first pivot of the list.

    b) Use a quick sort to put the times in descending order.

    c) If you used a bubble sort to sort the list from part b) into ascending order,
        how many comparisons would you have to make? (Don't actually carry out a bubble sort.)

Q7   Find the pivot for the list 104, 97, 111, 108, 95, 91.

Q8   Sort the numbers 0.8, 1.2, 0.7, 0.5, 0.4, 1.0, 0.1 into ascending order using a quick sort.
Write down the pivots you use at each step.

Q9   Use the binary search algorithm to locate 'Brooklyn' in the list below:

    1) Bronx   2) Brooklyn   3) Manhattan   4) Queens   5) Staten Island.

Q10 a) Use a quick sort to list these vegetables in alphabetical order:

onion, carrot, parsnip, swede, turnip, leek, endive

b) Use the binary search algorithm on the ordered list to locate:

(i) onion

(ii) endive

(iii) parsnip

(iv) rhubarb

> **Tip:** You don't need to know this, but endive is a leafy vegetable similar to chicory.

Q11 Give one advantage and one disadvantage of:

a) the first-fit algorithm

b) the first-fit decreasing algorithm

c) the full-bin packing algorithm

Q12 Six items of weights 5 kg, 11 kg, 8 kg, 9 kg, 12 kg and 7 kg need to be packed into boxes that can hold a maximum weight of 15 kg.

a) Find a lower bound for the number of boxes needed.

b) Pack the items into the boxes using the first-fit algorithm.

c) Pack the items into the boxes using the first-fit decreasing algorithm.

d) Pack the items into the boxes using the full-bin packing algorithm.

For parts b)-d), say how many boxes are needed, how much space is wasted and whether the solution is optimal (if you can say).

Q13 Abigail and Chas are filling boxes with items for a charity to send abroad. Each box must weigh no more than 600 g, and the items to pack weigh (in grams):

300, 290, 30, 160, 50, 210, 320, 130, 90, 40 and 120.

a) Find a lower bound for the number of boxes.

b) Abigail decides that the best way to pack her boxes is to arrange the items in descending order of weight, then put each item in the first box that can take it.

(i) What is this algorithm called?

(ii) Use this algorithm to pack the boxes

c) Chas puts the items in the boxes as he picks them up from the row, filling each box as far as possible in turn.

(i) What is this algorithm called?

(ii) Use this algorithm to pack the boxes

d) Which, if any, of the algorithms gives an optimal solution?

Exam-Style Questions — Chapter 1

1   77   83   96   105   78   89   112   80   98   94

(a) Use a quick sort to arrange the list of numbers above into ascending order.
      You must clearly show the pivots you use at each stage.

(5 marks)

(b) A list of six numbers is to be sorted into ascending order using a bubble sort.

   (i)   Which number(s) will definitely be in the correct position after
          the first pass?

(1 mark)

   (ii)   After how many passes will the list definitely be in ascending order?

(1 mark)

   (iii) Write down the maximum number of swaps needed to
          sort a list of six numbers into ascending order.

(1 mark)

2   Consider the following algorithm:

   Step 1:   Input A, B with $A < B$

   Step 2:   Input $N = 1$

   Step 3:   Calculate $C = A \div N$

   Step 4:   Calculate $D = B \div N$

   Step 5:   If both C and D are integers, output N

   Step 6:   If $N = A$, then stop. Otherwise let $N = N + 1$ and go back to Step 3.

(a) Carry out the algorithm with $A = 8$ and $B = 12$. Record your results.

(3 marks)

(b) (i)   What does this algorithm produce?

(1 mark)

   (ii)   Using your answer to part (i) or otherwise, write down the output that
          would be produced if you applied the algorithm to $A = 19$ and $B = 25$, and
          explain your answer. You do not need to carry out the algorithm again.

(2 marks)

3   A joiner has planks of wood that are 3 m long. He needs to cut pieces of wood from the planks in the following lengths:

$$1.2 \text{ m} \quad 2.3 \text{ m} \quad 0.6 \text{ m} \quad 0.8 \text{ m} \quad 1.5 \text{ m} \quad 1.0 \text{ m} \quad 0.9 \text{ m} \quad 2.5 \text{ m}$$

(a)   Calculate a lower bound for the number of planks of wood he will need to use.

(2 marks)

(b)   Use the first-fit bin packing algorithm to fit the lengths of wood onto the planks. State how many planks are needed and how much wood is wasted.

(3 marks)

(c)   (i)   Use the full-bin packing algorithm to fit the lengths of wood onto the planks. Again, state how many planks are needed and how much wood is wasted.

(3 marks)

(ii)   Is this solution optimal? Explain your answer.

(1 mark)

4   Mark   Adam   Dan   James   Stella   Helen   Robert

(a)   Use a quick sort to list the above names in alphabetical order.
Show clearly the pivots you use.

(4 marks)

(b)   (i)   Use the binary search algorithm on the list from part (a) to locate the name 'Adam'.

(3 marks)

(ii)   Use the binary search algorithm again to try to locate the name 'Laura' in the list.

(3 marks)

1. Graphs

The graphs you find in Decision Maths look quite different to the ones you'll know from other parts of maths. Here they're all about showing how different people, places or things are connected.

Learning Objectives:

- Be able to identify and draw different types of graph.
- Find the degree of a vertex.
- Identify and draw paths, cycles and connected graphs.
- Identify and draw trees and spanning trees.
- Draw graphs from adjacency matrices and distance matrices.
- Use adjacency matrices and distance matrices to represent graphs.

Graphs

> A **graph** is made up of points (called **vertices** or **nodes**) joined by lines (called **edges** or **arcs**).

Graphs can be used to **model** or **solve** real-life problems.

- In this graph, the **vertices** represent towns and the **edges** represent roads.
- The graph **doesn't** show where the towns are in relation to each other — just how they are **linked** by roads.

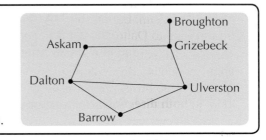

Bipartite graphs

Bipartite graphs have two sets of vertices.
The edges only join vertices in **one set** to vertices in the **opposite set**.

- This bipartite graph shows the jobs a group of students would prefer to do at the end-of-term barbecue.

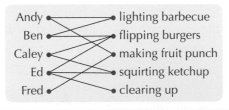

- The edges can only join students to jobs. So you could never join Andy and Caley, or "lighting barbecue" and "flipping burgers".

- In this bipartite graph, both groups have the same members. The graph shows how the members of a quiz team voted to choose a captain.
- The column on the left shows who voted, and the one on the right shows who they voted for.
- You can see that each team member voted twice, and Gurjit got the most votes.

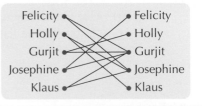

Tip: There's more about bipartite graphs in Chapter 6.

Networks

In a **weighted graph**, or **network**, each edge has a number associated with it.
This number is called the **weight** of the edge.

- Weights often give you **lengths**.
  This network shows points
  in a nature reserve and the
  footpaths joining them.
  The weights represent the
  lengths of the footpaths.
- Weights can also be used to
  show things like **costs** or **times**.

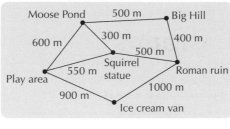

Tip: Typical costs shown
on a network include
the cost of travelling
between two points, or
the cost of connecting
two points in some way,
e.g. by installing wiring
or piping, or by building
roads or paths.

Digraphs

Sometimes edges have **directions**, e.g. to show one-way streets.
If they do, they're called **directed edges** and the graph is a **digraph**.

- The edges on this digraph show the bus routes between the towns.
- There's a direct bus from
  Dalton to Askam, but not
  from Askam to Dalton.
- There's no direction on the
  edge connecting Broughton and
  Grizebeck, so buses run between
  them in **both directions**.

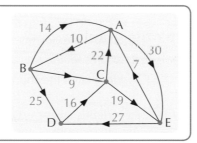

- This is a **weighted digraph**.
- There are two edges between A and B
  and two edges between A and E.
  For each of those pairs, you can travel
  between them in either direction but
  the weights are different depending
  on which direction you go.

Subgraphs

A **subgraph** of graph G is a graph where all the vertices and edges are in G.

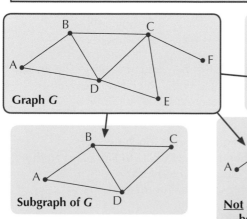

Graph G

Subgraph of G

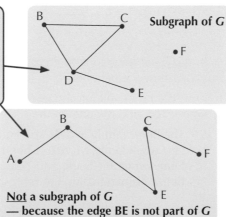

Subgraph of G

<u>Not</u> **a subgraph of G**
— because the edge BE is not part of G

Tip: One way to think of
a subgraph is that if you
take a graph, then rub a
few bits out, what you're
left with is a **subgraph** of
the original graph.

Complete graphs

In a **complete graph**, all the vertices are **directly connected** to each other.

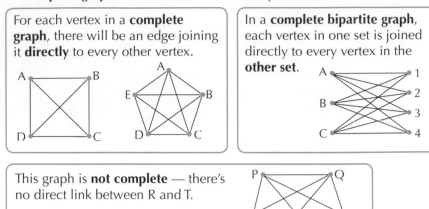

For each vertex in a **complete graph**, there will be an edge joining it **directly** to every other vertex.

In a **complete bipartite graph**, each vertex in one set is joined directly to every vertex in the **other set**.

This graph is **not complete** — there's no direct link between R and T.

Exercise 1.1

Q1 An electrical circuit has six components, A, B, C, D, E and F.

A is connected to D and E.   D is connected to A, B, C and E.
B is connected to C, D and F.   E is connected to A and D.
C is connected to B, D and F.   F is connected to B and C.

Draw a graph to represent the circuit.

Q2 The following roads connect six towns, P, Q, R, S, T and U:
From P to Q is 60 km, P to T is 50 km, Q to R is 70 km,
U to T is 40 km, R to S is 35 km, U to R is 30 km and S to T is 65 km.
None of the roads intersect.

a) Represent the roads listed above as a weighted graph.

b) How far is the shortest route from U to Q?

Q3 Five friends answered a survey about which sports they like to play.
Akio likes football and tennis; Betty likes tennis and hockey; Clare likes netball; Daisy likes football and hockey; Emma likes tennis.
Draw a bipartite graph to represent this information.

Q4 Are the following graphs complete? Give reasons for each answer.

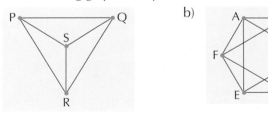

a)

b)

Q5 The Borer family live far apart and keep in touch by letter.
Last week Dolly wrote to Cheryl, Cheryl wrote to Flora and Nellie, Flora wrote to Cheryl, and Zelda wrote to Flora.
Draw a bipartite graph to represent this information.

Q6 Draw a complete graph with: a) 3 vertices,   b) 7 vertices.

Q7 Without trying to draw one, calculate how many edges
    there are on a complete graph with 40 vertices.

Q8 This is Graph G:

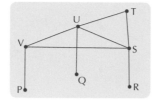

a) State which of the following is not a subgraph of G,
   giving a reason for your answer.

(i)   (ii)   (iii)

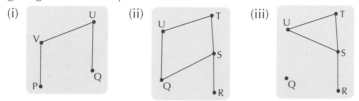

b) Draw a subgraph of G with 5 vertices and 5 edges.

Degree of a vertex

The **degree** or **valency** of a vertex is the number of edges connected to it.

The sum of the degrees is always **double** the number of edges — it's a count
of how many **edge ends** there are. So the sum of degrees is **always even**.

Example

Calculate the degree
of each vertex in
this graph.

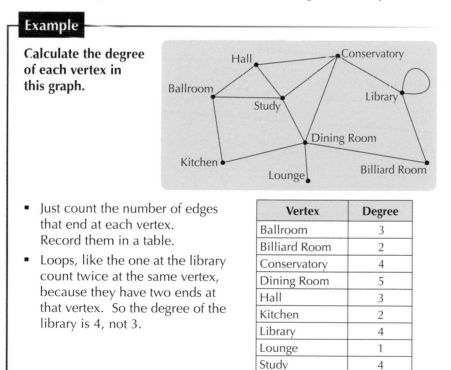

- Just count the number of edges
  that end at each vertex.
  Record them in a table.

- Loops, like the one at the library
  count twice at the same vertex,
  because they have two ends at
  that vertex. So the degree of the
  library is 4, not 3.

Vertex	Degree
Ballroom	3
Billiard Room	2
Conservatory	4
Dining Room	5
Hall	3
Kitchen	2
Library	4
Lounge	1
Study	4

Tip: Here, there are 14
edges and the sum of the
degrees is 28 (2 × 14).

A vertex with an odd degree is **odd**, and one with an even degree is **even**.
So in the example above, the Billiard Room, Conservatory, Kitchen, Library
and Study are all even, and the rest are odd.

Q1 Hint: Check each answer by confirming (sum of degrees) = (twice number of edges).

Q1   Find the degree of each vertex in the following graphs.

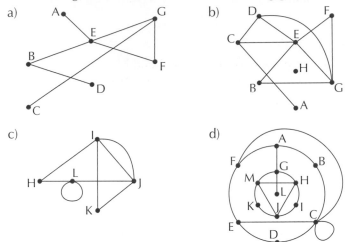

a)

b)

c)

d)

Q2   Aroon made this table for a graph with five vertices, P, Q, R, S, T.

Vertex	P	Q	R	S	T
Degree	2	3	1	4	1

Explain how you can tell that Aroon has made a mistake.

Q3   Copy the following graphs and add edges to each one to make all the vertices even.

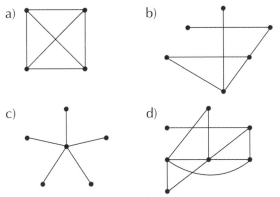

a)

b)

c)

d)

Q4   Ibrahim made this table for a graph with four vertices, P, Q, R and S.

Vertex	P	Q	R	S
Degree	3	5	6	2

How many edges does his graph have?

Q5   By deleting the least possible number of edges, draw a subgraph of the graph on the right where every vertex is even.

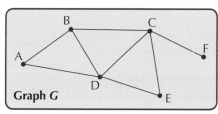

Q5 Hint: A vertex with a degree of zero counts as an even vertex.

Q6   Draw a graph with:
- a) four vertices, of degrees 2, 3, 2 and 1
- b) five vertices, of degrees 2, 5, 4, 4 and 1
- c) three vertices, of degrees 4, 1 and 1
- d) four vertices, of degrees 1, 5, 2 and 6

Q6 Hint: Don't forget that a loop adds 2 to the degree of a vertex.

Paths and cycles

A **path** is a route in a graph — a **sequence of edges** that are all **connected end to end**. A path can't go through any vertex more than once.

Graphs like graph G, shown on the right, contain lots of paths.

Graph G

One path in graph G is ABDECF.   Another is CBAD.

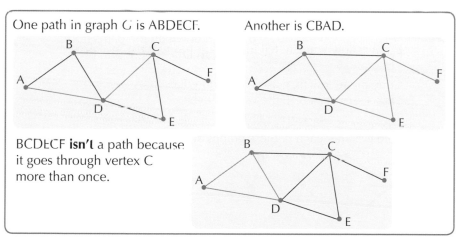

BCDECF **isn't** a path because it goes through vertex C more than once.

A **cycle** (or **circuit**) is a **closed path** — a path that brings you back to your **starting point**. The end vertex is the **same** as the start vertex.

So on graph G, ABDA is a cycle.   CEDBC is also a cycle.

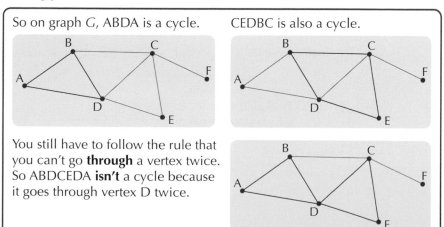

You still have to follow the rule that you can't go **through** a vertex twice. So ABDCEDA **isn't** a cycle because it goes through vertex D twice.

Two **vertices** are **connected** if there's a **path** between them
— it doesn't have to be direct.

A **graph** is **connected** if all its vertices are connected.

Tip: You can show that
G is connected because
you can join two of its
vertices by a path which
visits every vertex.
E.g. you can get from A
to F by the path ABDECF
— and because this path
visits every vertex, you
can connect any two
vertices of *G* using part
of the path.

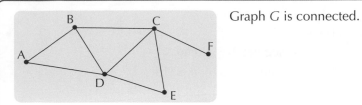

Graph *G* is connected.

This subgraph of *G* is **not** connected
— you can't get from some vertices to
others. E.g. there's no path between
B and C, or between E and A.

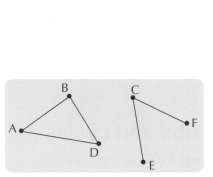

Exercise 1.3

Q1

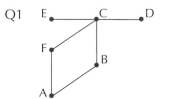

a) Is E connected to F?

b) Write down all the paths from:
(i) E to D   (ii) B to D

Q2   State whether each of these graphs are connected or not connected.

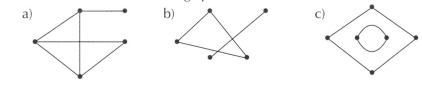

Q3   Identify whether the following are
paths on the graph on the right.
If they are not paths, explain why.

a) TURP

b) SRPVQ

c) TRQVPRS

Q4

Q4 Hint: Remember —
a cycle can't go through
a vertex more than once.

Find all the cycles for this graph
which start from A and visit every vertex.

Q5   Liang and Sue are friends. Weizhe and Sue are friends.
      Liang and Nelly are friends. Kevin and Nelly are friends.
      Weizhe and Nelly are friends.

      Draw a graph to represent this information and hence:

      a) Find a path from Kevin to Sue.

      b) Write down, if possible, a cycle starting with Weizhe.

      c) Write down, if possible, a cycle starting with Kevin.

Q6   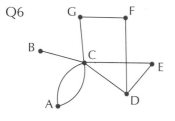   In this graph:

      a) How many cycles start from A?

      b) How many cycles start from C?

      c) Which vertex cannot be part of any cycle?

Trees and spanning trees

A connected graph which contains no cycles is called a **tree**.

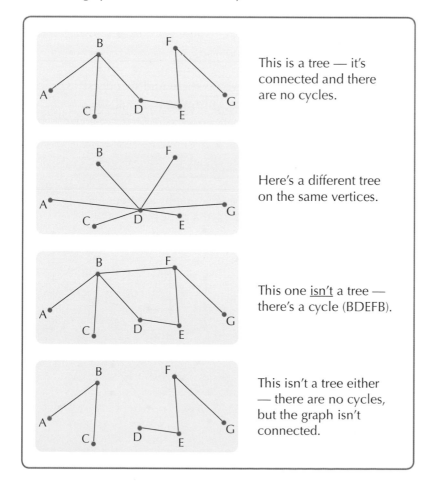

This is a tree — it's connected and there are no cycles.

Here's a different tree on the same vertices.

This one <u>isn't</u> a tree — there's a cycle (BDEFB).

This isn't a tree either — there are no cycles, but the graph isn't connected.

Tip: You could make this last example into a tree by adding an edge joining any of A, B or C to any of D, E, F or G.

Spanning trees are **subgraphs** that are also **trees**, **and** that include **all** the vertices of the original graph.

So if you're asked to draw a spanning tree of a graph, you can **only** delete **edges** from the original graph.

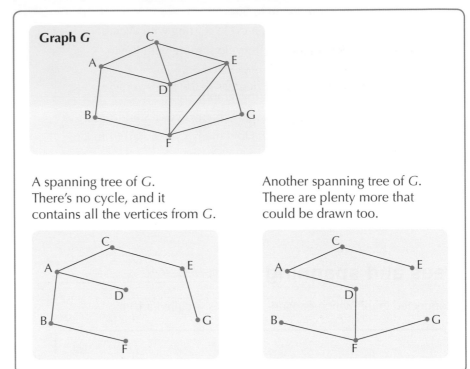

Graph G

A spanning tree of G. There's no cycle, and it contains all the vertices from G.

Another spanning tree of G. There are plenty more that could be drawn too.

Both the spanning trees above have seven vertices and six edges. In fact, the number of edges in any tree is **always** one less than the number of vertices.

Exercise 1.4

Q1 State whether each of the following graphs are trees. For each one that is not a tree, give a reason.

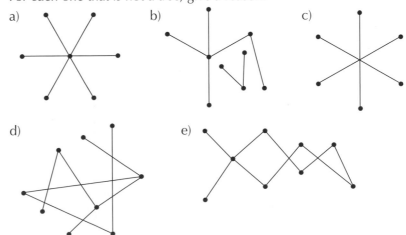

a)   b)   c)

d)   e)

Q2 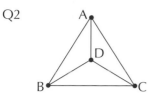 Draw ten different spanning trees for the graph shown on the left.

Q3 A tree has 15 vertices.

State: a) the number of edges in the tree,
b) the sum of the degrees of the tree's vertices.

Q3 Hint: If you can't remember how the number of edges and the degrees of vertices are related, go back to p.35.

Q4 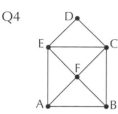 Draw a spanning tree for this graph.

Q5 Sara made this table for a connected graph with vertices A, B, C and D.

Vertex	A	B	C	D
Degree	3	4	5	2

Q5 Hint: Think about how many edges there are in a spanning tree.

a) How can you tell from the table that Sara's graph isn't a tree?
b) How many edges should be deleted to get a spanning tree?

Adjacency matrices and distance matrices

Adjacency matrices

Adjacency matrices show the number of links between each pair of vertices.

To **draw** an adjacency matrix from a **graph**, go through each space in the matrix and count the number of **direct connections** from the vertex at the left of the row to the vertex at the top of the column.

Tip: A matrix is just a set of numbers arranged into rows and columns. You can think of the matrices you get in D1 as just being a type of table — you might even come across questions that call them tables instead of matrices.

Example 1

Represent this graph with an adjacency matrix.

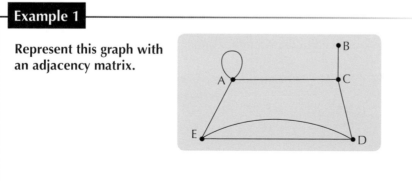

- The graph has five vertices, so we need a matrix with five rows and five columns.
- Label the rows and columns with the names of the vertices.

$$\begin{array}{c} \;\;A\;\;B\;\;C\;\;D\;\;E \\ \begin{matrix}A\\B\\C\\D\\E\end{matrix}\left(\phantom{\begin{matrix}\;\;\;\;\;\;\;\;\;\;\\ \\ \\ \\ \end{matrix}}\right) \end{array}$$

- The first row shows the number of links to each vertex from A.

- There's a loop from A to A. You can go in either direction, so it counts as 2 links.

- There's no direct link from A to B, so put a zero here...

$$\begin{array}{cc} & \begin{array}{ccccc} \text{A} & \text{B} & \text{C} & \text{D} & \text{E} \end{array} \\ \text{A} & \begin{array}{ccccc} 2 & 0 & 1 & & \end{array} \end{array}$$

- ... and there's one direct link from A to C, so that goes in the next space.

- Fill in the rest of the matrix in the same way.

- Notice that the completed matrix is symmetrical along the diagonal from top left to bottom right.

$$\begin{array}{cc} & \begin{array}{ccccc} \text{A} & \text{B} & \text{C} & \text{D} & \text{E} \end{array} \\ \begin{array}{c} \text{A} \\ \text{B} \\ \text{C} \\ \text{D} \\ \text{E} \end{array} & \left(\begin{array}{ccccc} 2 & 0 & 1 & 0 & 1 \\ 0 & 0 & 1 & 0 & 0 \\ 1 & 1 & 0 & 1 & 0 \\ 0 & 0 & 1 & 0 & 2 \\ 1 & 0 & 0 & 2 & 0 \end{array}\right) \end{array}$$

You might have to **draw a graph** using the corresponding adjacency matrix.

Example 2

Draw the graph represented by this adjacency matrix.

$$\begin{array}{cc} & \begin{array}{ccccc} \text{J} & \text{K} & \text{L} & \text{M} & \text{N} \end{array} \\ \begin{array}{c} \text{J} \\ \text{K} \\ \text{L} \\ \text{M} \\ \text{N} \end{array} & \left(\begin{array}{ccccc} 0 & 1 & 1 & 1 & 0 \\ 1 & 0 & 1 & 0 & 2 \\ 1 & 1 & 0 & 0 & 1 \\ 1 & 0 & 0 & 2 & 0 \\ 0 & 2 & 1 & 0 & 0 \end{array}\right) \end{array}$$

Tip: If it helps you to remember which way round is which, add 'from' and 'to' labels at the side and top of your matrices.

- Start by drawing the vertices.
- Use the first row to draw the edges from J — there's one to each of K, L and M.

$$\begin{array}{cc} & \begin{array}{ccccc} \text{J} & \text{K} & \text{L} & \text{M} & \text{N} \end{array} \\ \text{J} & \left(\begin{array}{ccccc} 0 & 1 & 1 & 1 & 0 \end{array}\right. \end{array}$$

- Use the second row to draw the edges from K. There's already an edge between K and J, so we don't need to draw another one.

$$\begin{array}{cc} & \begin{array}{ccccc} \text{J} & \text{K} & \text{L} & \text{M} & \text{N} \end{array} \\ \begin{array}{c} \text{J} \\ \text{K} \end{array} & \left(\begin{array}{ccccc} 0 & 1 & 1 & 1 & 0 \\ 1 & 0 & 1 & 0 & 2 \end{array}\right. \end{array}$$

- Add one edge from K to L and two from K to N.

- Use the other rows to add the remaining edges. Remember, two links from M to M means a loop.

Tip: The sum of all the numbers in the adjacency matrix for an undirected graph is always even. That's because each edge is counted twice, as you can travel along it in either direction.

Distance matrices

Distance matrices show the **weights** between vertices.
To draw a distance matrix from a **weighted graph**, go through each space in the matrix and write down the weight between the two vertices.

As with adjacency matrices, you only include **direct links** — don't start adding weights together.

Be really careful with **directed edges**. A weight on a directed edge only goes in **one** space of the matrix.

Tip: There's more about weighted graphs on p.33.

Example 1

Represent this graph with a distance matrix.

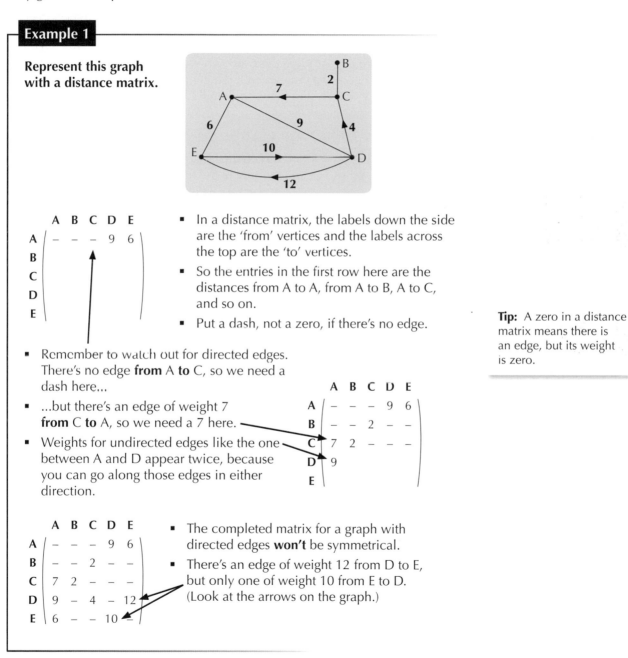

- In a distance matrix, the labels down the side are the 'from' vertices and the labels across the top are the 'to' vertices.
- So the entries in the first row here are the distances from A to A, from A to B, A to C, and so on.
- Put a dash, not a zero, if there's no edge.

Tip: A zero in a distance matrix means there is an edge, but its weight is zero.

- Remember to watch out for directed edges. There's no edge **from** A **to** C, so we need a dash here...
- ...but there's an edge of weight 7 **from** C **to** A, so we need a 7 here.
- Weights for undirected edges like the one between A and D appear twice, because you can go along those edges in either direction.

- The completed matrix for a graph with directed edges **won't** be symmetrical.
- There's an edge of weight 12 from D to E, but only one of weight 10 from E to D. (Look at the arrows on the graph.)

Example 2

Draw the graph represented by this distance matrix.

	V	W	X	Y	Z
V	–	8	–	12	–
W	8	–	–	–	9
X	5	–	–	2	1
Y	7	–	–	–	–
Z	–	–	1	–	–

Tip: It's up to you how you arrange the vertices when you're drawing a graph like this. Try to lay them out so that you can draw a straight edge from any vertex to any other vertex if you need to.

- Start by drawing the vertices.
- Look for **repeated weights** to find any **undirected edges**. Here there are two — the weights are the same in both directions between V and W, and between X and Z.

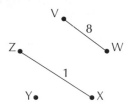

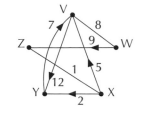

- The other numbers in the matrix represent **directed edges**. Remember, the labels down the **side** of the matrix are the '**from**' vertices, and across the **top** are the '**to**' vertices.

Exercise 1.5

Q1 Hint: Remember, a loop counts for 2 connections in an adjacency matrix.

Q1 Represent each of these graphs with an adjacency matrix.

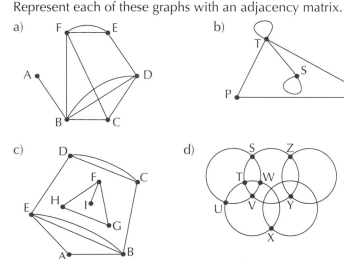

Q2 Construct a graph from each of these adjacency matrices.

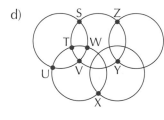

a)

	P	Q	R	S	T	U
P	0	1	0	0	0	0
Q	1	0	1	0	0	1
R	0	1	0	1	0	0
S	0	0	1	0	1	1
T	0	0	0	1	0	1
U	0	1	0	1	1	0

b)

	A	B	C	D	E	F
A	0	0	0	1	0	0
B	0	0	0	1	0	1
C	0	0	0	2	1	0
D	1	1	2	0	2	0
E	0	0	1	2	0	1
F	0	1	0	0	1	0

c)

	A	B	C	D	E	F
A	0	0	0	0	0	1
B	0	0	1	0	1	0
C	0	1	0	1	1	0
D	0	0	1	2	1	0
E	0	1	1	1	2	0
F	1	0	0	0	0	0

d)

	U	V	W	X
U	0	2	0	1
V	2	0	1	1
W	0	1	0	0
X	1	1	0	4

Q3 A complete graph has four vertices, W, X, Y and Z.
Without drawing the graph, write out the adjacency matrix.

Q3 Hint: See page 34 for the definition of a complete graph.

Q4 Represent each of the following graphs using a distance matrix.

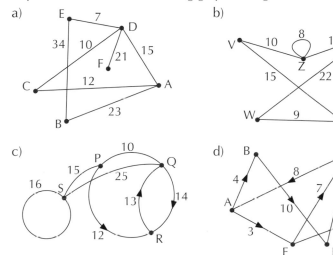

a)

b)

c)

d)

Q4 c), d) Hint: Be careful with the direction of the arrows.

Q5 Construct a graph from each of these distance matrices.

a)

	A	B	C	D	E	F
A	–			–	20	–
B	–	–	10	–	–	30
C	–	10	–	–	15	–
D	–	–	–	–	25	40
E	20	–	15	25	–	–
F	–	30	–	40	–	–

b)

	A	B	C	D	E	F
A	10	12	–	–	–	–
B	12	–	14	–	18	–
C	–	14	–	–	16	–
D	–	–	–	–	–	20
E	–	18	16	–	–	–
F	–	–	–	20	–	–

c)

	P	Q	R	S	T	U
P	–	–	–	–	–	25
Q	32	–	–	–	–	–
R	–	40	–	–	–	20
S	–	–	30	–	–	–
T	–	–	–	19	–	–
U	–	–	24	–	41	–

d)

	T	U	V	W	X	Y	Z
T	22	26	25	–	–	–	21
U	–	–	33	–	–	–	–
V	20	–	–	–	–	15	–
W	–	–	–	–	14	–	–
X	–	–	–	14	–	13	–
Y	–	–	–	–	13	–	8
Z	–	–	–	–	–	8	–

e) The matrix in part d) represents a road system.
    (i)   Explain why the system is not viable.
    (ii)   Describe how you could make the system viable
        by changing the direction of one edge.

2. Minimum Spanning Trees

Learning Objectives:

- Use Kruskal's algorithm to find a minimum spanning tree for a given graph.
- Use Prim's algorithm to find a minimum spanning tree for a given graph or distance matrix.

A minimum spanning tree connects the vertices of a weighted graph using the least possible total weight. In this section, you'll see two methods for finding the minimum spanning tree of a graph, and one method for a matrix.

Minimum spanning trees

> A **minimum spanning tree** (MST) is a spanning tree where the total weight of the arcs is as **small as possible**.

- So a **minimum spanning tree** (also known as a **minimum connector**) is the shortest way to **connect** all the vertices of a graph.

- Minimum spanning trees are used in real life — for example, they come in handy for cable or pipe-laying companies. Suppose they need to connect several buildings in a town, then they'd want to find the **cheapest path** — this may be the **shortest** route, or have the **easiest** ground to dig up.

- Being absolutely certain that you've got the minimum spanning tree by eye is tricky, so using an **algorithm** helps.

Tip: See page 40 if you've forgotten what spanning trees are. And remember — an **arc** is just another name for an **edge**.

Kruskal's algorithm

Kruskal's algorithm gives one method for finding minimum spanning trees.

> 1. List the arcs in **ascending order of weight**.
> 2. Pick the arc of **least weight** — this starts the tree.
> 3. Look at the **next arc** in your list.
>   - if it forms a cycle, **DON'T** use it and go on to the next arc.
>   - if it **doesn't** form a cycle, add it to the tree.
> 4. Repeat step 3 until you've joined **all** the vertices.

Tip: Kruskal's algorithm is a 'greedy algorithm'. That means you make the choice that seems best at each stage, without worrying about later choices.

Tip: If a network has n vertices then, as with any spanning tree, there will always be $(n - 1)$ arcs in its minimum spanning tree.

Example

Use Kruskal's algorithm to find a minimum spanning tree for this network.

- Step 1 is to make an **ordered list** of the arcs.
- You can put arcs of the **same weight** in **any order** — for example, it doesn't matter which way round you put AD and AB, or BC and AC.

Arc	Weight
BD	3
AD	4
AB	4
BC	5
AC	5
DE	6
CE	8

- The **shortest arc is BD**, so that starts the tree, and you can mark the edge as 'used' in the table.

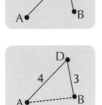

Arc	Weight	Used?
BD	3	✓

- The next arc, **AD**, **doesn't** form a cycle, so it can be added on.

AD	4	✓

- AB would form a cycle, so it's **rejected**.

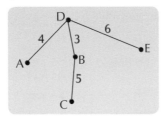

AB	4	✗

- Continue down the list like this until **all** vertices are connected, meaning the MST is **complete**.

Arc	Weight	Used?
BD	3	✓
AD	4	✓
AB	4	✗
BC	5	✓
AC	5	✗
DE	6	✓
CE	8	✗

Tip: You'll often be asked to find the weight of your MST. This is easy — just add all the weights up. So the weight of the MST in this example is $3 + 4 + 5 + 6 = 18$.

- There are often **a few different** minimum spanning trees that can be found for a network — and you might be asked to find them all.
- In the example above, **AB** could have been used instead of AD, or **AC** instead of BC.
- All the different combinations of these arcs give **three more MSTs**:

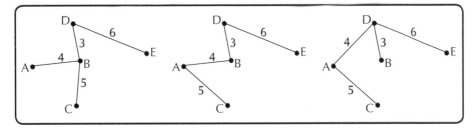

Tip: These minimum spanning trees all have the same weight.

Exercise 2.1

Q1 a) List the arcs of the network below in ascending order of weight.

b) Use Kruskal's algorithm to find a minimum spanning tree for the network. Draw your spanning tree clearly, labelling each arc with its weight.

c) State the weight of your minimum spanning tree.

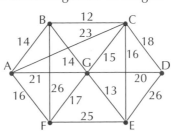

Q1 Hint: Don't worry if parts of your MST aren't connected to start with. Keep going and you should find that it all connects up in the end.

Q2 The matrix below represents the distances, in km, between six towns.

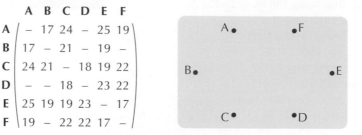

	A	B	C	D	E	F
A	–	17	24	–	25	19
B	17	–	21	–	19	–
C	24	21	–	18	19	22
D	–	–	18	–	23	22
E	25	19	19	23	–	17
F	19	–	22	22	17	–

a) Draw a weighted network to represent the information given in the table. Copy the vertices shown next to the matrix and use them to plan your diagram.

b) Using your weighted network, and Kruskal's algorithm, find a minimum spanning tree for this network and state its weight. List the arcs and the order in which you chose them.

Q3 The matrix on the right represents the distances, in metres, between computer terminals in an office. The computers need to be linked using electronic cables.

By drawing a weighted network diagram, use Kruskal's algorithm to find the most efficient way to link the computers. State the total amount of cabling needed. Show your method clearly.

	P	Q	R	S	T	U
P	–	7.5	–	3.8	1.9	2.7
Q	7.5	–	3.5	1.6	1.9	–
R	–	3.5	–	4.1	2.6	2.2
S	3.8	1.6	4.1	–	–	–
T	1.9	1.9	2.6	–	–	3.3
U	2.7	–	2.2	–	3.3	–

Q4 A park warden has identified nine attractions in a park, and is planning to lay a number of pathways so that visitors can visit each attraction. He wishes to use the minimum amount of materials possible when laying the pathways and so plans to join the nine attractions to form a minimum spanning tree. The cost of laying the pathways is £175 per metre.

The diagram below shows the distances between the attractions in metres, and all the possible routes on which pathways can be laid.

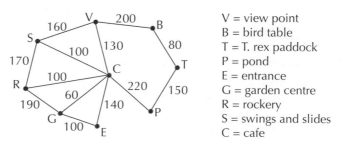

V = view point
B = bird table
T = T. rex paddock
P = pond
E = entrance
G = garden centre
R = rockery
S = swings and slides
C = cafe

By using Kruskal's algorithm to find a minimum connector, state the total cost of the pathway needed to join all nine attractions. List the arcs carefully in the order in which they are chosen.

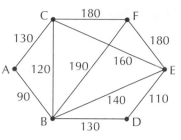

Q5 The diagram on the right represents the distances, in metres, between six till points in a department store. The tills need to be linked using cabling.

a) Using Kruskal's Algorithm, find the minimum amount of cabling required. Show the order in which the arcs are selected.

b) When installing the cabling, the computer engineer instructs the store owner that till points B and F must be directly linked in order for the system to operate correctly. Modify your tree from part (a) to find the new minimum amount of cabling that will be required.

Q5 b) Hint: The modified spanning tree will no longer be a minimum spanning tree.

Q6 The graphs below shows the paths between the ten most popular rides in a theme park, and the distances between them in metres.

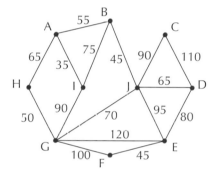

A sudden snowfall blocks all the pathways in the theme park and the park maintenance team only has enough equipment to unblock one path at a time. Use Kruskal's algorithm to work out which paths should be cleared first in order to make all ten rides accessible as quickly as possible. What is the minimum total length of path the team will need to clear?

Prim's algorithm on graphs

Prim's algorithm is another method for finding minimum spanning trees. It does the same job as Kruskal's algorithm, but in a slightly different way. You need to know both algorithms, so make sure you learn these three steps:

1. Start the tree by picking **any vertex**.
2. Look at each arc that joins a vertex **already in** the tree to one **not yet in** the tree. Add the one with the **least weight** to the tree. (If more than one arc could be chosen, pick one at random.)
3. Repeat step 2 until you've joined **all** the vertices.

Tip: When you're using Prim's algorithm, you don't have to check for cycles like you did with Kruskal's algorithm. Connecting to a vertex outside the tree will never make a cycle.

Example

Use Prim's algorithm to find a minimum spanning tree for the network on the right.
Find the weight of the minimum spanning tree.

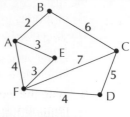

Tip: In this example, the dashed grey lines represent the edges you could have added at each stage, but rejected.

- Pick a vertex to start the tree.
  I've randomly chosen to start with E.
- There are **two arcs** that join E to vertices not yet in the tree, EA and EF. They're both the same weight (3), so choose one at random — I've picked **EA**.

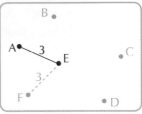

- There are three arcs that join a vertex **in** the tree (A or E) to a vertex **outside** the tree: AB (2), AF (4) and EF (3).
- **AB** has the **least weight**, so that's the one to add.

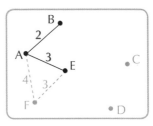

- Now the choice is from arcs AF (4), EF (3) or BC (6) — they each join a vertex in the tree (A, B or E) to one not yet in the tree.
- **EF** has the **least weight**, so it's added next.

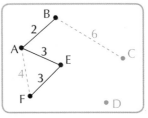

- Nearly there now — the next choice is from BC (6), FC (7) or FD (4).
- **FD** has **least weight**, so that's the one to add.

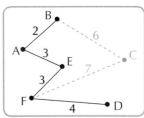

- Finally, C could be joined by BC (6), FC (7) or DC (5).
- **DC** has the **least weight**, so that's the final arc.

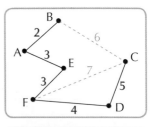

- The **weight** of the completed minimum spanning tree is

  $2 + 3 + 3 + 4 + 5 = \boxed{17}$

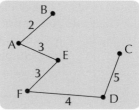

Q1 a) Use Prim's algorithm to find a minimum spanning tree for the network shown below, starting at node A.

Q1 Hint: Remember, a node is just another name for a vertex.

Draw your spanning tree clearly, labelling each arc with its weight.

b) State the weight of your minimum spanning tree.

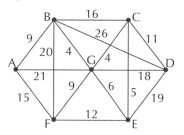

Q2 A university has seven campuses, A–G, located at various sites across the north of England. The diagram below shows the cost, in hundreds of pounds, of linking each site to a new computer network.

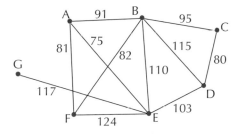

It is required to connect all the sites to the network as cheaply as possible. Using Prim's algorithm, find the weight of the minimum connector, and hence the minimum cost of connecting all the sites. State the order in which you choose your arcs clearly. Start with node D.

Q2 Hint: Don't forget, the weights are in hundreds of pounds.

Q3 Eight towns are to be connected to an electricity grid.

The nodes in the network below represent the eight towns. The arcs represent possible ways to link the towns to the grid, and the numbers on each arc represent the length, in km, of the power lines needed to link them.

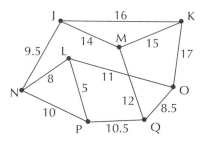

Using Prim's Algorithm, and starting with town J, find the way to link the towns to the grid that keeps the total length of power lines as short as possible. State the total length of power lines used.

Q4 A new security system is
    being installed at a zoo.
    The diagram on the right
    shows the nine points
    where security cameras
    are to be placed, and the
    length of cabling, in metres,
    required to connect them.

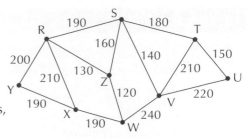

    Listing the arcs carefully in the order in which they are chosen, use
    Prim's algorithm, starting from point R, to find the least possible
    length of cabling needed to join all nine cameras together.
    Calculate the total cost of linking up the cameras if the cabling
    costs £1.25 per metre to install.

Q5 The diagram on the right represents
    the possible routes and travelling
    times, in minutes, to walk between
    seven locations.

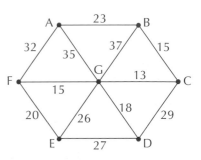

    a) Using Prim's algorithm and
        starting at point G, find a
        minimum spanning tree for this
        network. Show the order in
        which the arcs are selected.

    b) Veronica is at point G. She wants to visit points A–F today, and
        end up back at G. She can only return to G by retracing her
        steps along routes she has already walked.
        Use your answer to a) to find the least time it would take
        Veronica to visit points A–F and return to G at the end.

Q5 b) Hint: Veronica
can return to G more
than once on her route
if she needs to.

Q6 a) At an animal research centre in Africa, ten research sites need
        to be joined by wooden bridges, to allow the researchers access
        to each site. The network diagram below shows all the feasible
        locations for bridges and the prices, in £, of building bridges
        between these sites.

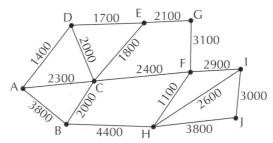

        Apply Prim's algorithm to find a minimum spanning tree and
        hence state the minimum total cost of building bridges between
        the research sites. Start at site J.

    b) During the rainy season a landslide destroys the bridge between
        sites C and F and the ground is not sufficiently firm for the bridge
        to be rebuilt. Between which two sites would you advise the
        researchers to build a bridge to ensure the network of bridges still
        provides access to and from all sites? Explain your answer.

Prim's algorithm on matrices

The easiest way of putting a graph into a computer is to use a matrix.
Prim's algorithm can be used on a distance matrix, which makes it very useful.

> **Tip:** Kruskal's algorithm **doesn't** work on matrices.

1. Pick **any vertex** to start the tree.
2. **Cross out** the **row** for the new vertex and **number** the corresponding **column**.
3. Find and circle the **smallest weight** that's in **any** numbered column **and** that hasn't been crossed out yet.
   (If more than one entry could be chosen, pick one at random.)
4. The entry you've just circled represents the **next arc** to add to the tree. The column it's in represents the **start vertex** of the arc, and the row it's in represents the **new vertex**.
5. Repeat steps 2-4 until all the rows are crossed out.

Example

Use Prim's algorithm to find a minimum spanning tree for the graph represented by this distance matrix.

List the arcs of the minimum spanning tree in the order you selected them.

$$\begin{array}{c|ccccc} & A & B & C & D & E \\ \hline A & - & 4 & - & 3 & 3 \\ B & 4 & - & 5 & - & 6 \\ C & - & 5 & - & 8 & 7 \\ D & 3 & - & 8 & - & 2 \\ E & 3 & 6 & 7 & 2 & - \end{array}$$

- Pick a **starting vertex**
  — A is as good as any.
- **Cross out** the 'A' row and **number** the 'A' column.

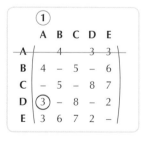

- The **smallest** number in the 'A' column that isn't deleted is 3. This appears twice, so **circle** either of them.
- The first arc to add is **AD** (A from column A, D from row D) — weight 3.

- D is the new vertex, so **cross out** the 'D' row and **number** the 'D' column.

- The smallest number in the A or D columns that isn't deleted is 2, so **circle** it.
- The second arc to add is **DE** (weight 2).

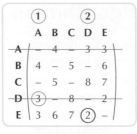

- E is the new vertex, so **cross out** the 'E' row and **number** the 'E' column.

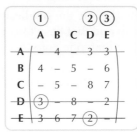

- The smallest number in the A, D or E columns that isn't deleted is 4, so **circle** it.
- The third arc to add is **AB** (weight 4).

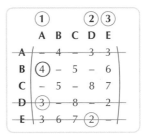

- B is the new vertex, so **cross out** the 'B' row and **number** the 'B' column.

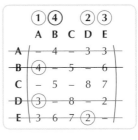

- The smallest number in the A, B, D or E columns that isn't deleted is 5.
- The fourth arc to add is **BC** (weight 5).

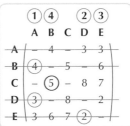

Tip: There's no need to show each step separately — I've just done it here to make things clearer. Your answer to a question like this should be the final matrix with all the circles and crossings-out, plus the list of arcs in the order they were added. You don't have to draw the MST unless you're asked for it — I've just included it here to show you what it looks like.

- After crossing out the **final row** and numbering the **final column**, you know you've finished.
- Remember to include an ordered list of the arcs of the minimum spanning tree.
- The total weight of the MST is: 2 + 3 + 4 + 5 = 14

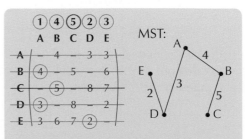

The arcs of the MST were added in the order: **AD, DE, AB, BC**

Q1 The matrix on the right shows the distances between six nodes. Use Prim's algorithm on this matrix, starting at node A, to find a minimum connector for the network represented by the matrix.

List the arcs in the order in which they are chosen and state the weight of your minimum connector.

	A	B	C	D	E	F
A	–	13	24	20	25	22
B	13	–	18	15	19	14
C	24	18	–	21	17	16
D	20	15	21	–	23	22
E	25	19	17	23	–	18
F	22	14	16	22	18	–

Q2 The matrix on the right represents a network of seven villages, labelled A-G, and the distances between them in km.
Using Prim's algorithm on this matrix, and starting with node C, find the weight of the minimum spanning tree required to join the seven villages. List the arcs in the order in which they are chosen and draw the minimum spanning tree.

	A	B	C	D	E	F	G
A	–	3.1	4.4	2.9	3.3	2.7	1.9
B	3.1	–	4.1	3.5	2.7	–	3.7
C	4.4	4.1	–	–	4.4	4.3	4.2
D	2.9	3.5	–	–	2.8	1.9	3.2
E	3.3	2.7	4.4	2.8	–	4.5	2.6
F	2.7	–	4.3	1.9	4.5	–	1.1
G	1.9	3.7	4.2	3.2	2.6	1.1	–

Q3 A college wants to install a number of photocopiers (A-E) which must be networked and linked to the main college computer system (F). The distances, in metres, between the locations are given in the matrix on the right.

	A	B	C	D	E	F
A	–	250	175	210	330	195
B	250	–	185	135	260	270
C	175	185	–	155	230	410
D	210	135	155	–	280	340
E	330	260	230	280	–	300
F	195	270	410	340	300	–

If cabling costs £3 per metre, find the minimum cost of connecting the photocopiers to the network.

Use Prim's algorithm on the matrix, starting at node F.

Q4 A cable TV company wishes to join the villages of Worsthorne (W), Cliviger (C), Furstwood (F), Roggerham (R) and Haggate (H) to its network.
The matrix on the right shows the distances in miles between the villages.

	W	C	F	R	H
W	–	2.4	1.3	1.2	3.1
C	2.4	–	2.6	3.9	6.1
F	1.3	2.6	–	2.5	4.3
R	1.2	3.9	2.5	–	1.9
H	3.1	6.1	4.3	1.9	–

Find the minimum length of cabling required to complete the job, using Prim's algorithm and starting at Worsthorne.

Q5 A new reservoir, R, is to be built to supply the water to five towns T1–T5. The matrix shows the distances in miles between the reservoir and the five towns.

Find the minimum length of piping needed to join all five towns to a network of pipes connected to the reservoir and draw your minimum spanning tree.
Use Prim's algorithm, starting at R.

	R	T1	T2	T3	T4	T5
R	–	13	22	15	24	9
T1	13	–	16	18	16	11
T2	22	16	–	31	26	14
T3	15	18	31	–	19	17
T4	24	16	26	19	–	20
T5	9	11	14	17	20	–

3. Dijkstra's Algorithm

Learning Objectives:

- Be able to use Dijkstra's algorithm to find the shortest path between two vertices.

Dijkstra's algorithm is a bit different to Kruskal's and Prim's — it's used for finding shortest paths between vertices instead of minimum spanning trees.

Dijkstra's algorithm

Dijkstra's algorithm is a foolproof way to find the **shortest path** between **any two vertices** in a graph. In other words, Dijkstra's is the algorithm you need when you want to find the shortest (or quickest, or cheapest) way to join **two specific points**.

- For example, if you're driving between **two cities** with a complicated **road network** between them, it's useful to know which route is **quickest**. Many satnav systems use a version of Dijkstra's algorithm to do this.

- Basically, the algorithm **labels** each vertex with the length of the **shortest path** found so far from the starting point. The labels are **updated** if you find a shorter path, until you're sure that you've got the shortest distance to that vertex. The algorithm works through the vertices in this way until the **end vertex** is reached.

Tip: Don't confuse this with finding the shortest route that visits **all** the vertices — this is covered in D2.

Tip: Once you've given a vertex a **final value**, you can't change it.

---

1. Give the **start vertex** the **final value '0'**.

2. Find all the vertices **directly connected** to the vertex you've just given a final value. Calculate a **working value** for each of these vertices using the formula:

$$\text{working value} = \frac{\text{final value at}}{\text{previous vertex}} + \frac{\text{weight of arc}}{\text{between previous}}{\text{vertex and this one}}$$

If one of these vertices already has a working value, replace it **only** if the new working value is **lower**.

3. **Compare** the working values of all the vertices that **don't** have a final value yet. Pick the **smallest working value** and make this the **final value** of that vertex. (If two vertices have the same smallest working value, pick either.)

4. Repeat steps 2 and 3 until the **end vertex** has a final value (this is the length of the shortest path).

5. Trace the route **backwards** from the end vertex to the start vertex to find the shortest path. An arc is only included in the path if:

$$\begin{array}{c}\textbf{weight} \\ \textbf{of arc}\end{array} = \begin{array}{c}\textbf{difference in final} \\ \textbf{values of its vertices}\end{array}$$

Tip: Sometimes there's more than one shortest route. If there is, you'll find two possible arcs leading off from a vertex when you're tracing the route back. Read the question carefully — they might want both of the shortest routes.

In **questions** on Dijkstra's algorithm, you'll usually be given a graph with **boxes** to complete. Here's what goes in each box: ➡

Vertex	Order of labelling	Final value
Working values		

This will probably sound quite confusing at first.
Following through an **example** should help make things clearer.

Use Dijkstra's algorithm to find the shortest route between A and G.

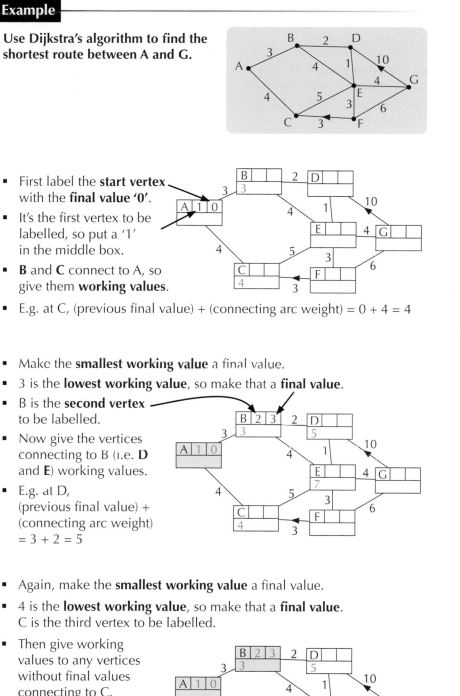

- First label the **start vertex** with the **final value '0'**.
- It's the first vertex to be labelled, so put a '1' in the middle box.
- **B** and **C** connect to A, so give them **working values**.
- E.g. at C, (previous final value) + (connecting arc weight) = 0 + 4 = 4

Tip: The working values are shown in green in this example.

- Make the **smallest working value** a final value.
- 3 is the **lowest working value**, so make that a **final value**.
- B is the **second vertex** to be labelled.
- Now give the vertices connecting to B (i.e. **D** and **E**) working values.
- E.g. at D, (previous final value) + (connecting arc weight) = 3 + 2 = 5

- Again, make the **smallest working value** a final value.
- 4 is the **lowest working value**, so make that a **final value**. C is the third vertex to be labelled.
- Then give working values to any vertices without final values connecting to C. In this case that's only **E** — F is connected to C by a **directed edge** that only goes **from** F **to** C, not from C to F.

Tip: Watch out for sneaky directed edges — there's another one from G to D.

- 4 + 5 = 9, but this is greater than the current working value for E, so **don't** replace it.

- You're probably getting the idea now. Make the smallest working value a **final value**. In this case it's **5** (making D the **4th** vertex to be labelled).

- Give a working value to all vertices connecting to D without final values. Again, it's only E. (G is connected by a **directed edge** running in the opposite direction.)

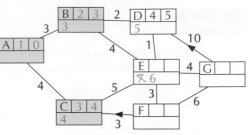

- The working value coming from D to E is 5 + 1 = 6. This is **smaller** than the current working value for E, so **replace it**.

- **E** has the **smallest working value** (6), (in fact, the only working value). Make that its **final value**.

- Give the vertices connecting to E (F and G) working values.

- So at F, 6 + 3 = 9 and at G, 6 + 4 = 10

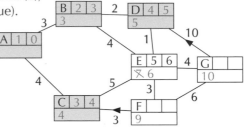

- **F** has the **smallest working value** of 9, so make that its final value.

- 9 + 6 = 15 is **greater** than G's current working value, so leave it as 10.

- G is the only vertex left. Make its working value the **final value**.

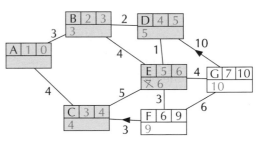

- You've now got a final value at the **end vertex** — this is the length of the **shortest route**.

- Now it's time to figure out the **route**. An arc's on the path if:

> Weight of arc = Difference in final values of arc's vertices

Working backwards from G (the **end vertex**):

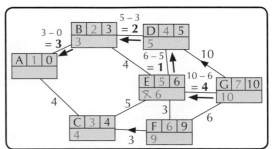

- The arc **EG** is on the path, because the **difference** in the final values of E and G is **4**, which is the length of the arc **EG**.

- The arc **DE** is on the path, because the **difference** in the final values of D and E is **1**, which is the length of **DE**.

- And so on, all the way back to **A**.

So the **shortest route** from A to G is **ABDEG**.

Q1 a) For the network on the right, apply Dijkstra's algorithm to find the length of the shortest route from A to G.

b) By working backwards through the network, identify the shortest route.

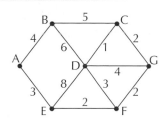

Q2 The network below represents a network of towns and possible routes between them. The numbers represent the times, in minutes, to travel between the towns.

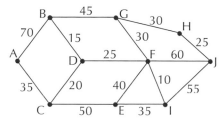

Apply Dijkstra's algorithm to find the quickest route from town A to town J.

State the time it would take to travel this route.

Q3 The diagram below represents nine locations in a village, and the numbers represent the time, in minutes, needed to cycle between the locations. A newspaper delivery boy collects his newspapers from the shop at P at 6.30 am, and needs to deliver to house T first.

By applying Dijsktra's algorithm, find the optimal route that the newspaper boy should take.

State whether the owner of house T will get his newspaper before he leaves for work at 6.40 am.

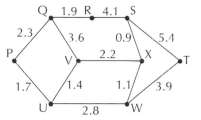

Q3 Hint: Don't forget about the last part of this question. Always read the whole question — you've not necessarily finished once you've found the shortest route.

Q4 The city of Rochley is shown in the diagram below. Key locations in the city are indicated as follows:

A = Airport   TH = Town Hall   S = Statue of Edsger Dijkstra
P = Park   H = Hotel   SP = Swimming Pool
CH = Church   GC = Golf Course   B = Bus Station

The numbers indicate the times, in minutes, to walk between the various locations.

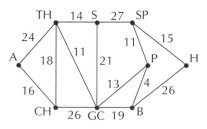

A pilot lands at the airport and decides to walk to the hotel.

Apply Dijkstra's algorithm to advise the pilot on the quickest route to walk, and state how long the journey will take.

Q5 Hint: It looks like you have to run the algorithm twice here, starting from each depot. But if you start at the warehouse and work backwards, you only need to do it once to see which depot is nearest.

Q5 The network below represents two storage depots (D1 and D2), a warehouse (W), and a number of other buildings (A – I), all located on an industrial estate. The distances between the buildings are given in metres.

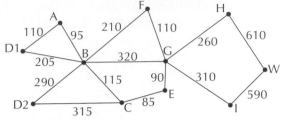

A fork-lift truck is urgently required at the warehouse. It can be borrowed from either D1 or D2.

Apply Dijkstra's algorithm to find out which depot is nearest to the warehouse. State the optimal route that the fork-lift truck should take from your chosen depot to the warehouse.

Q6 The diagram on the right represents a network of university buildings within a city centre and the time taken to walk between them, in minutes.

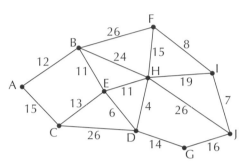

David plans to walk from his Hall of Residence (A) to the Lecture Hall (J).

What is the latest time he could leave his Hall of Residence in order to arrive on time for a 9 am lecture? State the optimal route he should take.

Q7 The network diagram on the right shows a number of bus routes around a city. The values are the costs of travelling by bus in pence. Ammar lives at location A and wishes to travel to the shopping centre, located at I.

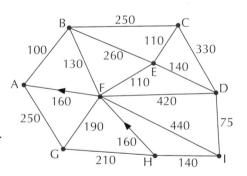

a) Using Dijkstra's algorithm, find the cheapest bus route Ammar could take, and state the total cost of his journey.

b) The bus company introduces a direct bus from A to C for £2. How, if at all, would this change your answer to part a)?

Q7 b) Hint: You don't need to run the whole algorithm again — just work out the new routes.

Q8 Hint: Remember to read the question carefully — don't assume you'll always be asked for a route from A to H.

Q8 For the network diagram on the right, find the shortest possible route from B to G.

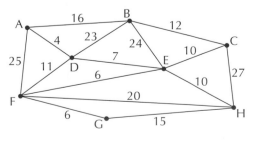

Show your working clearly and state the optimal length of route.

Q9 During some roadworks in the town of Kentley (K), a large piece of equipment is needed. This piece of equipment is stored in Bington (B). The distances (in km) between the towns in the area are shown on the diagram below.

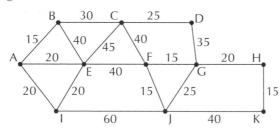

Q9 Hint: Remember, if you end up with two possible choices for the lowest working value, pick one of them at random.

If the machinery can be transported at a maximum speed of 20 km/h, what is the shortest time needed to get the piece of equipment from Bington to Kentley?

Q10 The network diagram below shows a number of cities (D–M) and the cost, in £, of flying between the cities.

Ambreen plans to travel from her home at E, for a city break in city L.

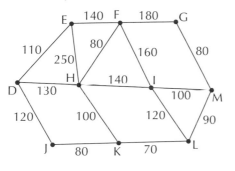

Using Dijkstra's algorithm, plan the most cost-effective route Ambreen could take, and state the total cost.

What other factors might Ambreen wish to take into account when planning her journey?

Q10 Hint: This question asks about 'other factors'. Remember that with real-life contexts, there may be reasons why the path with the least weight might not be the best choice.

Q11 The network below represents a system of underground rail routes, and the time (in mins) to travel between the stations A–O.

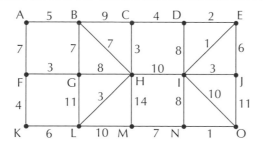

What is the minimal possible journey time from A to O, and which route should you take to make it in this time?

What assumptions have been made in your answer?

Review Exercise — Chapter 2

Q1 Explain what the following are: a) network b) digraph c) tree d) spanning tree

Q2 Padmaja is a town planner. She has prepared a scheme for a town centre where the road system is to be completely one-way.

The one-way system connects five points, A, B, C, D and E. Padmaja's scheme has direct one-way streets from A to B, D to A, B to D, C to B, D to C, and E to A.

a) Draw a digraph to represent Padmaja's scheme.

b) How would you get from C to A?

c) Suggest a flaw in Padmaja's plan.

Q3 Doris and Harry are friends, Beryl and Harry are friends, Beryl and Melvyn are friends, Norman and Harry are friends, and Norman and Melvyn are friends.

a) Draw a bipartite graph to represent this information.

b) Which of the five friends is most popular within the group?

> **Q3 Hint:** You'll need to draw each link twice here.

Q4 Graph G is shown on the right.

a) Draw two subgraphs of G.

b) How many arcs do you need to add to G to make it into a complete graph?

c) Describe a possible path in G.

d) Describe a possible cycle in G.

e) Graph G is currently connected. Delete some edges so that it isn't connected any more.

f) List the degree of each vertex of G. Explain the link between the number of edges and the sum of the degrees.

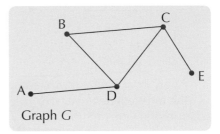

Graph G

Q5

	P	Q	R	S	T	U
P	0	1	0	1	0	0
Q	1	0	1	0	0	1
R	0	1	0	1	2	0
S	1	0	1	2	0	0
T	0	0	2	0	2	0
U	0	1	0	0	0	0

This is the adjacency matrix for a graph. Without drawing the graph, find:

a) a path from P to T

b) a cycle starting from Q

c) the degree of vertex R

d) the number of edges in the graph

Q6 The arcs in the network shown on the right represent possible ways to lay pipes in a planned sewerage system. The numbers on each arc represent the cost, in hundreds of pounds, for laying the pipe. The nodes represent houses which must be connected to the sewerage system.

Using Kruskal's algorithm, plan the most cost-effective way to join all the houses to the sewerage system. State the cost of connecting the pipes in the way you have planned.

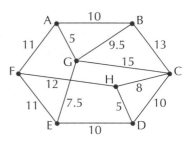

Q7   a) Describe the differences between Prim's algorithm and Kruskal's algorithm for finding the minimum connector of a network.

   b) For the network shown on the right, apply Prim's algorithm to find a minimum connector, starting at:
   (i) node A   (ii) node D
   What do you notice about your answers?

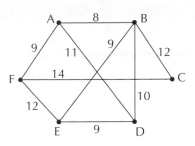

Q8   The distance matrix on the right represents a graph with six vertices. Starting at vertex S, apply Prim's algorithm to the matrix to find a minimum spanning tree of the graph.

   Draw your minimum spanning tree, listing the arcs in the order in which they were added, and state its total weight.

	P	Q	R	S	T	U
P	–	12	–	15	9	–
Q	12	–	–	10	–	17
R	–	–	–	14	11	8
S	15	10	14	–	–	12
T	9	–	11	–	–	–
U	–	17	8	12	–	–

Q9   A rail network is being planned for a city and the surrounding area. Initially, seven stations are planned. The distances, in km, between the seven sites are given in the matrix on the right.

   Apply Prim's algorithm, starting at X, to find the most efficient way to join the seven sites, and draw the minimum spanning tree.

	T	U	V	W	X	Y	Z
T	–	4.4	–	8.9	7.9	10.5	18.0
U	4.4	–	17.4	9.6	–	13.6	–
V	–	17.4	–	15.4	12.6	19.3	22.4
W	8.9	9.6	15.4	–	–	16.6	23.1
X	7.9	–	12.6	–	–	14.4	18.3
Y	10.5	13.6	19.3	16.6	14.4	–	3.9
Z	18.0	–	22.4	23.1	18.3	3.9	–

Q10 Using Dijkstra's algorithm on the graph on the right:
   a) Find the shortest route from A to G.
   b) Delete edge DE.
      Now find the shortest route from A to G.

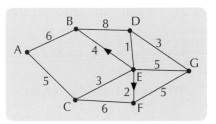

Q11 The network below indicates possible routes for laying electrical cable between locations S–Z in a furniture factory. The distances are given in metres.

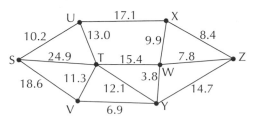

The manager of the factory needs to run a cable from S to Z.

State the optimal route for the cable and the minimum length of cabling required.

If cabling costs £2.50 per metre, state the cost of the cabling needed.

1   **Figure 1** shows the potential connections for a sprinkler system between greenhouses at a
    plant nursery. The numbers on each arc represent the cost in pounds of each connection.

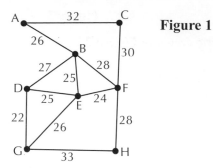

Figure 1

a)   Use Kruskal's algorithm to find a minimum spanning tree for the network in
     Figure 1. List the edges in the order that you consider them and state whether
     you are adding them to your minimum spanning tree.

(3 marks)

b)   State the minimum cost of connecting the sprinkler system.

(1 mark)

c)   Draw the minimum spanning tree obtained in a).

(2 marks)

d)   If Prim's algorithm had been used to find the minimum spanning tree,
     starting from E, find which edge would have been the final edge added.
     Show your working.

(2 marks)

e)   State two advantages of Prim's algorithm over Kruskal's algorithm for finding
     a minimum spanning tree.

(2 marks)

2   The table shows the lengths, in miles, of the roads between five towns.

a)   Use Prim's algorithm, starting from A, to find a
     minimum spanning tree for this table. Write down
     the arcs in the order that they are selected.

(3 marks)

b)   Draw your tree and state its total weight.

(2 marks)

c)   State the number of other spanning trees that
     are the same length as your answer in part (b).

(1 mark)

	A	B	C	D	E
A	–	14	22	21	18
B	14	–	19	21	20
C	22	19	–	21	15
D	21	21	21	–	24
E	18	20	15	24	–

3

A B C connected to 1 2 3 4 (Figure 2)

A B C D E (Figure 3)

Figure 2   **Figure 3**

a) Name the type of graph drawn in **Figure 2**.

(1 mark)

b) State the number of edges that would need to be added to **Figure 2** to make the graph complete.

(1 mark)

c) State the number of edges that would need to be added to **Figure 3** to make the graph connected.

(1 mark)

d) What is the sum of the orders of the vertices in **Figure 3**?

(1 mark)

e) Explain why it is impossible to add edges to **Figure 3** so that all vertices have an odd order.

(2 marks)

4 The diagram below shows a network of forest paths. The number on each edge represents the time, in minutes, required to walk along the path.

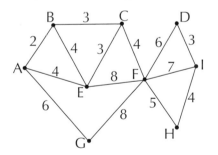

a) Write down the number of edges in a minimum spanning tree of the network shown.

(1 mark)

b) Use Dijkstra's algorithm to find the fastest route from A to I. State how long the route will take.

(6 marks)

c) A new path, taking x minutes to walk along, is to be made between G and H. The new path reduces the time required to walk between A and I. Find and solve an inequality for x.

(2 marks)

1. Eulerian Graphs

Route inspection problems are where you have to find the shortest possible route that travels along every edge of a network at least once — e.g. a postman's delivery route or a park ranger's patrol.

Eulerian and semi-Eulerian graphs

To find the **shortest route** through a network, first you decide if you'll have to **repeat** any **edges**. To do this, you need to work out if a graph is **traversable**:

> If a graph is traversable, it's possible to start at **any point** and draw along each edge **exactly once** (without taking your pen off the paper).

In this section graphs will all be one of three things — **Eulerian**, **semi-Eulerian** or **neither**. Which of the three they are will tell you to what level the graphs are **traversable**.

To find if a graph is Eulerian, semi-Eulerian or neither, you look at the **degree** of each **vertex**. The degree of a vertex is the number of edges coming out of it (see page 35).

> If **all** the vertices in a graph have an **even** degree, the graph is **Eulerian**

- The three graphs below are all **Eulerian**. Every vertex is **even**.

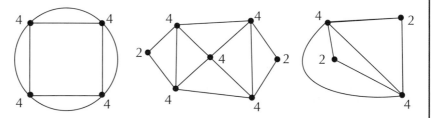

- For an **Eulerian graph**, it's possible to find a route that goes along each arc **exactly once** and finishes back at the **starting point**.

- Or to look at it another way, if the graph represents **roads**, it's possible to walk down each of them **exactly once** before getting back to your **starting point**.

- You find the routes by **inspection** (just by looking at the graph) and they all have the **same length** — the total weight of the network.

Example

Find a route for the graph below that traverses each arc exactly once.

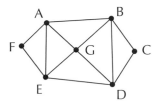

- All the vertices are even, so the graph is **Eulerian** — this means you can start at **any point**.

- A possible route is: A G D B C D E G B A F E A

- Another route is: E D C B D G A F E A B G E

Tip: No matter which route you take, it'll always involve passing through the same number of vertices (13 in this case).

If **exactly two vertices** have an **odd degree**, (and the rest are even), the graph is **semi-Eulerian.**

- The graphs below are all **semi-Eulerian**. There are **exactly two** odd vertices.

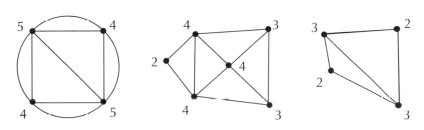

- For a **semi-Eulerian** graph, it's possible to find a route that goes along every edge on the graph **exactly once**, but only if you start at one odd vertex and end up at the **other** odd vertex.

Example

Find a route for the graph below that traverses each arc exactly once.

Tip: There's no way you could start and finish at A without repeating some edges, no matter which path you take.

- The degrees of the vertices are: A = 5, B = 4, C = 4 and D = 5.

- Two vertices are odd and the rest are even, so this graph is semi-Eulerian — this means you have to start and end at the odd vertices (A and D).

- A possible route is ABDCA around the square, then ABDCA around the circle then across the diagonal to D, i.e. A B D C A B D C A D

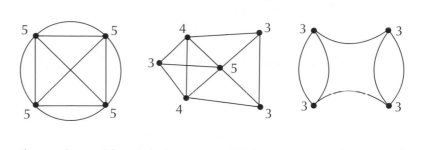

If a graph has **more than two odd vertices**, it's **neither Eulerian nor semi-Eulerian**.

- The graphs below are **neither** Eulerian nor semi-Eulerian.

- If a graph is **neither** Eulerian nor semi-Eulerian, you **can't traverse it**.

- There's **no route** that travels along each edge exactly once. You'd have to go along some of them **twice**.

The bridges of Königsberg is a famous example. The city of Königsberg was set on both sides of a river, with two islands in the middle. **Seven bridges** connected the **four different parts** of the city.

- The problem was to find a **route** that crossed **each bridge exactly once** and ended up back at the **starting point**. As only the **connections** between the different parts of the city were important, the problem could be **simplified** using a graph.

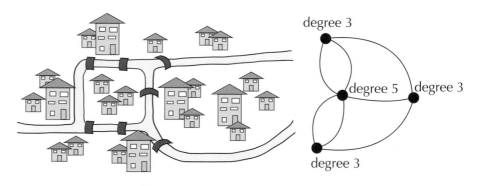

- The **vertices** represent the **land masses** (one for each side of the river and one for each island) and the **edges** represent the **bridge connections**.

- The Swiss mathematician Euler showed that there was **no solution** to the problem — there was **no way** to walk through the city and cross each bridge **once** and only once. There are **more than two** odd vertices, so the city is **not traversable**.

Q1 For each of the following, say whether the graph is Eulerian, semi-Eulerian or neither.

a)   b)   c)

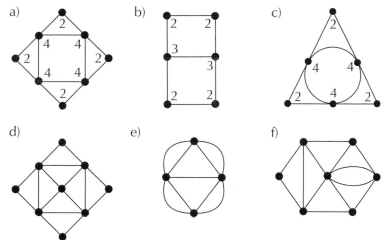

d)   e)   f)

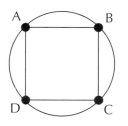

Q2 The graph below is Eulerian. Find a route that traverses it, starting at vertex A.

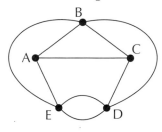

Q3 The graph below is semi-Eulerian. Find a route that traverses it, starting at vertex A and ending at vertex C.

Q4 The graph below is Eulerian. Find a route that traverses it, starting at vertex A.

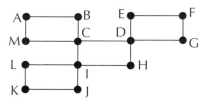

2. Route Inspection Problems

The route inspection problem is also called the Chinese postman problem because it was first discussed by a Chinese mathematician in the 1960s. His name was Kwan Mei Kwo, and he wasn't actually a postman.

Finding the shortest route

Route inspection problems ask you to find the **shortest route** through a network that goes along **each edge at least once** before returning to the **starting point**.

- It's the route that, say, a **railway engineer** would take if he had to **inspect** all the tracks in the most **efficient** way possible.
- In **Chinese postman** terms, the postman wants to find the **shortest route** that allows him to deliver letters to **every street** in a city, and brings him back to his **starting point** for a cup of tea.
- As you might expect, there are **algorithms** for finding the quickest route for each **type** of graph you might come across.

It's **not always possible** to find an inspection route without **repeating** some edges — in these cases, you'll need to choose **which** edges to repeat to make the route as short as possible. The first step is to consider whether the graph is **Eulerian**, **semi-Eulerian**, or **neither** (see pages 66-68).

Eulerian graphs

- In an **Eulerian graph**, you can travel along each edge **exactly once** and end up back at your **starting point**, no matter which point you start from.
- Because you've gone down **each** edge **once**, you find the length of the route by just **adding up** all the **edge weights**.

Length of inspection route in an Eulerian graph = weight of the network

Example

Find an inspection route for the network below.
Your route must start and finish at A. State the length of the route.

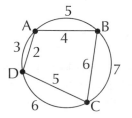

- The graph is Eulerian — the vertices all have even degrees (they're all 4). A possible inspection route is: A B C D A B C D A (once round the quadrilateral, then once around the circle).
- Length of the route = sum of weights
$$= 4 + 6 + 5 + 2 + 5 + 7 + 6 + 3$$
$$= 38$$

Q1 a) Find an inspection route starting at vertex C for the graph below and state its length.

b) Find an alternative inspection route starting at C and show that the two routes have the same length.

Q1-4 Hint: Remember, an inspection route is the shortest possible route that goes along every edge at least once.

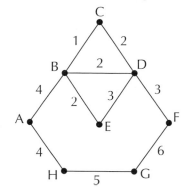

Q2 Find an inspection route starting at E for the Eulerian network below. State the length of the route.

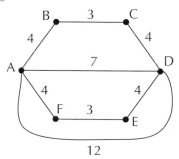

Q3 The paths in a park are represented by the network below. Each path needs to be checked for cracks. Find an inspection route and state its length (the numbers represent distance in hundreds of metres).

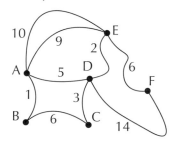

Q4 The network below represents the corridors in the school science block, which Kevin the caretaker has to patrol to make sure that no poisonous snails have escaped from their enclosures. Find an inspection route he can use, and state its length.

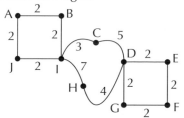

The numbers represent distance in tens of metres.

Semi-Eulerian graphs

For an inspection route in a semi-Eulerian network, you have to repeat the **shortest path** between the two **odd vertices**. You can think of it as **adding arcs** to the network so that all the vertices are **even**.

Length of inspection route in a semi-Eulerian graph	=	Weight of network	+	Weight of the shortest path between the two odd vertices

Examples

Tip: There's no set method for finding the shortest path — you just do it by inspection. That means considering each option and working out which is the shortest.

a) Find an inspection route for the network on the right. Your route must start and finish at B. State the length of the route.

- The vertices have orders A = 3, B = 4, C = 2, D = 3, E = 4 and F = 2.

- So the graph is semi-Eulerian — the odd vertices are A and D.

- The shortest path between them is **AED**, of length 10 (5 + 5), so extra edges **AE** and **ED** are added (shown in pinky purple).

Tip: The added paths have been underlined here to show when they've been used.

- A possible route is BCDEFAB<u>DEAE</u>B.

- The weight of the network = 3 + 6 + 4 + 5 + 4 + 3 + 5 + 4 + 8 = 42

- Length of inspection route = Weight of network + weight of shortest path between odd vertices

  = 42 + 10 = 52

b) Find an inspection route for the network on the right. Your route must start and finish at A. State the length of the route.

- The orders here are A = 2, B = 5, C = 2, D = 4, E = 3, F = 4, G = 4.

- Again, you have a semi-Eulerian graph, so you need to add a path between the two odd vertices (B and E).

- By inspection, the shortest path between them is BCDE, which has a length of 2 + 1 + 2 = 5.

Tip: By effectively making the graph Eulerian, you can start from any vertex if you want to.

- A possible route is ABC<u>DEDCB</u>DGEFGBFA.

- Length of inspection route
  = weight of network + weight of shortest path = 33 + 5 = 38

- You only have to repeat the shortest path if you want to **start** and **end** at the **same vertex**. There might be a situation where it's fine to **start** in **one place** and **end** in **another**, such as a paperboy's delivery route starting at the post office and ending at his house.

- You can only do this if you start at one **odd vertex** and end at the other. In this case, you don't repeat any paths, so the length of the route will just be equal to the **network weight**.

Q1 a) Find the shortest route between the two
         odd vertices in the semi-Eulerian
         network to the right.

     b) Find an inspection route for the
         network starting at A.

     c) Find the length of the route.

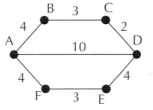

Q2 a) Find the shortest route between the two
         odd vertices in the semi-Eulerian
         network to the right.

     b) Find an inspection route for the
         network starting at B.

     c) Find the length of the route.

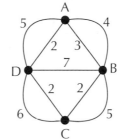

Q3 a) What are the two odd vertices in this graph?

     b) There are two possible shortest paths
         between these vertices. What are these
         and what is their weight?

     c) Find an inspection route for the graph,
         starting and finishing at vertex E.

     d) What is the total weight of this route?

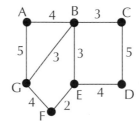

Q4 The network shows the relative amount of time
     each section of a racecourse takes.

     a) If race is to cover every part
         of the circuit and start and end
         at A, which would be the quickest
         section to repeat?

     b) The organisers want a complete
         circuit to last at least 1 hour.
         What would be the minimum value of t?

     c) Suggest a route starting and ending at A.

Q5 Some children are taking part in an orienteering challenge, where they
     must collect a flag that's been hidden along each path before reporting
     to a teacher at any of the 8 checkpoints, who marks their finishing time.
     Distances are in hundreds of metres.

     a) Which are the two odd vertices in this
         semi-Eulerian network?

     b) What is the shortest route between
         the two odd vertices?

     c) Find an optimal route around the network,
         starting at A and ending at any point.

     d) What is the length of your route?

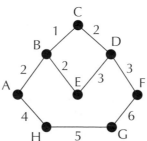

Q5 c) Hint: Be careful
here — this isn't a
typical question, as
you're not starting at an
odd vertex.

Other graphs

Finding inspection routes for graphs with **more than two** odd vertices is a little trickier than for the Eulerian and semi-Eulerian networks you saw in the previous sections.

However, in D1 the **maximum** number of odd vertices you'll ever have to worry about is **4**. Networks **never** have an odd number of odd vertices (page 68), so you only need to worry about solving problems with graphs that have **exactly 4 odd vertices** (as you'll never have 3 odd vertices).

For a network with 4 odd vertices:

> 1. Identify all of the **odd vertices** in the graph (say A, B, C and D).
>
> 2. Write down **all** the possible **pairs** you can make from the odd vertices — there will only ever be **3 possible pairings**: [AB and CD], [AC and BD], [AD and BC].
>
> 3. For each of the three combinations, find the **shortest path** between **each pair** then **add** the two distances together.
>
> 4. Use the set of pairs that gives the **smallest combined** weight as your **repeated paths**.

Tip: The order of the pairs doesn't matter — AC and BD is the same as DB and CA.

This will make more sense with an example:

Example

Find an inspection route for the network below. Your route must start and finish at E. State the length of the route.

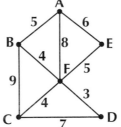

- First, find the **degrees** of the vertices: A = 3, B = 3, C = 3, D = 2, E = 2, F = 5.

- Then pick out the vertices with **odd degrees**. In this case, the vertices are A, B, C and F.

- Then **pair off** the vertices with **odd degrees** in **all** the possible ways:

  > AB and CF
  > AC and BF
  > AF and BC

- Once you've found all the pairings, work out the **minimum total distance** between each set of pairs:

> AB + CF = 5 + 4 = 9
> AC + BF = 12 + 4 = 16
> AF + BC = 8 + 8 = 16

Tip: There are lots of different paths from A to C. By inspection, AFC is the shortest (12).

- Now choose the **set** of pairs with the **smallest total distance**. Here it's AB and CF, with a total of 9. These are the two paths that will be **repeated** in the inspection route:

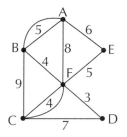

- The graph is now **Eulerian** so you can find an inspection route through it. A possible route is E A B C F A̲B̲ F D C̲F̲ E.

- To find the **length** of the route, add the **weight** of the network to the distance of the added paths.

  Length = [5 + 8 + 6 + 5 + 4 + 9 + 4 + 3 + 7] + 9 = 60

- In a network with 4 odd vertices you can **reduce** the distance of an inspection route if you're **not** restricted to starting and finishing at the **same vertex**.

- In this case, the shortest inspection route will **start** and end at **two** of the odd vertices, and will **repeat** the **shortest path** between the **other two** odd vertices.

To find the shortest inspection route with **different start and end points**:

1. Write down **each pair** of **odd** vertices. With 4 odd vertices you'll get 6 pairs — if your vertices are A, B, C, D, then the pairs would be AB, AC, AD, BC, BD and CD.

2. Find the **shortest distance** between each pair by **inspection**.

3. The pair with the **smallest value** is the path to **repeat** in your route inspection (starting and ending at either of the two **other** points). If the shortest path is AD, then your inspection route should start at B and end at C, or vice versa (and repeat AD).

Tip: If you're told a specific start or end point, just go through these steps but leave out any pairs that include the point(s) you need to start or end from. For example, if you need to start at A and end anywhere, just find the shortest paths between BC, BD, and CD.

Examples

A feather duster salesman wants to travel along each street in a housing estate. He can start his journey at any point, and end it at any point.
The graph represents the streets in the estate, and the numbers represent the lengths of each street in hundreds of metres.

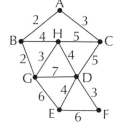

a) **Find the vertices that the salesman could start at to minimise his journey.**

- There are four odd vertices, so you're going to **start and end** at **two of them**. You have to **repeat the path** between the other two odd vertices, so make sure it's the **shortest possible**.

- The odd vertices are B, C, D, E.
  The distance between each possible pair is:
  BC = 5, DE = 4, BD = 8, CE = 9, BE = 8, CD = 5

- The distance between **D and E** is shortest, at only 4, so that's the path you need to repeat — you start at **either** of vertices **B or C**, and end at the **other**.

b) **Find the length of his journey.**

- To find the length of the journey, just add up the path lengths, remembering to include the one you've added (DE, 4 units long):

$$[2 + 3 + 4 + 5 + 3 + 4 + 2 + 7 + 5 + 6 + 4 + 3 + 6] + 4 = \boxed{58}$$

- Remember to always **check the units** — the weights represent **hundreds of metres**, so the journey is actually 5800 metres long, or 5.8 km.

- Sometimes, the usual 'inspection route' or 'Chinese postman' problem is **changed** so that the person has to go down **each path twice**. Perhaps they'll be inspecting each **pavement**, or delivering leaflets to **both sides** of the streets.

- This actually makes it **easier** to solve. It effectively **doubles** the edges at each vertex, making all the vertices **even**. The network is now **Eulerian**, so you can **traverse** it, and the length of the inspection route will just be **double the weight** of the original network.

Example

The feather duster salesman decides to go down each street twice, once on each side. What is the length of his new route?

- The original network weight is 54.

- As the salesman wants to go down each street twice, the network becomes Eulerian because the degree of each vertex is doubled. So the distance travelled must just be 54 × 2 = 108 units.

- The salesman therefore travels **10 800 metres** or **10.8 km**.

Tip: You know this from the last example — the weight was 58, so it's 54 without the added path.

Exercise 2.3

Q1 a) Identify the odd vertices in the graph below.

b) Write down all the possible ways of pairing the odd vertices and work out the weight of each pairing.

c) Find an inspection route for the network, starting at vertex A, and state its length.

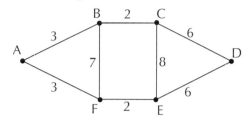

Q2 a) Identify the odd vertices in the graph below.

b) Write down all the possible ways of pairing the odd vertices and work out the weight of each pairing.

c) Find an inspection route for the network starting and ending at vertex G and state its length.

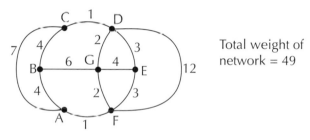

Total weight of network = 49

Q3 The number of market stalls in a town centre is shown in the network below. The weights represent the number of stalls on each street. A safety inspector wants to start at A and walk along each road, pass each stall at least once, and finish back at A, repeating the smallest possible number of stalls.

a) Why does she have to pass some stalls more than once?

b) Using the Chinese postman algorithm, find the minimum number of stalls she will have to pass more than once.

c) Give a possible route.

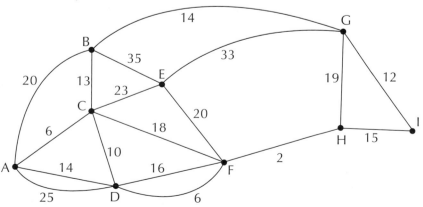

Q4   The network below shows the paths in a park. The numbers represent the length (in m) of each path. The total length of the paths shown is 2890 m. What is the length of the shortest route that the park keeper can take if he starts and ends at his hut (H) and walks along each path at least once?

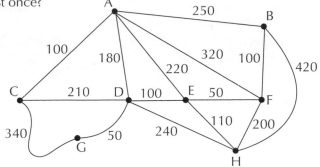

Q5   The diagram below shows the main roads in a town. The weights represent the length of each road in km, and the total weight of the network is 71. Peter has been asked to inspect these roads and so he needs to pass along each road at least once. He lives near K and wants to finish there, but he can start at any point. How long would the shortest possible inspection route be?

Q5 Hint: Remember, when you don't have to start and finish at the same vertex you only need to repeat one path, not two.

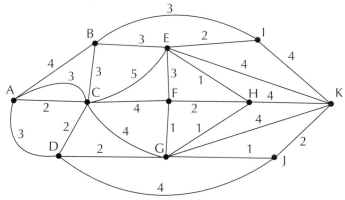

Q6   a)   The network below represents the corridors in a building. The weights are the lengths of the corridors in metres. The total length is 765 m. In order to sweep the corridors the cleaner must go along each corridor at least once. If the cleaner can start and finish at different points, find an inspection route and calculate its length.

Q6 Hint: Remember, the shortest route will always be one that starts and ends at odd vertices.

b)   The cleaner decides to go along each corridor twice, sweeping on the left the first time and on the right the second time. What would the length of a new inspection route be?

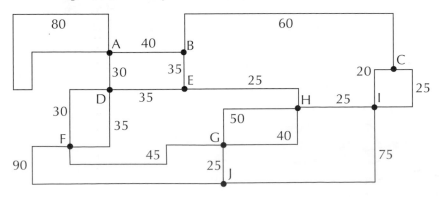

Review Exercise — Chapter 3

Q1 Say whether each of these graphs is Eulerian, semi-Eulerian or neither.

a)   b)

c)   d)

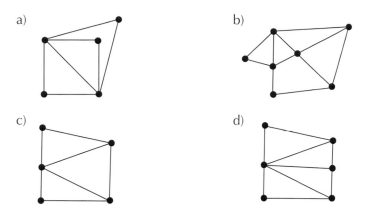

Q2 Identify the odd vertices in the graph below.
Write down all the possible ways of pairing the odd vertices.

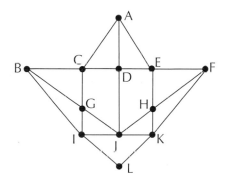

Q3 Find the length of the shortest "Chinese postman" route for each of these networks.
Start and end at vertex A.

a)   b)   c)

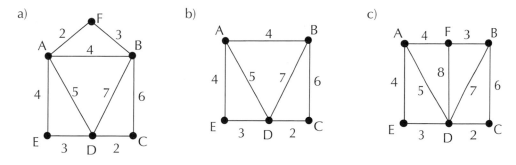

Q4 Repeat question 3. But this time you can start and finish at any vertices.
State which vertices you're starting and finishing at.

Q5 a) Find the shortest route between the two odd vertices in this semi-Eulerian network.

b) Find the length of an inspection route for this network, starting and ending at H. You don't need to find the route.

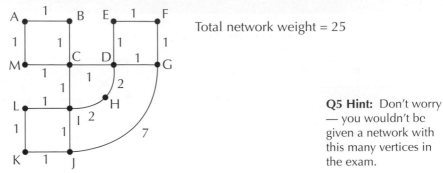

Total network weight = 25

Q5 Hint: Don't worry — you wouldn't be given a network with this many vertices in the exam.

Q6 a) Identify the odd vertices in the network below.

b) Write down all the possible ways of pairing the odd vertices and work out the weight of each pairing.

c) Find the length of an inspection route for the network starting and finishing at vertex A. You don't need to find the route.

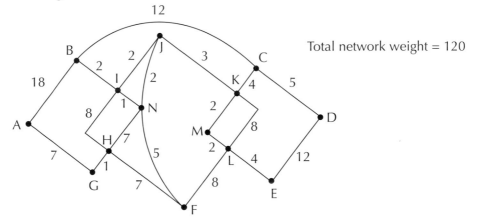

Total network weight = 120

Q7 The network below represents the paths in a funfair, where the entrance and exit are found at E.

a) Jonny wants to see the attractions on every path before leaving. Calculate the length of the shortest route he can take.

b) Suggest a possible inspection route starting and ending at E.

c) Jonny decides he wants to walk down each path twice to make sure he doesn't miss any attractions. What would be the distance of his new route?

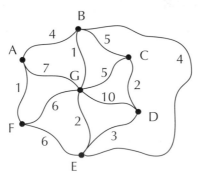

Numbers show distances in tens of metres.

Total weight = 560 m

1   A machinist is embroidering logos on sportsbags. The two logos are shown below.

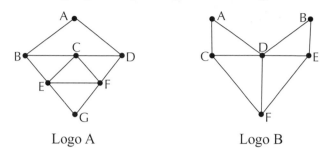

Logo A   Logo B

(a)   Say whether each logo consists of an Eulerian graph,
      a semi-Eulerian graph or neither.

(2 marks)

(b)   The sewing machine needle is positioned at any starting point, and sews a route
      without stitching any line more than once. It can be lifted and moved to a
      new starting point.

      (i)   For each logo, how many times must the needle be lifted?

(2 marks)

      (ii)   For logo A, state an efficient starting vertex.

(1 mark)

(c)   Extra arcs are added to each logo to make them Eulerian.
      State the minimum number of arcs that must be added to each logo.

(2 marks)

2   The diagram on the right shows all the streets in a town,
     and their lengths in metres.

     Angus is considering moving to the town and
     wants to walk down each street at least once.
     He parks his car at K.

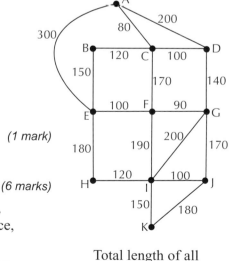

(a)   Explain why it is not possible to walk down each
      street only once and return to the starting point.   *(1 mark)*

(b)   Find the length of the shortest route Angus
      could follow, starting and finishing at K.   *(6 marks)*

(c)   Angus's friend offers to drop him off at any point,
      and after he's walked down each street at least once,
      to pick him up from any point.

      (i)   Find the length of the optimal route for Angus.   *(2 marks)*

      Total length of all
      the roads = 2740 m

      (ii)   State the vertices from which Angus could
             start in order to achieve this optimal route.

(1 mark)

3   The diagram below shows the paths in a park, and the time taken to walk them in minutes.

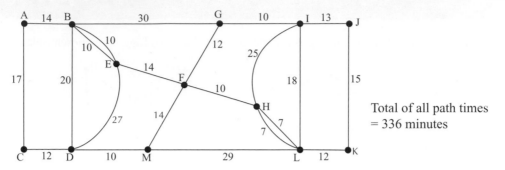

Total of all path times
= 336 minutes

Alice the park keeper needs to walk down each path to check for storm-damaged trees.
She parks her car at F.

(a)   Find the time for the quickest route Alice could follow,
       starting and finishing at F.

(6 marks)

(b)   If Alice starts at point B, and can finish at any point:

   (i)   What point should she end at for the optimal route?
          Show your working.

(2 marks)

   (ii)   How long will it take her to walk along all the paths now?

(1 mark)

4   The diagram below shows the distances between towns in miles.
     The total road distance is 106 miles.

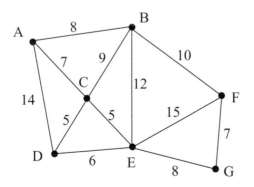

Jamie is inspecting the hedgerows along the roads.
He needs to go along each road, starting and finishing at A.

(a)   Find the length of the optimal 'Chinese postman' route for Jamie.

(6 marks)

(b)   There are ice-cream shops at points C and E. If Jamie follows his optimal route,
       how many times will he pass an ice-cream shop?

(2 marks)

(c)   Jamie decides it would be better if he went along each road twice.
       What is the length of his new optimal route?

(2 marks)

Chapter 4

1. Activity Networks

Critical path analysis is a way of planning a project, making sure that tasks are done in the correct order and reducing the amount of time wasted. The first thing you need to consider is which jobs need doing first.

Complicated projects, like building a house, involve lots of different activities that have to be done in a **specific order**. Often there will be a range of tasks that **can't be started** until others are finished.

- You can't put the roof of a house on until the walls have been built, but the walls can't be built until the foundations are in place. If any of these are done in the **wrong order**, the project just **wouldn't work**.

- If you want to get the house built as **quickly** and **cheaply** as possible, you have to do a lot of **planning** (there's no point in the decorator turning up on the same day as the bricklayer and hanging around for 3 months).

- Setting up a **precedence table** can help organise a project so that the smallest possible amount of time and money are **wasted**.

Learning Objectives:

- Be able to fill in and interpret precedence tables.
- Be able to use precedence tables to create activity networks.
- Be able to use activity networks to create precedence tables.
- Understand the need for dummies and be able to use them when creating activity networks.

Precedence tables

Precedence tables keep track of which activities need doing **before** others. This way, you know which activities need to be done before you can continue. Once you know how they work, they're quite easy to make and understand.

- The left-hand column just lists the **activities** in the task. They're usually represented by **letters** so you can refer to them easily, e.g. the schedule for getting ready in the morning might include A — wash hair and B — dry hair.

- The right-hand column shows which activities need to be done **before** the activity in the left-hand column can be **started**. For example, if the activity in the left-hand column is B (dry hair), then the right-hand column would show A (wash hair) — there's no use doing them the other way round.

Tip: The left-hand column contains one activity per row, but the right-hand column can have any number. If an activity needs four others to finish before it can start, put them all in the right-hand column.

Example

Complete the precedence table to show the activities involved in baking an apple pie.

- Just go through each activity and think about whether it can be done at any point, or whether it **relies** on something else being done.

Activities	Immediately preceding activities
A — Mix pastry	
B — Roll out pastry	
C — Grease tin	
D — Line tin with pastry	
E — Chop apples	
F — Stew apples	
G — Fill pastry with filling	
H — Add pastry lid	

- A, C and E don't rely on anything — they all use raw ingredients or baking equipment, so leave their right-hand columns blank.

- You can't roll the pastry (B) until the pastry has been mixed (A).

- You can't line the tin with pastry (D) until the tin and pastry are ready, so D relies on B (rolling the pastry) and C (greasing the tin).

- Stewing the apples (F) needs the apples to be chopped first (E).

- To fill the pastry with filling (G), you need to have the pastry already in the tin (D) and the stewed apples prepared (F).

- There's no use adding the lid (H) unless you've filled the pastry (G).

- Now put this information in the precedence table:

Activities	Immediately preceding activities
A — Mix pastry	—
B — Roll out pastry	A
C — Grease tin	—
D — Line tin with pastry	B, C
E — Chop apples	—
F — Stew apples	E
G — Fill pastry with filling	D, F
H — Add pastry lid	G

Exercise 1.1

Q1 Activities A and B are independent of each other. Activity C must wait until B has finished and activity D can only start once A has finished. E can begin when all the other activities have been completed. Draw a precedence table for these activities.

Q2 The activities below describe the process of making a pepperoni pizza. Create a precedence table for these activities.

Activities	
A.	Prepare the pizza base
B.	Make the tomato sauce topping
C.	Spread the sauce on the pizza base
D.	Add the pepperoni to the pizza
E.	Add the cheese to the pizza
F.	Put the pizza in the oven

Q3 The activities below describe the process of ironing a shirt. Create a precedence table for these activities.

Activities			
A	Put up the ironing board	E	Iron the body
B	Fill the iron with water	F	Iron the collar
C	Switch on the iron	G	Switch off the iron
D	Iron the shirt sleeves	H	Empty the iron of water

Activity networks

Precedence tables are good at showing a list of activities that need doing, but their main use is to help you to set up **activity networks,** which make the information **easier to understand**.

- In activity networks, **arcs** represent the **activities**, and **nodes** represent the **completion of activities**, or **events**.

- The nodes are **numbered** as they're added to the network. The **first** one is numbered zero and is called the **source node**, and the **last** one is called the **sink node**.

Tip: If you need a reminder about arcs and nodes, see page 32.

Constructing activity networks can be quite difficult because you need to **think ahead** and consider what later activities are going to depend on. If an activity relies on two activities, say C and D, you need to make sure C and D end at the same node before you draw their arcs.

Example

Show the precedence table from the apple pie example on the previous page as an activity network.

- Start by drawing your source node. Once you've drawn this, add an arc coming out of it for each activity that **doesn't depend** on other activities being completed — in this case it's A, C and E.

- For each **new arc**, add a **new node**, and number the nodes 1-3. Add **arrows** to show the direction of the arcs.

Tip: If you add lots of nodes at once, number them in alphabetical order.

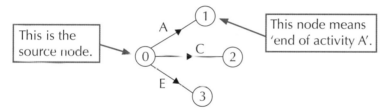

This is the source node. [node 0, arc A to node 1, arc C to node 2, arc E to node 3] This node means 'end of activity A'. [points to node 1]

- Now look at the first activity without an arc (B). This activity **depends** on A happening first, so draw an arc coming out of node 1.

- Be careful though — if you look at the next activity without an arc (D), you'll see that it relies on both B and C, so make sure those finish at the **same node**. Once you've added B, you can also add D.

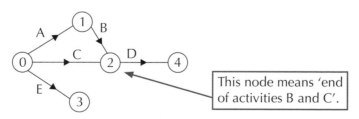

This node means 'end of activities B and C'. [points to node 2]

- The next activity without an arc is F, and the precedence table tells you it **can't start** until E has finished, so draw the arc coming out of node 3. However, like before, make sure to look ahead to see which activities rely on F happening first — activity G relies on **both** D and F, so make the arc end at node 4 along with D.

- Once you've added G, you can just add the final activity (H) and finish the network.

- H is the last activity and no other activities rely on it, so the node that represents the end of activity H is called the **sink node**.

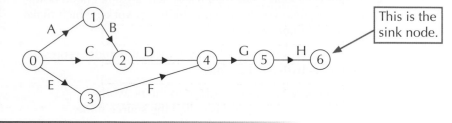

This is the sink node.

You can also go in the other direction, and use an activity network to create a precedence table. For each activity, its immediately preceding activities are the ones that lead into (or point towards) the node it's coming from.

Example

Create a precedence table for the activity network below.

There are no activities leading into the source node, so A and B have no precedences.

A is the only activity pointing towards node 1, so that's the only precedence for C.

2 activities point at node 3 (C and D), so they're the precedences for the 2 activities pointing out (F and G).

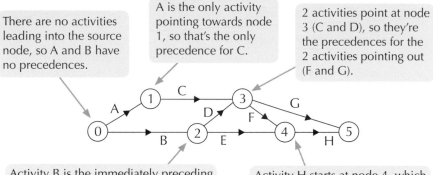

Activity B is the immediately preceding activity for the two activities coming out of node 2 — D and E.

Activity H starts at node 4, which has 2 immediately preceding activities — E and F.

Activities	Immediately preceding activities	Activities	Immediately preceding activities
A	—	E	B
B	—	F	C, D
C	A	G	C, D
D	B	H	E, F

Exercise 1.2

Q1 Draw an activity network to represent the precedence table below.

Q1 Hint: Remember to look ahead at which activities depend on each other before drawing the arcs.

Activities	Immediately preceding activities
A. Butter the bread	—
B. Open the tin of tuna	—
C. Add mayonnaise to the tuna	B
D. Spread the tuna on the bread	A, C

Q2 Draw an activity network to represent the precedence table below.

Activities	Immediately preceding activities
A	—
B	—
C	A
D	A
E	B, C

Q3 Draw an activity network to represent the activities below.

Activities
A. Remove the spare wheel from the boot of the car.
B. Jack up the car.
C. Remove the wheel nuts from the wheel being changed.
D. Remove the wheel being changed from the car.
E. Put the spare wheel on the car.
F. Add and tighten the nuts on the spare wheel.
G. Lower the car.

Q3 Hint: You might find it easier to create a precedence table before starting your activity network.

Q4 Create a precedence table to represent the activity network below.

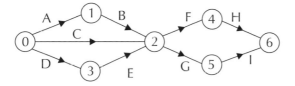

Dummies

In some activity networks you'll find '**dummies**'. These **aren't real activities**, but they help show that one real activity **depends** on another real activity when it's not clear otherwise.

Dummy activities are shown in a network by **dotted lines**.

Example 1

Show the information in the table below as an activity network.

Activity	Immediately preceding activities
A	—
B	A
C	—
D	A, C

- If you start the network as usual, you can make the source node and then add arcs for activities A and C (as they don't rely on anything).

- Here's where the problem comes in. B relies on A, which is simple enough, but D relies on A **and** C. You can't draw an arc from both as that would look like you've added an activity, so you draw a **dummy** instead. This takes you from node 1 to node 2 without adding activities that weren't there to start with.

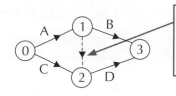

This is the dummy. It shows that D relies on A without adding any activities.

Example 2

Show the information in the table below as an activity network, using exactly two dummies.

Activity	Immediately preceding activities	Activity	Immediately preceding activities
A	—	E	B, C
B	—	F	C
C	—	G	D
D	A	H	D, E, F

- The first bit's straightforward. Activities A, B and C don't depend on any other activities. Activity D depends only on A.

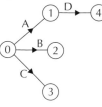

- Activity F depends only on activity C, but activity E depends on **both B and C**. You need a dummy to show this. It's also worth noting that H relies on both E and F, so make them end at the same node.

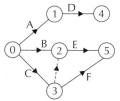

- You now hit another problem — activity G depends only on D, but H relies on D, E and F, so you're going to need another dummy.

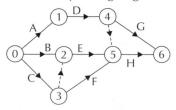

- No activities depend on G or H, so make these two arcs end at the **sink node**. You only ever have **one** final node.

No two activities can be shown between the same pair of events —
each activity must be shown between a **different** pair of nodes.
Sometimes a dummy is needed so that you can stick to this rule.

Example 3

Show the information in the table below as an activity network.

Activity	Immediately preceding activities
A	—
B	A
C	A
D	B, C

- You can't do it like this —
  activities B and C are between
  the **same pair** of nodes.

- A dummy activity solves the
  problem — now each activity is
  between a **unique pair** of nodes.

Tip: If two activities
start at the same node,
they must always finish
at different ones.

Exercise 1.3

Q1 Draw an activity network to represent the precedence table below.
You will need one dummy.

Activity	Immediately preceding activities
A	—
B	—
C	A, B
D	B

Q2 a) Draw an activity network to represent the precedence table below.
You will need two dummies.

Activity	Immediately preceding activities	Activity	Immediately preceding activities
A	—	E	A, B
B	—	F	C, D
C	A	G	C, D, E
D	A, B	H	G

b) Explain the reasons for the dummies you used.

Q3 Draw a precedence table for the activity networks below.

a)

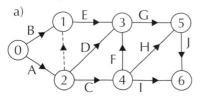

b)

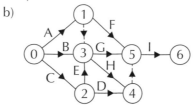

Q3 Hint: When there's
a dummy going into a
node, look at the node
the dummy's coming
from for the immediately
preceding activities.

2. Critical Paths

- Be able to calculate the early and late event times for activities in a project.
- Be able to identify the critical activities and the critical path in an activity network.
- Be able to calculate the total float for activities in a network.

In most projects there will be some activities that need to be done as soon as possible (e.g. buying the raw materials), and others that can be left a few days, (e.g. clearing sawdust off the floor). The activities that need doing straight away are called critical activities, and a set of critical activities forms a critical path.

Early and late event times

- When planning a project, you normally have a **deadline** to stick to, so **how long** each activity takes (its **duration**) is important.

- The duration of an activity is shown in **brackets** next to the activity. You'll usually be told the units — minutes, hours, weeks etc.

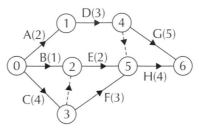

Tip: Remember, an event is the completion of an activity (see p.85).

- Each node or 'event' has an **early event time** and a **late event time**:

> **Early event time**
>
> This is the **earliest time** you can reach an event.
> It depends on the durations of the **preceding activities**.
>
> You work out an **early event time** by adding the **activity duration** to the **previous** early event time. If there's a **choice** of paths to a node you use the **biggest** number.

> **Late event time**
>
> This is the **latest time** you can get to an event **without** increasing the duration of the entire project.
>
> To work out late event times, you start at the **sink node**, and work back towards the source. You subtract each **activity duration** from the **late event time** of the node it leads to. If there's a choice of paths, you use the **smallest** number each time.

The convention is to use boxes at each node to represent early and late event times. The numbers show the time since the **start of the project**.

The **early event time** goes in the **top box**.

The **late event time** goes in the **bottom box**.

Fill in the early and late event times for the activity network below.

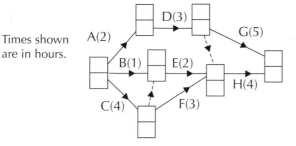

Times shown are in hours.

- Start by adding a zero in the source node then write the duration of each activity leading from it in the next set of nodes.

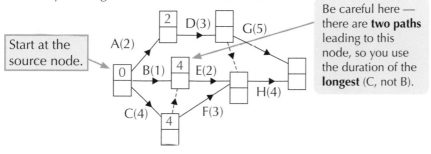

Start at the source node.

Be careful here — there are **two paths** leading to this node, so you use the duration of the **longest** (C, not B).

Tip: You include the dummies when choosing which path to use — their length is always zero.

- Then just do this for the other nodes, making sure you check each path.

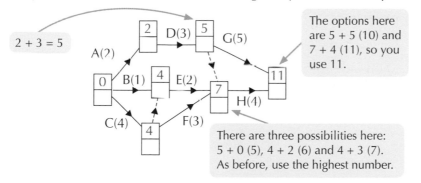

2 + 3 = 5

The options here are 5 + 5 (10) and 7 + 4 (11), so you use 11.

There are three possibilities here: 5 + 0 (5), 4 + 2 (6) and 4 + 3 (7). As before, use the highest number.

Tip: The critical time for the project is 11 hours — there's more on this on p.94.

- Then start from the sink node and work out the late event times by subtracting the duration of the smallest path from the previous event.

At the source node, the late event time is always 0.

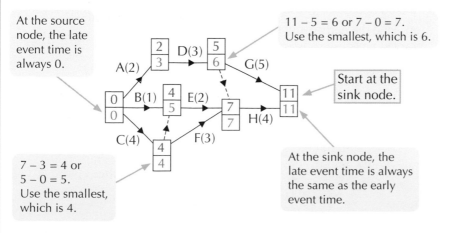

11 − 5 = 6 or 7 − 0 = 7. Use the smallest, which is 6.

Start at the sink node.

7 − 3 = 4 or 5 − 0 = 5. Use the smallest, which is 4.

At the sink node, the late event time is always the same as the early event time.

Tip: The node after A means you can start activity D at any point between 2 and 3 hours into the project. Any earlier is impossible, and any later means the project would take more than 11 hours.

Q1 Hint: Remember to start from the sink node when you're working out the late event times.

Q1 The early event times for a project are shown on the network below. Work out the late event times for the project.

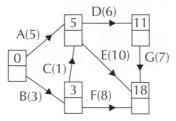

Q2 The late event times for a project are shown on the network below. Work out the early event times for the project.

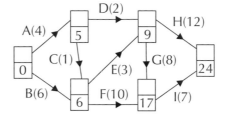

Q3 The early event times for a project are shown on the network below. Work out the late event times for the project.

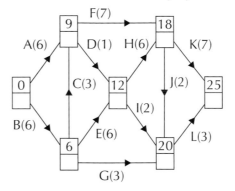

Q4 Below is the activity network used by a computer program to scan the computer for viruses, where times shown are in minutes.

a) Find the early event times for nodes in the network.

b) How long does the virus scan last?

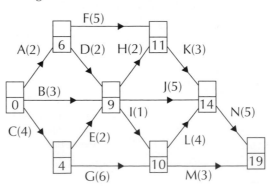

Q5 a) Work out the early and late event times for the project shown by the activity network below.

b) What is the total time for the project?

Q5-8 Hint: You'll need to replace the numbered nodes with boxes to show the early and late event times for these questions.

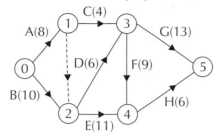

Q6 Work out the early and late event times for the project shown by the activity network below.

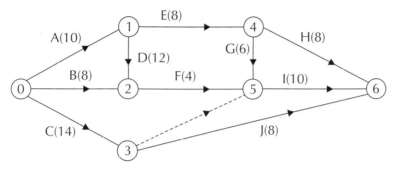

Q7 Below is the activity network for a construction project, where each letter represents a task to be completed and each number in brackets shows the duration in days. Work out the early and late event times.

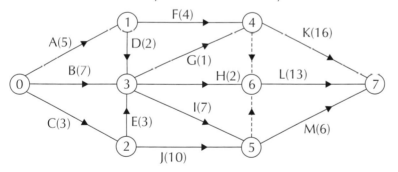

Q8 The network below shows the activities involved in manufacturing cars, where the numbers show the duration of each activity in hours. Work out the early and late event times for the project.

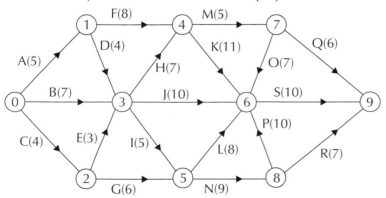

Critical paths

To be able to finish a project you need to complete **all** of the activities involved. With some activities, you can wait a while before starting them and still get everything else done on time, but with others you have to start them **as soon as possible** or you'll delay the project — these are called the **critical activities**.

> - If the duration of a critical activity **increases**, the duration of the **whole project** increases by the **same amount**.
>
> - A **critical path** runs from the **source node** to the **sink node** and is made up of **critical activities**. The **nodes** lying on this path are called **critical events**.

- For a node on a **critical path**, the **early and late event times** are the same.

- This means they **must** be started at a particular time — there's no 'slack'.

- **Adding up** the **durations** of the activities on the critical path gives you the duration of the **whole project** or the 'critical time'.

Example 1

Determine the critical activities and the length of the critical path for the network below.

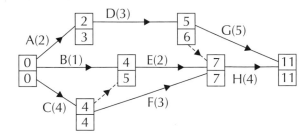

- To find the critical activities, look at the **early and late event times** at each node. You'll find the critical activities between nodes where the early event time is the **same** as the late event time — in other words, both numbers in the box are the same.

- Including the source node and the sink node, there are 4 **critical events**. The **critical activities** are those **between** these nodes — C, F and H.

- The other nodes all allow 'slack', so A, B, D, E and G aren't critical.

- So the critical activities are C, F and H, and the length of the critical path is 4 + 3 + 4 = 11.

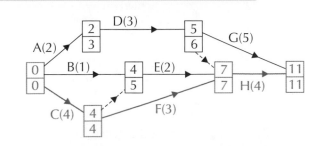

You can have an activity network with **more than one** critical path, all of which have the same durations — the **total duration** of the project.

Example 2

Determine the critical activities and the critical paths in the activity network below.

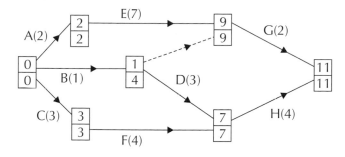

- Remember, critical activities are found between two critical nodes. The [1, 4] node isn't critical (the two numbers are different), so the activities either side of it can't be critical — B and D aren't critical.

- All the other nodes do have matching top and bottom numbers, so A, C, E, F, G and H are critical activities.

- The six critical activities form two different critical paths: The first is A E G and the second is C F H.

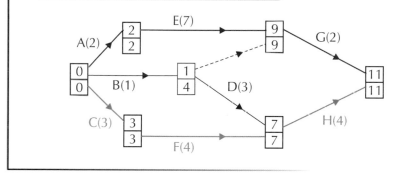

Tip: Not all the critical activities will necessarily be part of the same critical path — once you've found the critical activities, you need to look at the network and find any paths they form from source node to sink node by eye.

Critical activities always happen between critical events, but activities between critical events **aren't always critical** — if there are **multiple** activities between nodes then it's possible **some are** critical and **some aren't**.

An activity is only critical if:

$$\textbf{Activity Duration} = \begin{array}{c}\textbf{Event time of}\\\textbf{critical node after}\end{array} - \begin{array}{c}\textbf{Event time of}\\\textbf{critical node before}\end{array}$$

Tip: You can check that this is true for the critical activities in the examples above.

Tip: For critical events, the early and late event times are the same, so the "event time" is just this number.

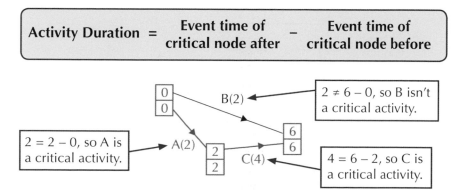

Exercise 2.2

Q1   Identify the critical activities in the network below.

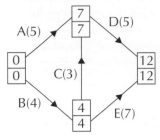

Q2   Identify the critical path in the network below.

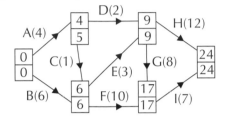

Q3   Identify the critical path(s) in the network below.

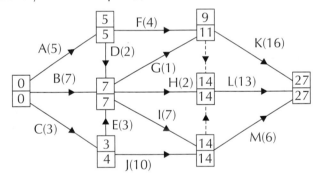

Q4   a) Find the values of *x*, *y* and *z* in the activity network below.
       b) Identify any critical paths in the network.

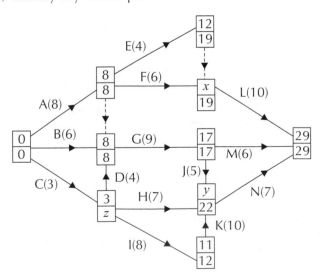

Floats

The **total float** of an activity is the **maximum amount of time** you can **delay starting it** if the whole project is still going to be **completed on time**. There's a formula for calculating the total float of an activity:

> **Total float of an activity = latest finish time – duration – earliest start time**

Tip: Critical activities have a float of 0 — they can't be delayed or the whole project will be delayed.

Example

Calculate the float of the activities B, D and F in the network from the example on page 94 (shown below). Times shown are in hours.

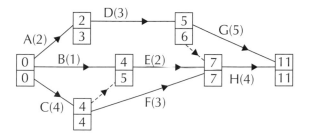

- Start by looking at B on its own:

The earliest start time for B.   The latest finish time for B.

- Total float for activity B = 5 – 1 – 0 = 4. This means you can start B at any point in the **first four hours** without delaying the project.

- Next, find the float for activity D:

The earliest start time for D.   The latest finish time for D.

- Total float for activity D = 6 – 3 – 2 = 1. This means you can delay D by a **maximum of 1 hour**.

- Use the same process to find the float of activity F:

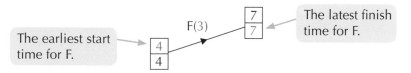

The latest finish time for F.   The earliest start time for F.

- Total float for activity F = 7 – 3 – 4 = 0. This means that there is a **float of 0** and activity F should be started **as soon as possible**.

- This shows that F is a **critical activity**.

Exercise 2.3

Q1 a) Calculate the float for the following activities.

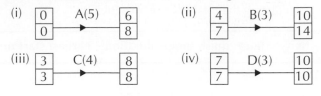

(i)
0	A(5)	6
0		8

(ii)
4	B(3)	10
7		14

(iii)
3	C(4)	8
3		8

(iv)
7	D(3)	10
7		10

b) Activity E is a critical activity. Find the values of x, y and z.

x	E(6)	y
4		z

Q2 Calculate the total float of each activity in the network below.

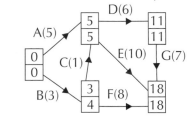

Q3 a) Calculate the total float of each activity in the network below.
  b) List the critical activities.

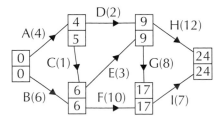

Q4, 5 Hint: You'll need to find the early and late event times before you can calculate the float of each activity.

Q4 Calculate the total float of each activity in the network below.

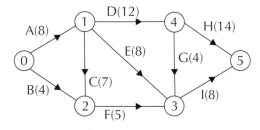

Q5 a) The network below shows the activities in a morning routine, where times are in minutes. Calculate the float of each activity.
  b) Identify the critical path in the activity network.

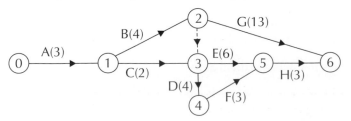

3. Scheduling

So far you've seen how to draw activity networks and find the critical activities. Now you can use this information to schedule projects, making sure they're completed in the shortest amount of time possible and with the smallest possible number of workers.

Gantt charts

Gantt charts are also known as **cascade charts**, and they show the **possible time periods** that each activity can happen in for the project to be completed **on time**.

You plot a single activity on a Gantt chart like this:

- First, look at the **early** and **late event times** for the activity:

The numbers you're going to use are shown in orange.

- Now, draw a **timeline** to represent your project.

- On the timeline, draw a **solid box** that starts at the **early starting time** for the activity (1) and is as long as its duration (4).

- Then, draw a box with **dotted edges** starting at the right edge of the solid box and ending at the **late finishing time** (7).

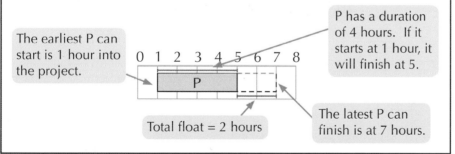

The earliest P can start is 1 hour into the project.

P has a duration of 4 hours. If it starts at 1 hour, it will finish at 5.

Total float = 2 hours

The latest P can finish is at 7 hours.

Learning Objectives:

- Be able to draw a Gantt chart from an activity network.
- Be able to interpret Gantt charts and say which activities will be happening and when.
- Be able to schedule a project so that it's completed within the critical time.
- Be able to calculate the lower bound for the number of workers.

Tip: The dotted box shows how much you can delay the activity — it represents the float.

Example

Display the information in the activity network below on a Gantt chart. Times shown are in hours.

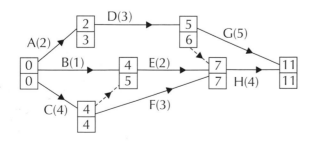

- This is the activity network from the example on page 94.
- The project duration is **11 hours**, so make sure your timeline goes to 11. Once you've set up the timeline, just fill in each activity using the method above.

- The **critical activities** go along the **top** — they'll form one or more critical paths, and there's no flexibility as to when they can start or finish.

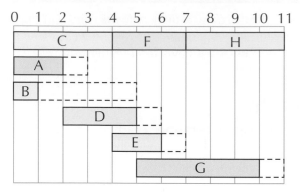

- The **times** along the top are the hours that have passed since the project **started**. The times could alternatively be in days, months, etc.

- Activity B has a duration of 1 hour, and must be finished 5 hours into the project **at the latest**. The **dotted line** shows its **total float** of 4 hours. Activity B can happen anywhere within this rectangle.

- The earliest activity G can start is at 5 hours. It has a duration of 5 hours, and must be finished at 11 hours. It has total float of 1 hour, meaning its **start** could be **delayed** until 6 hours.

- The solid activity rectangles can slide **right** — as long as they stay within the **dotted rectangles**. But sliding them might affect **other activities**. E.g. if A slides forward an hour, then D must too. This means G has to slide later too.

You need to be able to **interpret** Gantt charts as well as construct them.

- You'll sometimes be asked what activities will be happening at a particular time. Some activities will **definitely** be happening at this time, whereas other activities only **might** be happening.

- Don't forget — the times along the top indicate the number of days or hours that have **elapsed**. So day 4 is the space **before** 4 on the scale.

Example

Which activities will definitely be happening and which might be happening at noon on day 4 of this 12-day project?

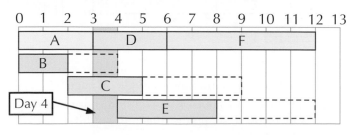

- Activity D falls on day 4, and is a **critical activity** (it has no float), so activity D will **definitely** be happening on day 4.

- Activities B and C could also be happening on day 4, but only in certain situations — B has to be **delayed** by 2 days, and C has to be started **no later** than 1 day after its earliest start time.

Exercise 3.1

Q1 a) State the float, if any, of the activities in the Gantt chart below.
    b) Identify the critical activities in the Gantt chart.

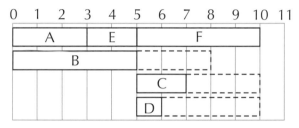

Q2 Below is the Gantt chart for a project, where times are in hours.
    a) Which activities will definitely be happening in the first 3 hours?
    b) Which activities could be happening after 6 hours?
    c) Which activities will definitely be happening after 10 hours?

Q2 b) Hint: Include any activities that will definitely be happening in your answer to this question.

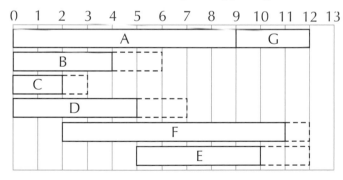

Q3 Below is the activity network for a project, where times are in weeks.
    a) What is the total length of the project?
    b) Which activities will definitely be taking place during week 4?

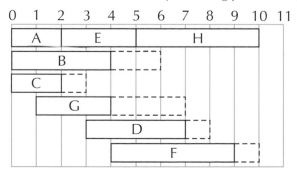

Q4 Below is the activity network for a project, where times are in days.

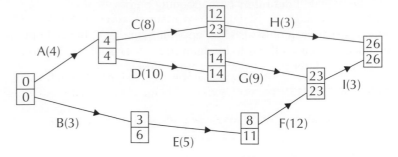

a) What is the critical path for the network?
b) Draw a Gantt chart for the network.
c) What activities will definitely be taking place after 12 days?

Q4 b) Hint: You might find drawing the Gantt chart easier if you calculate the floats of the activities first.

Q5 The network below shows the activities involved in cooking a meal. Times shown are in minutes.

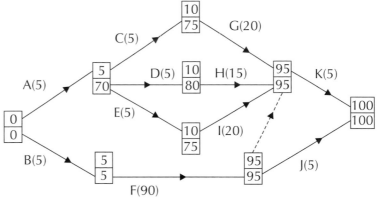

a) Identify the critical path(s) in the network.
b) Draw a Gantt chart for the network.
c) Ideally, activities G, H and I should finish around the same time as activity F. Suggest a good time to start these events.

Q5 b) Hint: You might find it easiest to use a timeline with segments 5 minutes long.

Q6 The network below shows the activities involved in a construction project, where times are shown in months.

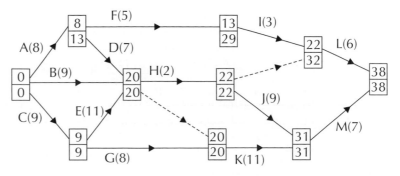

a) Draw a Gantt chart for this project.
b) Assuming everything is running to schedule, what activities must be taking place in the first week of months 14 and 25 of the project?

Scheduling

Gantt charts are useful for working out **how many people** are needed to complete a project on time. An employer wouldn't want to have people standing about, because they're all going to want to be **paid**.

- Scheduling diagrams show **which activities** are assigned to each worker, and **how many workers** are needed to finish the project by the deadline.

- There are some **rules** to follow when you're scheduling workers:

- Assume that **each activity** requires **one worker**.

- Once a worker starts an activity, they have to **carry on** with it until it's finished. They **can't** break off from the activity to get another one started.

- Assume that once a worker finishes one activity, they're ready to start on another **immediately** — workers in Decision Maths don't need a lunch break.

- If there's a **choice of activities** for a worker, they should always start on the one that must be **finished soonest** (which has the lowest latest finishing time).

Tip: Remember that the floats mean that activities can slide backwards or forwards.

Tip: If you have a choice of activities that need to be finished by the same time, look ahead and see what effect it will have if you choose one over the other.

Example

The Gantt chart below is for a project that must be completed in 12 hours. Schedule the activities and find the minimum number of workers required.

- There's no set method to doing this — you just look at the Gantt chart and work out the most sensible way of assigning workers to tasks.

- You can start by assuming you'll need **1 worker** to carry out the **critical activities**, and then the only other activity at the start is A, so you'll need another worker for that. Once A has finished, there are 3 possible tasks for the second worker, so choose the one that must finish **earliest** (D).

- Activity B has enough **float** that you can start it after D, so assign that to worker 2 as well. Activity E, however, needs a third worker.
G can then start as soon as E has finished, so the third worker can move straight onto that.

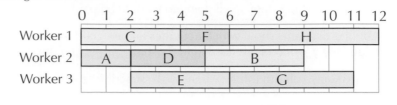

- You've now scheduled all of the activities — you need 3 workers in total.
It's convention to **shade out** any times when workers aren't busy:

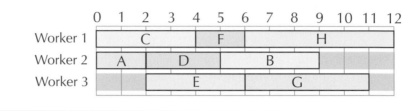

You can also schedule a project from an **activity network** — just look at the **early start and late finish times** for each activity. When you have a **choice** of activities to assign to a worker, assign the one with the **lowest late finish time**.

Example

Schedule the activities below to find how many workers are needed (times are in weeks).

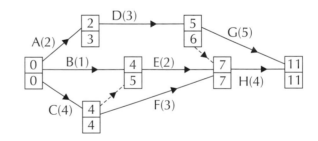

- Start by identifying the **critical path** — C F H, and assign one worker to it.

- You then have a choice of either A or B to assign to the second worker.
Activity A has the **earlier late event time**, so assign them to that.
You can then put the second worker on B or D — now B is more 'urgent', so that's their next task. This actually gives them time to complete activity D as well before its late event time of 6 weeks.

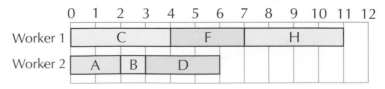

- Now you're left with two activities. E has to start before 5 weeks, so that needs a third worker to complete it, but G can wait until the 6th week to start — you can assign this to either the second or third worker.

```
      0  1  2  3  4  5  6  7  8  9  10 11 12
Worker 1 |    C    |    F    |    H    |
Worker 2 | A | B | D   |      G         |
Worker 3 |         |   E   |            |
```

- So three workers are needed in total.

Sometimes a **change of plan** in a project means that one or more activities have to be **delayed** — a worker might fall ill, or the parts might not arrive before assembly was due to start.

You can use a **scheduling diagram** to work out if a change will **delay** the overall project so that it can't be completed within the **critical time**.

Example

During the first week of the project in the example above, worker 1 is summoned for 1 week of jury duty starting in the 7th week of the project. Will this delay the project at all?

- Start by checking if there's any **shaded** space after the activity that would allow them to **delay** the start. In this case there isn't any as worker 1 is completing the critical activities.

- Next, look to see if any other workers can complete the activity that's affected instead. Worker 3 is free from week 7, and so they can complete activity H instead of worker 1.

- Therefore the project will not be delayed.

Tip: If you do push an activity forwards, be careful to check that there are no activities that rely on it scheduled to start straight after.

Exercise 3.2

Q1   Schedule the following project and state how many workers are needed.

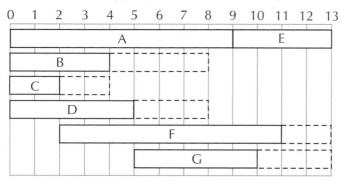

Q1 Hint: Remember — if more than one activity can start at the same time, pick the one that has to be completed first. In this case, it's C.

Q2   Schedule the following project and state how many workers are needed.

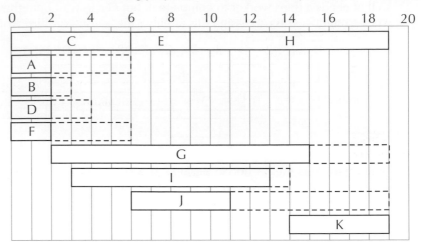

Q3 a) Hint: It's a good idea to check that your Gantt chart matches the activity network — e.g. to make sure that all immediately preceding activities have been taken into account.

Q3   a) The network below shows the activities involved in production of model aeroplanes. Use the information to produce a Gantt chart.

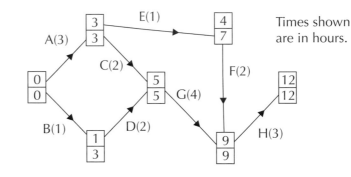

b) Schedule the activities and state how many workers are needed.

c) Bruno, the workshop manager, decides that for health and safety reasons activities E and C can't be carried out at the same time. Will this cause the production to take longer? Explain your answer.

Q3 c) Hint: Remember, first check if there's 'free time' (shaded space) after the scheduled activities that allows them to be delayed without affecting the total project time. If not, check if any other workers can complete the affected activities.

Q4   a) Below is an activity network for a restoration project, where times are shown are in days. Find the early and late times of the events.

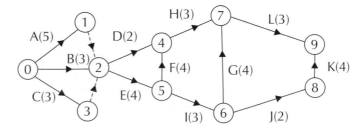

b) Schedule the activities and state how many workers are needed.

Q4 b) Hint: Even though the question doesn't ask for it, you might find it easier to make a Gantt chart first.

c) The day before the project is due to start, a worker calls to say he has missed a connecting flight to return from a holiday and will be held up by 2 full days. Will this delay the project, and if so for how long?

Lower bounds

The **lower bound** gives a **minimum** for the number of workers you'll need to complete the project **on time**. You can't definitely schedule the project using this number of workers, but you'll need **at least** this many.

> The lower bound for the number of workers is: | The smallest integer | $\geq \dfrac{\text{sum of all activity durations}}{\text{critical time of project}}$

Tip: This formula might look a bit messy, but it just means "calculate the bit on the right then round up".

Example

Calculate the lower bound for the number of workers needed to complete the project below within the critical time. The times are all in days. The sum of all the durations of activities is 38 days.

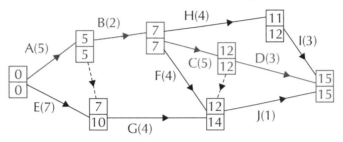

- The critical time of the project is 15 days, so just put the numbers into the formula above.

$$\frac{\text{sum of all activity durations}}{\text{critical time of project}} = \frac{38}{15} = 2.53$$

- The smallest integer greater than 2.53 is 3, so the lower bound is 3.

Tip: You might have noticed this is similar to the lower bounds you found for packing algorithms in chapter 1 — it's basically just the same thing, but with workers instead of bins.

- There's a fair chance that the lower bound **won't** be enough workers to complete the project within the **critical time** — it doesn't take into account the **overlap** and **orders** of activities.

- The Gantt chart for the activity network in the example above shows that on day 11, **four** activities **must** be happening — three workers **isn't enough** to finish on time.

- Constructing a **scheduling diagram** from the Gantt chart shows that you do need **four workers** to complete the project in **15 days**.

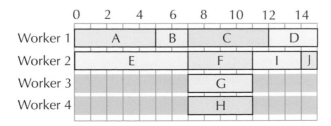

- If you don't have enough workers, the project will take **longer** than its **critical time**.

- If you're creating a scheduling diagram for **fewer** than the minimum number of workers, it's best to do it from the **activity network** so you don't miss any precedences.

Example

Only two workers are available to complete the project represented by the activity network in the previous example. Schedule the activities in the minimum number of days — how long will it take to complete?

- Just go through and assign each worker to the **first activity available**. If you have a choice of activities, it's a good idea to go for the one that has to be finished **sooner** (the one with earliest late finishing time). However, this won't **always** give you the best solution, so try playing around with the schedule a bit to see if it can be done in less time.

- By this method, worker 1 starts on A while worker 2 starts on E, then worker 1 starts on B as soon as they've finished A, as it's the **only** one that can be started at the same time.

- Once B and E have been completed, there are 4 activities to assign (C, F, G and H). The two that need to be finished **earliest** are C and H, so assign those.

- Then just do this for the rest of the activities until they're all assigned.

- With 2 workers, the project will take 19 days to complete.

Tip: Because you're using less than the lower bound of workers, you'll have to ignore some of the floats when scheduling the activities — some activities will end up finishing after their late finish time.

Tip: Instead of starting from scratch, you could use the schedule and activity network from p.107 and just tweak it.

Tip: As you can see, it's often worth reducing the number of workers even though the overall project takes longer as a result. Here you use half the number of workers but the length of the project only increases by 3 days.

Exercise 3.3

Q1   Calculate the lower bound of workers needed for the following projects if they are to be completed on time.
   a) Sum of durations: 56, critical time: 8
   b) Sum of durations: 37, critical time: 13
   c) Sum of durations: 90, critical time: 18
   d) Sum of durations: 193, critical time: 56

Q2 Find the lower bound for the number of workers needed to complete the project below in the critical time.

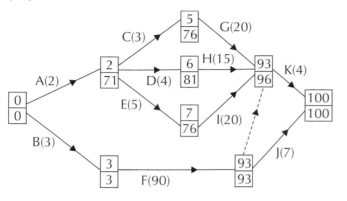

Q3 a) Find the lower bound for the number of workers needed to complete the project below in the critical time (times are given in hours).

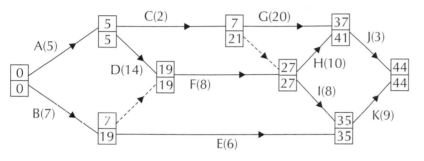

b) Schedule the activities in this project, ensuring it is completed in the minimum possible amount of time. How many workers are needed?

c) Does your answer to b) match the lower bound for the project?

d) One of the workers has had to pull out of the project and there isn't time to find a replacement. How long will it take to complete now?

> **Q3 b) Hint:** Don't forget to check that your schedule matches the network and allows for any preceding activities.

> **Q3 d) Hint:** You don't have to start from scratch here — look at the schedule you made in part b) and adapt it.

Q4 Below is a network showing the activities involved in restoring a medieval castle.

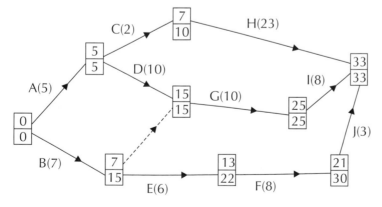

a) Work out the lower bound for the number of workers needed.

b) Create a schedule for this project, making sure it is completed in the minimum number of days possible.

c) If only two workers are available, schedule the activities in the minimum number of days possible.

Review Exercise — Chapter 4

Q1 Activities A and B don't depend on any other activities. Activity C depends on activity A, activity D depends on activity B, and activity E depends on both activities C and D.

　a) Draw a precedence table to represent this information.

　b) Draw an activity network for the project.

Q2 Draw an activity network for the precedence table below. You'll need 2 dummies.

Activity	Immediately preceding activities
A	—
B	—
C	A, B
D	A, B
E	C
F	C
G	D
H	E, G
I	E, F, G

Q3 a) Find the early and late event times for the activity network below.

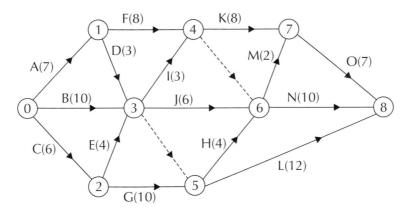

　b) Identify any critical paths in the network.

Q4 Calculate the total float of the activities in the network below.

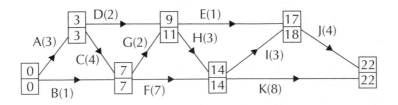

Q5 Shaniqua is creating a video for a school project and has drawn up a plan listing all the tasks she has to complete by the end of the year. Below are the tasks and their durations (in days).

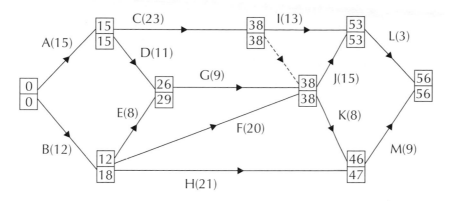

a) Draw a Gantt chart for the project.

b) If everything is going to schedule, which activities will definitely be happening at noon on:
   (i) Day 16 of the project?
   (ii) Day 31 of the project?

c) Shaniqua is told she can enlist any number of year 7s to help complete her project. Schedule the project so that it's completed within its critical time, assuming year 7s are able to complete the tasks in the correct times.

d) How many year 7s will she need?

Q6 a) Find the numbers represented by the letters *a–g* in the activity network below.

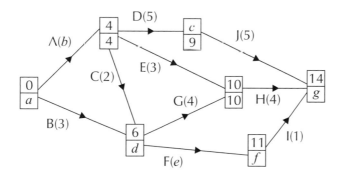

b) (i) Explain what is meant by a critical path.
   (ii) Identify both critical paths in the activity network.

c) Explain why activity E isn't a critical activity.

d) State the critical time for the project. (The times given are in hours.)

e) Work out the total float for activities B, E and I.

f) Draw a Gantt chart for the project.

g) Calculate the lower bound for the number of workers required to complete the project in the critical time.

h) Construct a scheduling diagram to show that the lower bound number of workers is sufficient to complete the project in the critical time.

1   The network in **Figure 1** shows the activities involved in a process.
    The number in brackets on each arc gives the time, in days, taken to complete the activity.

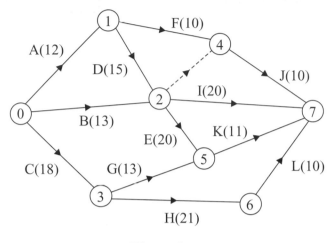

Figure 1

a) Calculate the early event time and the late event time for each event.
    Show them on a copy of the diagram.

    (4 marks)

b) Determine the critical activities and the length of the critical path.

    (2 marks)

c) Calculate the total float on each of activities F and G. Show your working.

    (3 marks)

d) Draw a cascade (Gantt) chart for the process.

    (4 marks)

e) Calculate a lower bound for the number of workers needed to complete
    the project in the minimum time. You must show your working.

    (2 marks)

f) Schedule the activities, using as few workers as possible,
    so that the project is completed in 58 days.

    (3 marks)

g) Comment on your answer to part f) regarding the lower bound
    you calculated in part e).

    (1 mark)

2   a)   This precedence table contains
         information about a project. Draw
         an activity network for the project,
         using exactly two dummies.
                                    (5 marks)

    b)   Explain why each dummy is needed.

                                    (2 marks)

Activity	Immediately preceding activities
A	—
B	—
C	A
D	B, C
E	B
F	D
G	E
H	F, G
I	F, G
J	H, I

3   **Figure 2** shows an activity network for a project. The duration of each activity is shown
    in days. The sum of all the activity times is 112 days.

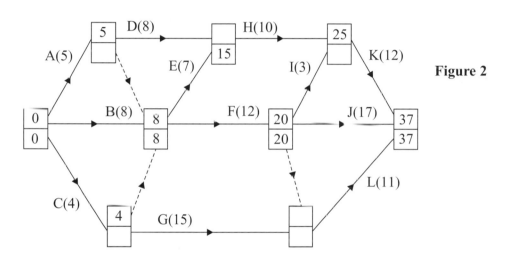

Figure 2

    a)   Some of the early and late event times are shown.
         Complete the diagram by calculating the missing early and late event times.
                                                                        (3 marks)

    b)   There are two critical paths for this network. State them both.
                                                                        (2 marks)

    c)   Find a lower bound for the number of workers required to complete
         the project in the critical time. Show your working.
                                                                        (2 marks)

    d)   Which activities must be happening on day 23? Explain how you know this.
                                                                        (3 marks)

    e)   Schedule the activities so that the project is completed in the minimum
         number of days. You must use as few workers as possible.
                                                                        (3 marks)

    f)   The supervisor realises at midday on day 14 that activity D has not yet
         been started. Determine if the project can still be finished on time.
         Explain your answer.
                                                                        (2 marks)

1. Linear Programs

Learning Objectives:

- Be able to understand and use all of the definitions used in linear programming.
- Be able to set up a linear program from a wordy problem, and vice versa.

Linear programming is a way of finding the optimal solution to a problem, subject to certain constraints. It's useful when a company wants to maximise profit (or time efficiency, etc.), but is limited by costs and resources.

Definitions

The **aim** of linear programming is to produce an **optimal solution** to a **problem** — e.g. to find the solution that gives the **maximum profit** to a manufacturer, based on **conditions** that would affect it, such as **limited time** or **materials**. Before you start having a go at linear programming problems, there are a few **terms** you need to know:

Decision variable

In any problem, you'll have things that are being **produced** (or **bought** or **sold** etc.) — e.g. jars of jam or different types of books. The **amount** of each thing is represented by letters — x, y, z etc. These are called the **decision variables**.

Constraints

The **constraints** are the **factors** that **limit** the problem, e.g. a limited number of workers available. The constraints are written as **inequalities** in terms of the **decision variables**. Most problems will have **non-negativity constraints**. This just means that the decision variables **can't** be **negative** — it wouldn't make sense to have a solution that produces –2 books.

Tip: The non-negativity constraints are usually written as x, $y \geq 0$.

Objective function

The **objective function** represents the thing you're trying to **maximise** or **minimise**, e.g. **profit** or **cost**. It's usually an **equation** written in terms of the **decision variables**.

Feasible solution

A **feasible solution** is a solution that **satisfies** all the **constraints**. It'll give you a **value** for each of the **decision variables**. On a **graph**, the **set** of feasible solutions lie inside the **feasible region** (see page 119).

Optimal solution

You're aiming to **optimise** the objective function — that's finding a solution within the feasible region that maximises (or minimises) the **objective function**. This is an **optimal solution**, and there can be **more than one**.

In the following linear programming problem, identify the objective function, decision variables and constraints.

A company that produces inflatable penguins wants to maximise profits £P. They produce 3 types of penguin — emperor (E), gentoo (G) and Adélie (A). They must produce at least 10 of each type of penguin every day, but don't have the equipment to produce more than 50.

▪ The objective function is   profit, £P,   which needs to be maximised.

▪ The decision variables are the number of each type of penguin to be produced, i.e. the number of:

emperor (E), gentoo (G) and Adélie (A).

▪ The constraints are the limits on production:

The number of each type of penguin must be 10 or more.
The total number of penguins must be no more than 50.

Tip: Determining the constraints is the trickiest part in setting up linear programming problems. There's more on this in the next section.

Exercise 1.1

Q1   For the following linear programming problems, state the decision variables, the objective function and the constraints.

a)   Maximise $P = 5x + 7y$
Subject to $5x + 2y < 4$
$x + y \geq 1$
$x, y \geq 0$

b)   Minimise $C = 200h + 250a$
Subject to $50h + 20a \leq 1200$
$h + a \leq 30$
$h, a \geq 0$

c)   Maximise $W = 2x + 3y + 4z$
Subject to $x, y, z > 0$
$3x - y + z \leq 0$
$2x \geq y$

Q2   Briefly explain what is meant by non-negativity constraints.

Q3   A clothing company makes football shirts for both home and away kits. The company can produce up to 900 shirts per day (x home shirts and y away shirts) but is required to make at least twice as many home shirts as away shirts. Home shirts make £2 profit and away shirts make £1.50 profit, and the company wants to maximise its profits £P.

a)   What are the decision variables?

b)   What's the objective function?

c)   Explain whether or not the problem needs non-negativity constraints, and if so write them down.

d)   What are all the other constraints for this problem?

Setting up linear programming problems

Sometimes you'll have to set up the constraints and objective function yourself by **interpreting** the information given in the question. Often you'll be presented with a **wordy** problem and asked to turn the information into **inequalities** that describe the **constraints**.

Tip: If the question says "at least" you'll need a $\geq$ sign. If it says "no more than", "up to" or "cannot exceed" you'll need a $\leq$ sign. Don't get these confused with situations that need 'more than' ($>$) or 'less than' ($<$) a certain number.

- A company might be **limited** by **how many** products they can make — say, for example, they produce x balls and y frisbees, but only have machinery to produce **100 units a day**. This is shown by the inequality $x + y \leq 100$.

- They might also have a **quota** as to how many they must produce — if they have to produce **at least** 50 units a day, then $x + y \geq 50$.

- Sometimes sales figures show that a certain product sells better than another. In this case, they decide they want to produce **at least 3 balls, x, for every 2 frisbees, y.** Be **careful** not to fall for the trap here — the inequality **isn't** $3x \geq 2y$ as you might expect. That would allow 2 balls and 2 frisbees ($6 \geq 4$), which **isn't** at least 3 balls for every 2 frisbees. Another way of looking at it is that the **number of balls** must be **at least** $\frac{3}{2}$ (i.e. **1.5**) **times** the **number of frisbees**. This gives $x \geq 1.5y$, or $2x \geq 3y$.

- For the **objective function**, just look at **what** the company is trying to **maximise** or **minimise**, and how this is relevant to the **decision variables**. If the aim is to **maximise profit** (£P), then you'll want to know **how much** each variable makes when it sells. If balls (x) make £3 and frisbees (y) make £4 then the **objective function** is **£P = 3x + 4y**, which is to be **maximised**.

Sometimes when the question gives a **lot of information** all at once you might find it easier to set up a **table** to display it. This way you can just read off the inequalities from each row or column.

Example

Set up the following as a linear programming problem, identifying the objective function and writing out the constraints as inequalities.

A company makes garden furniture, and produces both picnic tables and benches. It takes 5 hours to make a picnic table and 2 hours to paint it. It takes 3 hours to make a bench and 1 hour to paint it. In a week, there are 100 hours allocated to construction and 50 hours allocated to painting. Picnic tables are sold for a profit of £30 and benches are sold for a profit of £10. The company wants to maximise their weekly profit.

- To make the information easier to process, put it into a table:

Item of furniture	Construction time	Painting time	Profit (£)
Picnic table	5	2	30
Bench	3	1	10
Total time available:	100	50	

- Now use the table to identify all the different parts of the problem and come up with the inequalities.
- The **decision variables** are the **number of picnic tables** and the **number of benches**, so let x = number of picnic tables and y = number of benches.

- The first **constraint** is for **construction** — making a picnic table takes 5 hours, so x tables will take $5x$ hours. Making a bench takes 3 hours, so y benches will take $3y$ hours. There are a **total** of 100 hours available, so this gives the inequality $5x + 3y \leq 100$.

- The second constraint is for **painting**. There are 50 hours available — a table takes 2 hours to paint and a bench takes 1 hour to paint, giving the inequality $2x + y \leq 50$.

- The **objective function** to be **maximised** is **profit**. Each picnic table makes a profit of £30, so x tables make a profit of £$30x$. Each bench makes a profit of £10, so y benches make a profit of £$10y$. Let P be the profit, then the aim is to maximise £$P = 30x + 10y$.

- So the problem can be written as:

  Maximise $\qquad\qquad\qquad$ £$P = 30x + 10y$
  Subject to the constraints $\quad 5x + 3y \leq 100$
  $\qquad\qquad\qquad\qquad\qquad 2x + y \leq 50$
  $\qquad\qquad\qquad\qquad\qquad x, y \geq 0$

Tip: Don't forget the non-negativity constraints (you can't have a negative number of picnic benches).

You may also be asked to go in the **other direction** and write out **inequalities** in **words**. This is fairly easy if you already know how to form inequalities, but it's still worth making sure you know how to do it.

Example

Maureen runs a theatre and needs to order three types of snack before the next show — ice cream (x), sweets (y) and crisps (z).

The member of staff who normally deals with ordering products is off sick, but he's left the details he uses for ordering snacks on his desk. Maureen wants to understand the information before ordering so that she doesn't make any mistakes.

Tip: This example uses 3 variables, but it's no different to those with 2 — just deal with each of the inequalities one at a time and keep in mind which letter represents which snack.

Describe, in words, what the following information shows.

$\qquad$ **Maximise** $\qquad\qquad\qquad$ **£$P = x + 0.5y + z$**
$\qquad$ **Subject to the constraints** $\;\; x, y, z \geq 20$
$\qquad\qquad\qquad\qquad\qquad\quad\; x + y + z \leq 120$
$\qquad\qquad\qquad\qquad\qquad\quad\; y \geq 2x$

- The objective function is **profit, £P**, and this needs to be **maximised**. Looking at the expression, ice cream and crisps make £1 profit and sweets make 50p.

- The first constraint says that x, y and z must be **at least** a certain value. Maureen must order at least 20 of each product.

- The next constraint has a $\leq$ sign, so it's setting a limit on the number of products she orders (perhaps because they don't expect more than a certain number of customers, or they have limited space). The **combined total** of snacks ordered must be **no more** than 120.

- The final constraint shows that the number of bags of sweets bought must be **at least twice** the number of ice creams bought. Or, in other words, she must buy **at least** 2 bags of sweets for every ice cream.

Q1 A company produces milk frothers, and are buying two components — heating elements (x) and frothing motors (y). The company accountant has produced the following linear programming problem for buying the two types of component:

$$\begin{aligned} \text{Minimise} \quad & £C = 2x + 3y \\ \text{Subject to the constraints} \quad & x, y \geq 5 \\ & x + y \leq 20 \\ & x + 2y \leq 30 \\ & 3y \leq 5x \end{aligned}$$

Describe, in words, what the objective function and constraints are.

Q1 Hint: Make sure you don't get the numbers the wrong way round on the final constraint (see page 116).

Q2 An electronics company makes two MP3 players — one has a 16GB capacity and the other 32GB. Loading software onto the MP3 players takes 5 mins for the 16GB model and 3 mins for the 32GB. In a single production run there are 3 hours in total available for loading software. Before leaving the factory, all MP3 players have to be checked by quality control. It takes 2 mins to check the 16GB model and 3 mins for the 32GB model. Quality control is available for 2½ hours per production run.

The company makes £40 profit from the sale of each 16GB model and £30 from the 32GB model — it wishes to maximise its potential profit per production run.

a) Complete the following table showing this information.

MP3 Player Size	Software	Quality control	Profit (£)
16GB			
32GB			
Total time			

b) Let x be the number of 16GB models produced per production run.
Let y be the number of 32GB models produced per production run.
Let £P be the total potential profit per production run.
Write down the objective function P in terms of x and y.

c) Write down the constraints for this linear programming problem.

Q2 Hint: This much text might look scary — just do it step by step and use the table to help.

Q3 A shop sells small and large boxes of fireworks. The suppliers charge £3 for a small box of fireworks and £6 for a large box. The shop has used information from pre-orders to come up with a list of constraints:

The shop wants to buy at least 90 boxes in total.
They will sell both small and large boxes.
They will sell at least twice as many small boxes as large.

The supplier can provide a maximum of 120 small boxes of fireworks and 80 large boxes.

Let x be the number of small boxes the shop buys from its suppliers and y be the number of large boxes it buys.

Formulate this information as a linear programming problem, writing out all the constraints as inequalities in terms of x and y and identifying a suitable objective function, stating how it would be optimised.

Q3 Hint: Optimising doesn't necessarily involve maximising profits — in this case it wants you to minimise something.

2. Solving Linear Programming Problems

Learning Objectives:
- Be able to plot the constraints of a linear programming problem on a graph and find the feasible region.
- Be able to use the objective line method to find the optimal solution to a problem.
- Be able to use the vertex method to find the optimal solution to a problem.
- Be able to find the optimal integer solution to a problem.

Now you know how to set up linear programming problems, you can start actually solving them. You need to know two ways of doing this — the objective line method and the vertex method. For both of these you need to start by plotting the constraints on a graph.

Feasible regions

Plotting the constraints on a **graph** helps you see the **feasible solutions** clearly (those that satisfy all of the constraints).

- Draw each of the **constraints** as a **line** on the graph. All you have to do is **change** the **inequality sign** to an **equals sign** and plot the line. If you find it easier, **rearrange** the equation into the form $y = mx + c$.

- Then you have to **decide** which bit of the graph you **want** — whether the solution will be **above** or **below** the line. This will depend on the **inequality sign**. If you're not sure, put the **coordinates** of a point (e.g. the origin) into the equation and see if it **satisfies** the inequality.

- Once you've decided which bit you want, **shade** the region you **don't want**. This way, when you put all the constraints on the graph, the **unshaded region** (the bit you want) is easy to see. Your finished graph should have an area, **bounded** by the lines of the **constraints**, that **hasn't** been **shaded**. This is the **feasible region**.

- If the inequality sign is < or >, use a **dotted line** — this means you **don't** include the line in the region. If the inequality sign is ≤ or ≥ then use a **solid** line, so the line **is included** in the range of solutions.

- Once you've drawn **all** the constraints on the graph, you'll be able to solve the problem. Don't forget the **non-negativity constraints** — they'll limit the graph to the **first quadrant**.

- The **coordinates** of any point inside the **unshaded area will satisfy all** the **constraints**.

Tip: To see which bit of the graph you want, rearrange the inequality into the form $y = mx + c$, then think about which sign you'd use.
For $y \leq mx + c$ (or <), you want the bit **underneath** the line, and if it's $y \geq mx + c$ (or >) then you want the bit **above** the line.

Example

On a graph, show the constraints $x + y \leq 5$, $3x - y \geq 2$, $y > 1$ and $x, y \geq 0$. Label the feasible region R.

- Rearranging the inequalities into '$y = mx + c$' form gives:
$$y \leq 5 - x$$
$$y \leq 3x - 2$$
$$y > 1$$

- The decision variables are represented by the x- and y-axes, and the non-negativity constraints $x, y \geq 0$ restrict us to the positive quadrant.

- Once you've sorted out your constraints, just draw a **set of axes** and plot each constraint on the **same** axes.

- For the first constraint, **replace** the ≤ with = and plot a straight line:

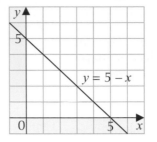

- To work out which section to **shade out**, choose a point **on one side** of the line and see if it **satisfies** the inequality — say the origin.

$y \leq 5 - x \Rightarrow 0 \leq 5 - 0$ This is **correct**, so shade out the **other side**:
(above the line)

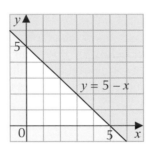

- The next inequality is $y \leq 3x - 2$ so draw the line of $y = 3x - 2$ and shade out the region that **doesn't** satisfy the inequality (in this case, shade everything above the line):

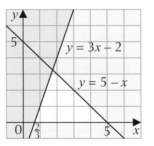

- For the final inequality, follow the usual method but notice the > sign — make the line **dotted** to show it's not included in the feasible region.

- The **feasible region** is the bit that's left **unshaded** — label this R.

Tip: You can check the feasible region is correct by choosing a point inside (say (2, 2)) and making sure it satisfies all the inequalities.

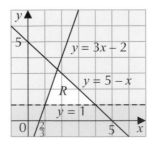

Q1 a) On the same set of axes, plot the following inequalities, shading out the region that doesn't satisfy the inequalities.

$y \leq 2x - 3 \qquad x \leq 4 \qquad y \geq 1$

   b) Label the unshaded feasible region R.

Q2 a) On the same set of axes, plot the following inequalities, shading out the region that doesn't satisfy the inequalities.

$y < \frac{x}{2} + 2 \qquad x \leq 5 \qquad y < 6 - x$

   b) Label the unshaded feasible region R.

Q2 Hint: Remember to check if the lines should be solid or dashed (see page 119).

Q3 Write down the constraints represented by the diagram below.

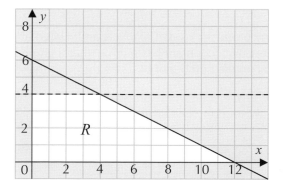

Q4 Write down the constraints represented by the diagram below.

Q5 a) On the same set of axes, plot the following inequalities, shading out the region that doesn't satisfy the inequalities.

$x > 1 \qquad y + 1 \geq x \qquad x + 2y - 10 \leq 0$

   b) Label the unshaded feasible region R.

Q5 Hint: Remember, rearranging them into the form '$y = mx + c$' will make graphing the inequalities easier.

Q6 PawsPlayPets produce collars for both cats and dogs. In a single
production run the company makes c cat collars and d dog collars.
For every two cat collars they make at least three dog collars.
A production run lasts two hours. A cat collar takes 3 minutes
to produce and a dog collar takes 2 minutes.

a) Write a list of constraints the company must follow in terms of
c and d, simplifying where possible.

b) Plot these constraints on a graph and label the feasible region R.

Q7 A small company produces two types of pen — black (y) and blue (x).
They're limited as to how many of each type of pen they can produce
each day by some constraints, shown on the graph below.

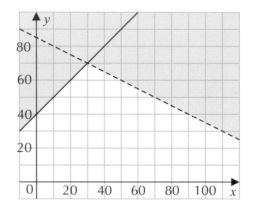

a) Write down the constraints shown by the graph.

b) An employee points out that they can't make more than 100 blue
pens or more than 60 black pens in a day. Add these constraints
to a copy of the graph.

c) There's another pair of constraints that haven't been taken into
account. What are these? Add them to the copy of the graph.

Q8 A textiles company produces x small blankets and y large blankets
in a day. The company accountant has put together a graph showing the
various constraints on the number of blankets they can make each day.

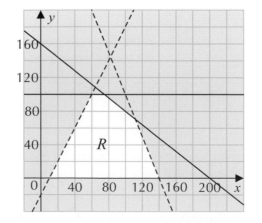

Write down all the constraints shown by the graph.

Optimal solutions — the objective line method

Once you've drawn a graph showing the constraints you can use it to **solve** the linear programming problem and find the **optimal solution**.

- All the points in the **feasible region** (see page 119) satisfy all the **constraints** in the problem.

- You need to be able to work out which point (or points) also **optimises** the **objective function**.

- The objective function is usually of the form $Z = ax + by$, where Z either needs to be **maximised** (e.g. profit) or **minimised** (e.g. cost) to give the **optimal solution**.

The Objective Line Method

1. Draw the **straight line** $Z = ax + by$, choosing a **fixed value** of Z (a and b will be given in the question). This is called an **objective line**.

2. If you're trying to **maximise** Z, move the line to the **right**, keeping it **parallel** to the original line. As you do this, the value of Z **increases**. The **optimal solution** will be the **last point** within the **feasible region** that the objective line touches.

3. If you're trying to **minimise** Z, the **optimal solution** will be the **last point** within the **feasible region** that the objective line touches as you slide it to the **left**. As you move it to the left, the value of Z **decreases**.

Tip: This is sometimes called the ruler method, as a good way to do it is to slide a ruler over the graph parallel to the objective line.

When you draw your **first** objective line, you can use **any value** for Z. Pick one that makes the line **easier** to draw — e.g. let Z be a **multiple** of both a and b so that the **intercepts** with the axes are **easy** to find.

Example

Maximise the profit $£P = 2x + 3y$ in the linear programming problem from the example on page 120. The graph below represents the constraints.

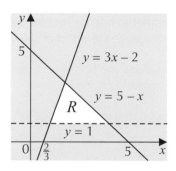

- Choose a value of P that's **divisible** by both 2 and 3 — say 6. If $P = 6$ then $6 = 2x + 3y$. When $x = 0$, $y = 2$ and when $y = 0$, $x = 3$.

- Now plot a **straight line** on the graph that goes through the points $(0, 2)$ and $(3, 0)$ — this is an **objective line**:

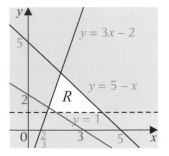

Tip: You might want to draw a few more lines using the ruler as you drag it along the page so you can keep track of where you are.

- Now take a **ruler** and place it along the line. Then **slide** it up and right keeping the ruler **parallel** to the line — as you do this, the value of P increases.

- Keep sliding the ruler until it's no longer within the **feasible region**. The **last point** within R it touches is the **optimal solution**.

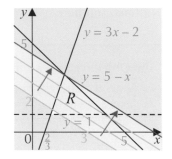

Tip: If you had to minimise P, you'd slide the ruler down and left.

- From the diagram you can see this point is the **intersection** between the lines $y = 3x - 2$ and $y = 5 - x$. To find the point of intersection, solve these **simultaneous equations**. This will give you the optimal solution.

- Substituting $y = 5 - x$ into $y = 3x - 2$ gives:

$$5 - x = 3x - 2 \ \Rightarrow \ 4x = 7 \ \Rightarrow \ x = \frac{7}{4}$$

- Putting $x = \frac{7}{4}$ into $y = 5 - x$ gives $y = \frac{13}{4}$

- Now put these values into the **objective function** to find P:

$$P = 2x + 3y = \frac{14}{4} + \frac{39}{4} = \frac{53}{4} = 13.25$$

- So the maximum value of P is 13.25, which occurs at $(\frac{7}{4}, \frac{13}{4})$.

Sometimes the optimal solution isn't just a single point.

- If the objective line is **parallel** to one of the **constraints**, you might end up with a **section of a line** that gives the **optimal solution**.

- If this happens, **any point** along the line is an optimal solution (as long as it's **inside** the **feasible region**).

- This shows that there can be **more than one** optimal solution to a problem.

Tip: If the optimal solution is a dotted line then the actual solution will just be a line very close to it. You don't need to worry about this in D1 though.

Q1 The following graph shows the feasible region of a linear programming problem. The objective function to be maximised is $Z = 2x + y$.

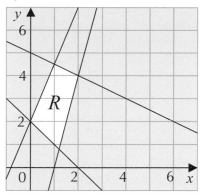

a) On a copy of the graph, show the objective line $2x + y = 2$.

b) Show at least two more objective lines, including the line that passes through the point that will give the optimal solution.

Q2 Use a copy of the graph below and the objective line method to maximise the following functions:

a) $Z = 2x + 3y$ b) $Z = 3x + 2y$ c) $Z = 3x - 2y$

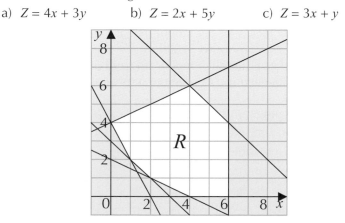

Q2 Hint: You're not given the equations of the constraints here, but you can read the coordinates off the graph.

Q3 Use a copy of the graph below and the objective line method to minimise the following functions:

a) $Z = 4x + 3y$ b) $Z = 2x + 5y$ c) $Z = 3x + y$

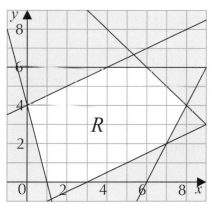

Q3 Hint: Minimising is done the same way as maximising, but instead of sliding the ruler up and right you slide it down and left.

Q4 A company produces a linear programming problem. The decision variables x and y are subject to the constraints shown on the graph:

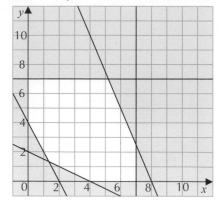

a) Two more constraints must be applied to the problem:

$$x + y \geq 3 \qquad x + y \leq 11$$

Add these to a copy of the graph and label the feasible region R.

b) The company wishes to maximise its takings $£T = 3x + 2y$. Use the objective line method to find the maximum takings, stating the values of x and y at this point.

c) The company decides that instead it would rather minimise its costs, $£C = x + 4y$. Use the objective line method and your graph from part a) to find the minimum cost, stating the values of x and y.

Q5 A linear programming problem is formulated as follows:

Minimise $C = 0.8x + 1.2y$
Subject to $x \geq 0$
$12 \leq y \leq 50$
$x + y \geq 40$
$6x + 5y \leq 300$

a) Plot a graph showing these constraints.

b) Use the objective line method to solve the problem.

Q6 A company that grows Christmas trees grows them to two different heights — 'indoor' and 'outdoor'. The land available is sufficient to grow 300 indoor trees. Outdoor trees require twice as much space as indoor trees.
The cost of water throughout the growing season is £4 per indoor tree and £5 per outdoor tree. The company has a £1000 water budget.
The cost of insecticides is £2 per indoor tree and £8 per outdoor tree. The budget for chemicals is also £1000.
The company makes £2 on each indoor tree and £5 on each outdoor tree, and wishes to maximise its profit (assuming all trees are sold).

a) If the company grows x indoor trees and y outdoor trees, write down the objective function stating clearly whether it should be maximised or minimised.

b) Show that the insecticide constraint is $x + 4y \leq 500$.

c) List all the other constraints.

d) Draw a graph of the feasible region.

e) Use the objective line method to solve the problem.

Optimal solutions — the vertex method

The **optimal solution** for the example on page 124 was found at a **vertex** of the **feasible region**. This isn't a coincidence — if you've had a go at some more linear programming problems, you'll have noticed that the optimal solutions **always** occur at a vertex (or an **edge**) of the feasible region. This gives you another way to solve the problem.

The Vertex Method

1. Find the x- and y-values of the **vertices** of the **feasible region**. You do this by solving the **simultaneous equations** of the **lines** that **intersect** at each vertex.

2. Put these values into the **objective function** $Z = ax + by$ to find the value of Z.

3. Look at the Z values and work out which is the **optimal value**. Depending on your objective function, this might be either the **smallest** (if you're trying to **minimise** Z) or the **largest** (if you're trying to **maximise** Z).

Tip: If two vertices A and B produce the same Z value, this means that all points along the edge AB are also optimal solutions.

Even if it looks **obvious** from the graph, you still have to **test** each vertex of the feasible region. Sometimes the **origin** will be one of the vertices — it's really easy to test, as the objective function will usually be equal to **0** there. Don't forget vertices on the **x-** and **y-axes** too.

Example

Minimise $Z = 8x + 9y$, subject to the constraints:

$$2x + y \geq 6$$
$$x - 2y \leq 2$$
$$x, y \leq 4$$
$$x, y \geq 0.$$

- Start by drawing the constraints on a graph. This way you'll be able to identify the vertices. Here A, B, C and D are the vertices of the feasible region R.

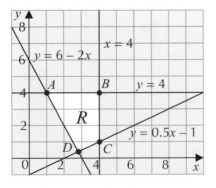

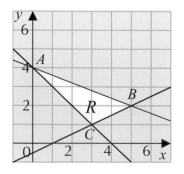

Point A is the intersection of the lines $y = 6 - 2x$ and $y = 4$, so A has coordinates $(1, 4)$.

Point B is the intersection of the lines $x = 4$ and $y = 4$, so B has coordinates $(4, 4)$.

Point C is the intersection of the lines $x = 4$ and $y = 0.5x - 1$, so C has coordinates $(4, 1)$.

Point D is the intersection of the lines $y = 6 - 2x$ and $y = 0.5x - 1$, which has coordinates $(\frac{14}{5}, \frac{2}{5})$.

■ Putting these values into the objective function $Z = 8x + 9y$:

$$\text{At } A, Z = (8 \times 1) + (9 \times 4) = 44$$
$$\text{At } B, Z = (8 \times 4) + (9 \times 4) = 68$$
$$\text{At } C, Z = (8 \times 4) + (9 \times 1) = 41$$
$$\text{At } D, Z = (8 \times 2.8) + (9 \times 0.4) = 26$$

■ So the minimum value of Z is 26, which occurs at $(\frac{14}{5}, \frac{2}{5})$.

Tip: You can sometimes just read off the coordinates from your graph (as long as it's accurate).

Tip: The coordinates of D were found by solving simultaneous equations, like in the example on page 124.

Exercise 2.3

Tip: Q1 is just a recap — you'll need to be able to solve simultaneous equations later in the exercise.

Q1 Solve the following simultaneous equations:
a) $y = 2x - 3$ and $y = 6 - x$
b) $x + 4y = 14$ and $9x - 2y + 26 = 0$
c) $2y = 4x - 19$ and $6x + 2y - 23 = 0$

Q2 Find the value of $P = 2x + 3y$ at each vertex of the feasible region in the graph below.

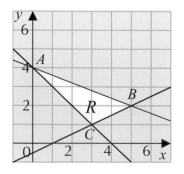

Q3 A linear programming problem has the following constraints:

$$y \le 4 \qquad y \le x + 2 \qquad y \ge 2x - 8 \qquad y \le 12 - 2x \qquad 2y \ge 4 - x$$

a) Plot these constraints on a graph and label the feasible region R.
b) The objective for this problem is to maximise $Z = x + 5y$. Use the vertex method to find an optimal solution.

Q4 A linear programming problem is formulated as follows:

Maximise $\qquad P = 3x + 7y$

Subject to the constraints $\qquad x - y \leq 15$

$\qquad\qquad 2x + 5y \geq 10$

$\qquad\qquad x - 2y + 40 \geq 0$

$\qquad\qquad y \leq 3x$

$\qquad\qquad 2x + y \leq 60$

$\qquad\qquad x, y \geq 0$

a) Plot these constraints on a graph, labelling the feasible region R.

b) Use simultaneous equations to show that two of the vertices of the feasible region have coordinates (25, 10) and (16, 28).

c) One of these two vertices gives an optimal solution. Which is it?

Q4 b) Hint: Use your graph from part a) to work out which lines are meeting at the points (25, 10) and (16, 28).

Q5 A linear programming problem is formulated as follows:

Minimise $\qquad C = 3x + y$

Subject to the constraints $\qquad y \leq 250$

$\qquad\qquad x - 2y + 400 \geq 0$

$\qquad\qquad y \leq 450 - x$

$\qquad\qquad y + 2x \geq 300$

$\qquad\qquad 2y \geq 100 + x$

a) Plot these constraints on a graph, labelling the feasible region R.

b) Use the vertex method to solve the problem, giving the coordinates of the optimal solution and stating the value of C at this point.

Q5 Hint: Remember, if it's not clear from the graph what the coordinates of a vertex are you should use simultaneous equations.

Q6 A company makes two different types of model train, steam and electric, and has the capacity to make up to 60 trains per week. Assembling a steam train takes 2 hours, while an electric train takes 1 hour. Painting and inscribing a steam train takes 1 hour, while the same process takes 4 hours for an electric train.
In a week the company dedicates 100 hours to assembling trains and 180 hours to painting and inscribing.
Steam trains sell for £32 profit, while electric trains sell for £20 profit. The company wants to maximise its profit.

a) Formulate this as a linear programming problem.

b) Use the vertex method to find an optimal solution and say how many of each train should be made.

Q7 A factory manufactures two different types of china ornaments — a cat and a dog. The factory must manufacture between 30 and 70 ornaments per production run. Sales figures show the factory should produce at least 2 dogs for every 5 cats, and that twice the number of cats must be at least 20 more than the number of dogs.
It costs the factory £2 to produce a cat ornament and £4 for a dog ornament. The factory wants to minimise costs.
Let x be the number of cat ornaments and y be the number of dog ornaments produced per production run. Let the costs be £C.

a) Formulate this as a linear programming problem, stating the objective function and listing all of the constraints.

b) Draw a graph to show the feasible region and use the vertex method to find the optimal solution of the problem formulated in a).

c) Comment on your solution — is this solution realistic?

Q7 Hint: 'At least 2 dogs for every 5 cats' is like saying 'the number of cats can not be bigger than $\frac{5}{2}$ times the number of dogs (see page 116).

Optimal integer solutions

- Sometimes it's fine to have **non-integer solutions** to linear programming problems — for example, if you were making different **fruit juices**, you could realistically have 3.5 litres of one type of juice and 4.5 litres of another.

- However, if you were making **garden furniture**, you couldn't make 3.5 tables and 4.5 benches — so you need **integer solutions**.

- You won't always be **told** whether a problem needs integer solutions, so you might have to **work it out** for yourself. It's common sense really — just think about whether you can have **fractions** of the **decision variables**.

You can use both the **objective line method** (page 123) and the **vertex method** (page 127) to find optimal integer solutions. It's important when using these that your **graph** is as **clear** as possible.

To use the **objective line method**:

- You use this method in exactly the **same way** as before, but instead of looking for the last **vertex** the line touches, you need to look for the last **point** with **integer coordinates** in the **feasible region**.

- This might be hard to do if your graph isn't very **accurate**, or if the scale isn't **clear**.

To use the **vertex method**

- Start by finding which **vertex** gives an optimal solution as before.

- Then, consider all the points with **integer coordinates** that are **close by**. Make sure you **check** whether these points still **satisfy** the **constraints** though — test this **before** you put the values into the objective function.

Tip: Some problems have optimal integer solutions that are far away from the vertices of the feasible region, but you don't need to worry about these for D1.

- To test the integer solutions that are close by, just **round** the coordinates of the optimal solution up and down to create **4 new sets of coordinates**, and test those.

- Here, the optimal solution is **between** 4 and 5 on the x-axis and **between** 8 and 9 on the y-axis, so the 4 points you'd test are (4, 8), (4, 9), (5, 8) and (5, 9).

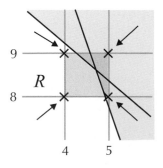

- It's easy to forget that **not all** the solutions near the optimal vertex will be **inside** the **feasible region** — you can check either **by eye** on an **accurate graph**, or put the **coordinates** into each of the **constraints**. In this case, (5, 8) and (5, 9) are outside the feasible region, so you'd just ignore those.

Example 1

The optimal solution to the problem on page 127 occurred at $(\frac{14}{5}, \frac{2}{5})$ (= (2.8, 0.4)). Find the optimal integer solution.

- Looking at the integers nearby gives you the points (3, 0), (3, 1), (2, 0) and (2, 1) to test.

- However, the point (3, 0) doesn't satisfy the constraint $x - 2y \leq 2$, and (2, 0) and (2, 1) don't satisfy $2x + y \geq 6$.

- So the optimal integer solution is at (3, 1), where $Z = (8 \times 3) + (9 \times 1) = \boxed{33}$

Tip: You won't always just end up with one solution — sometimes you'll have a few to test.

Example 2

A company makes designer dresses. It makes x ballgowns and y cocktail dresses, for a profit of £600 and £500 respectively, subject to the constraints $x + y \leq 9$, $3x - y \leq 9$, $y \leq 7$ and $x, y \geq 0$. Maximise the profit, $P = 600x + 500y$.

- Start by drawing the constraints on a graph:

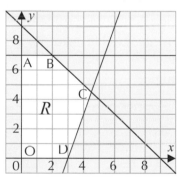

Tip: This example uses the vertex method, but you could also use the objective line method.

- The feasible region is the area *OABCD*, with coordinates $O(0, 0)$, $A(0, 7)$, $B(2, 7)$, $C(\frac{9}{2}, \frac{9}{2})$ and $D(3, 0)$.

- The value of P at each vertex is O: £0, A: £3500, B: £4700, C: £4950 and D: £1800.

- The maximum value of P is £4950, which occurs at $(\frac{9}{2}, \frac{9}{2})$ (= (4.5, 4.5)). However, making 4.5 dresses isn't possible, so an integer solution is needed.

- The integer coordinates near C are (4, 5), (5, 5), (5, 4) and (4, 4). (5, 5) and (5, 4) don't satisfy the constraint $3x - y \leq 9$ so are outside the feasible region.

- At (4, 5), $P = £4900$, and at (4, 4), $P = £4400$, so £4900 is the maximum profit.

- So the company needs to make 4 ballgowns and 5 cocktail dresses to make the maximum profit of £4900.

Q1 a) Identify the two constraints in the following graph (not including the non-negativity constraints).

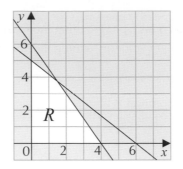

b) The point of intersection, P, between these two constraints gives the optimal solution for maximising the objective function $Z = 4x + 3y$. Find its coordinates.

c) Find the value of the objective function Z at P.

d) Find the value of Z at the closest points to P inside the feasible region that have integer coordinates.

e) Find the optimal integer solution.

Q2 The graph below shows the feasible region for a linear programming problem where Z is to be maximised.

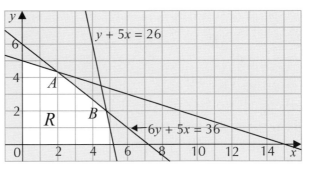

Q2 Hint: You may need to identify some of the constraints before finding the coordinates of the vertices.

a) Find the coordinates of the points labelled A and B.

b) Work out the value of $Z = 3x + 5y$ at the points A and B.

c) Deduce the optimal integer solution.

Q3 A linear programming problem has the following constraints:
$$0 \le 2y - x \le 6$$
$$5x + 2y \ge 12$$
$$4x + y \le 15$$

Q3 Hint: You'll need to plot 2 separate lines for the first constraint.

a) Plot these constraints on a graph and label the feasible region R.

b) The objective for this problem is to maximise $Z = x + 5y$. Find the optimal solution.

c) Find the optimal integer solution.

Q4 A linear programming problem is formulated as follows:

Maximise $\qquad Z = 9x + 8y$

Subject to the constraints $\qquad x + 4y \leq 100$

$\qquad\qquad\qquad\qquad\qquad 7x + 8y \leq 240$

$\qquad\qquad\qquad\qquad\qquad 7x + 6y \leq 210$

$\qquad\qquad\qquad\qquad\qquad x, y \geq 0$

a) Plot the constraints on a graph, labelling the feasible region R.

b) Find the optimal integer solution, stating the value of Z.

Q5 A linear programming problem is formulated as follows:

Minimise $\qquad C = 3x + 5y$

Subject to the constraints $\qquad 10 \leq x + y \leq 30$

$\qquad\qquad\qquad\qquad\qquad y \leq 3x$

$\qquad\qquad\qquad\qquad\qquad x + 4y \geq 20$

$\qquad\qquad\qquad\qquad\qquad x, y \geq 0$

a) Plot the constraints on a graph, labelling the feasible region R.

b) Find the optimal integer solution, stating the value of C.

Q6 A company makes two types of calculators — basic and scientific.
In each production cycle they can manufacture a total of 70 calculators.
The production involves two stages — construction and packaging.
The basic model takes 10 minutes to go through construction and
4 minutes to be packaged, while the scientific model takes 30 minutes
to go through construction but only 1 minute to be packaged.
The company has a maximum of 22½ hours for the construction stage
and 4 hours for packaging.
A basic calculator sells for £2.80 profit while a scientific calculator
sells for £4.60 profit, and the company wants to maximise profits.

a) Formulate this as a linear programming problem, defining the
decision variables and the objective function.

b) Plot the constraints on a graph and identify the feasible region.

c) Solve the problem and find an optimal solution.

Q6 c) Hint: Remember, you can't make a non-integer number of calculators.

Q7 Car Group Premium produce two types of car, offroad and hatchback,
by purchasing individual parts and assembling them at the factory.
In a single production run they must manufacture between 4 and 14
cars in total. From past sales figures they know they should produce
at least 3 offroaders for every 5 hatchbacks. The total production cost
of an offroader is £6000, while the production cost of a hatchback is
£3000. The company wants to minimise its costs.

Let x be the number of offroaders they produce per production run and
y the number of hatchbacks. Let the production cost be £C.

a) Formulate this as a linear programming problem, stating the
objective function and listing all of the constraints.

A further constraint is given by $2x \leq 3y + 4$.

b) Draw a graph to show the feasible region and solve the problem.

Review Exercise — Chapter 5

Q1 A company making photo frames have to purchase two raw materials: glass and wood.
They buy these in bulk — a pallet of glass costs £300 and a pallet of wood costs £200.
When ordering they must order a minimum of 5 pallets of glass and a minimum of 10 pallets of
wood. The total number of pallets purchased at a time must be at least 20. A further constraint
is given by $5x + 2y > 60$, where x is the number of pallets of glass and y is the number of pallets
of wood. The company wishes to minimise the cost of purchasing pallets of raw materials.

Formulate this as a linear programming problem, stating the objective function
and all of the constraints. You don't need to solve this problem.

Q2 Write down all constraints shown on the graph below.

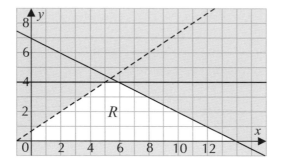

Q3 A company produces sticky notes in two varieties: standard size and jumbo size.
Their production process is subject to the following constraints, where x is
the number of standard packs and y is the number of jumbo packs:

$$x, y \geq 100$$
$$x + y \leq 500$$
$$y \leq 2x$$
$$x \leq 3y$$

a) Describe, in words, what each of these constraints shows.

b) Plot the constraints on a graph, labelling the feasible region R.

Q4 Use the graph below and the objective line method to maximise
the following objective functions:

a) $Z = x + y$ b) $Z = 2x + 5y$ c) $Z = 4x + y$

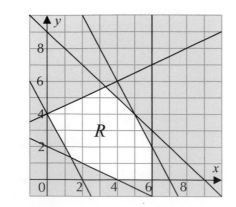

Q5   A linear programming problem is formulated as follows

    Maximise $Z = 3x + 2y$
    Subject to the constraints $x \geq 0$
                                      $2 \leq y \leq 6$
                                      $x + y \geq 4$
                                      $y \leq 9 - x$

a) Plot a graph showing these constraints.

b) Use the objective line method to solve the problem.

Q6   DontGetLost Ltd make satellite navigation systems for cars. They produce two models —
      square screen and widescreen. In each production run the company can manufacture
      a total of 25 machines but only a maximum of 10 can be widescreen. The square screen
      model takes half as long to produce as the widescreen model which takes 40 minutes.
      A production run lasts ten hours.

      The company wishes to maximise its profit — a square screen model generates £40 profit
      whilst the widescreen model generates £32 profit.

a) Formulate this as a linear programming problem. Define the decision variables and the
    objective function stating clearly whether this is to be maximised or minimised.

b) Plot the constraints on a graph and use the vertex method to solve the problem.

Q7 a) A linear programming problem has its optimal solution at (3.2, 2.8). Draw a diagram
        to illustrate this solution and the four closest points with integer solutions.

    b) State, with reason(s), whether or not you would need to test all four points in part b)
        in order to determine the optimal integer solution.

Q8   A company makes posters in two sizes: large and small. Large posters takes 10 minutes
      to print and small posters take 5 minutes to print. Each day has 250 minutes printing time.

      It takes 6 minutes to laminate a large poster and 4 minutes to laminate a small poster.
      There arc a total of 200 minutes laminating time each day.

      The company wants to sell at least as many large posters as small, and they need
      to sell at least 10 small posters each day. Large posters are sold for a profit of £6
      and small posters are sold for a profit of £3.50.

a) Write this out as a linear programming problem. Identify the decision variables,
    constraints and objective function.

b) Show the constraints for this problem graphically. Label the feasible region R.

c) Maximise the profit, using either the objective line method or the vertex method.
    Don't worry about integer solutions for now.

d) Use your answer to part c) to find the optimal integer solution.

1   Anna is selling red and white roses at a flower stall. She buys the flowers from a wholesaler, where red roses cost 75p each and white roses cost 60p each. Based on previous sales, she has come up with the following constraints:

- She will sell both red roses and white roses.

- She will sell more red roses than white roses.

- She will sell a total of at least 100 flowers.

- The wholesaler has 300 red roses and 200 white roses available.

Let x be the number of red roses she buys and y be the number of white roses she buys. Formulate this information as a linear programming problem.

Write out the constraints as inequalities and identify a suitable objective function, stating how it should be optimised. You do not need to solve this problem.

(7 marks)

2   The graph below shows the constraints of a linear programming problem. The feasible region is labelled R.

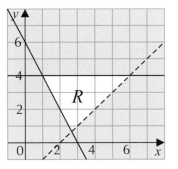

a)   Find the inequalities that produce R.

(4 marks)

b)   Find the coordinates of each vertex of R.

(4 marks)

The aim is to minimise $C = 4x + y$.

c)   Find the optimal solution and state where this value occurs.

(3 marks)

3   A company sells three packs of craft paper: bronze, silver and gold. Each pack is made up of three different types of paper: tissue paper, sugar paper and foil.

- The gold pack is made up of 6 sheets of foil, 15 sheets of sugar paper and 15 sheets of tissue paper.

- The silver pack is made up of 2 sheets of foil, 9 sheets of sugar paper and 4 sheets of tissue paper.

- The bronze pack is made up of 1 sheet of foil, 6 sheets of sugar paper and 1 sheet of tissue paper.

- Each day, there are 30 sheets of foil available, 120 sheets of sugar paper available and 60 sheets of tissue paper available.

- The company is trying to reduce the amount of foil used, so it uses at least three times as many sheets of sugar paper as of foil.

The company makes x gold packs, y silver packs and z bronze packs in a day.

a)   Apart from the non-negativity constraints, write out the other four constraints as inequalities in terms of x, y and z. Simplify each inequality where possible.

(8 marks)

b)   On Monday, the company decides to make the same number of silver packs as bronze packs.

(i)   Show that your inequalities from part (a) become
$$2x + y < 10$$
$$x + y \leq 8$$
$$3x + y \leq 12$$
$$2y \geq x$$
(3 marks)

(ii) On graph paper, draw a graph showing the constraints from part (i) above, as well as the non-negativity constraints. Label the feasible region R.
(5 marks)

(iii) Use your graph to work out the maximum number of packs the company can make on Monday.
(2 marks)

(iv) Gold packs are sold for a profit of £3.50, silver packs are sold for a profit of £2 and bronze packs are sold for a profit of £1. Use your answers to parts (ii) and (iii) to maximise the profit they make, and state how many of each type of pack they need to sell.
(3 marks)

1. Matchings

Learning Objectives:

- Know what bipartite graphs are and be able to draw them.
- Be able to use a bipartite graph to construct a matching.

Matchings are a way of allocating one set of nodes to another, taking into account what can and can't be matched. You'll often have to match people to tasks, based on what they can and can't do. The best way to work out a matching is to start with a bipartite graph — which you came across on p.32.

Bipartite graphs

The points in a graph are called **nodes** (or **vertices**) and the lines are called **arcs** (or **edges**) — this was covered in Chapter 2 (see page 32).

- A **bipartite graph** is made up of **two sets** of **nodes** that are **linked** by **arcs**. The arcs go from **one set** of nodes to the **other** — nodes within the **same set** can't be joined to each other.
- In lots of the examples you'll come across, one set of nodes will be the **people** and the other will be the **jobs** or **tasks** they have to do. You'll be told **who** can do which **job**.
- You might also come across bipartite graphs that have **two** sets of **people** — e.g. **girls** and **boys** being paired off for a dance.
- There doesn't have to be the **same number** of nodes in each set (like in the example below).

Tip: Sometimes the information will be given in a table instead of being written out.

Example 1

Jenny, Katie, Latika, Martyn and Nikki are planning a picnic. Jenny can bring sandwiches and crisps, Katie can bring sandwiches and pork pies, Latika can bring drinks, Martyn can bring pork pies and biscuits and Nikki can bring biscuits, quiche and crisps. Draw a bipartite graph to show this information.

First, list all the people on one side of the graph, and all the food (and drink) on the other side. Then draw lines connecting each person to all the items they can bring.

Tip: The lines show what each person can bring.

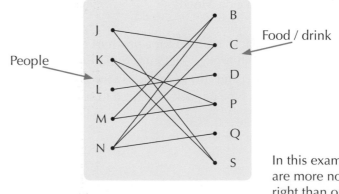

In this example, there are more nodes on the right than on the left.

Example 2

A teacher knows that some of her pupils are a bad influence on each other, so has drawn a bipartite graph (below) to help her work out a seating plan. Use the bipartite graph to work out who Poppy can sit by.

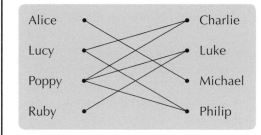

Just follow the arcs coming from Poppy's node — so

Poppy can sit by Charlie, Luke or Philip.

Tip: In this example, the lines show who each pupil can sit by.

Exercise 1.1

Q1 Four toddlers have the following preferences for snacks at nursery:
Ellie likes biscuits and satsumas
Isaac likes yoghurt and biscuits
Leah likes raisins
Rory likes biscuits, raisins and yoghurt
Draw a bipartite graph to show this information.

Q2 Draw a bipartite graph to show the following information:
A group of students play a variety of instruments. Jack can play the piano and saxophone, Kate plays the violin and flute, Andrea plays the guitar, saxophone and piano, Tom plays the cello and violin and Nicky plays the piano and flute.

Q3 In a factory, a group of workers can only undertake a job if they are trained for it. The table on the right details which jobs (labelled A-E) each worker is trained for.
Show this information in a bipartite graph.

	A	B	C	D	E
Toby	X				
Bill	X			X	
Anna		X			X
Sam	X	X	X	X	
Eve		X	X		

Q4 A family shares out household chores. Use the bipartite graph below to answer the following questions:
a) Which chores is David willing to do?
b) Who is happy to feed the dog?
c) Who is only prepared to do one chore?

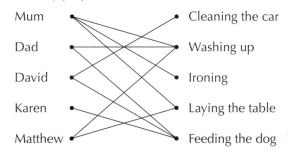

Matchings

Once you've drawn your bipartite graph showing who can do what, you need to work out a **solution** that assigns **one person** to **one job**. This is called a **matching**.

- In a matching, you can only have **one arc** for **each node** — so each person only does **one job** (and each job only has **one person** doing it). Matchings are **one-to-one**.

- You won't always be able to match **all** the nodes in one set with all the nodes in the other — it depends on who can do which tasks.

- If there are the **same number** of people as jobs, and each **job** is assigned to a **person**, the matching is said to be **complete**. So if there are x **nodes** in each set, a complete matching has x **arcs**.

- It's **not always possible** to have a complete matching — e.g. if there are **two jobs** that can only be done by the **same person**, one of the jobs **won't** be included in the matching.

- If a complete matching can't be done, you might have to find a **maximum** (or '**maximal**') **matching** — a matching that has the **greatest number** of arcs possible (so as many jobs as possible are being done). There can be **more than one** possible maximum matching.

Tip: You don't need to worry about the difference between 'maximal' and 'maximum' for D1.

Example 1

Use the bipartite graph from the previous page to come up with a complete matching for the teacher's seating plan.

- Start with the people who have the most **restrictions** — Alice can **only** sit by Michael and Ruby can **only** sit by Luke.

- Lucy and Poppy can both sit by either Charlie or Philip, so there are **two** complete matchings.

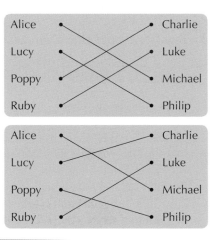

Example 2

Andy, Bahir, Carys and Daniel are going to a theme park. They can only afford to go on one ride each, and they each want to try out a different ride. Andy wants to go on the teacups or the big wheel, Bahir wants to go on the rollercoaster or the teacups, Carys wants to go on the log flume or the rollercoaster and Daniel only wants to go on the big wheel. Draw a bipartite graph to show this information, then use it to find a complete matching.

- List all the **people** on one side of the graph, and all the **rides** on the other side. Then draw lines linking each person to the rides they want to go on.

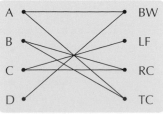

- To find a **complete matching**, you need to link **each person** to just **one ride**. Start with Daniel, as he **only** wants to go on the big wheel. This means that Andy will have to go on the teacups, then Bahir has to go on the rollercoaster and finally Carys has to go on the log flume.

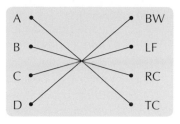

After a bad experience, Andy flatly refuses to go on the teacups again, so a complete matching is no longer possible.
Find a maximum matching for their next visit to the theme park.

Tip: Here, the information has changed, so you have to come up with a new matching. If it helps, draw out the new bipartite graph and work from that.

- Now, **both** Andy and Daniel **only** want to go on the big wheel — so you **won't** be able to find a complete matching. Just match as many people as you can for a **maximum matching**.

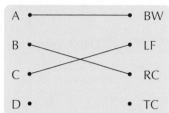

- You don't always have to draw your matching — you can just **write it out** instead. So this maximum matching would be Andy = big wheel, Bahir = rollercoaster and Carys = log flume.

Exercise 1.2

Q1 A group of friends are having a dinner party. Annabel is happy to make the starter or the dessert. Brendan is willing to provide drinks or the starter. Caroline is happy to make the main course or the dessert and Daniel is only willing to make the dessert.

a) Draw a bipartite graph to illustrate this information.

b) Find a complete matching for the model.

Q2 In Exercise 1.1 Question 1, the nursery has one snack available of each type for the toddlers. Find a complete matching so that every toddler has a snack that they like.

Q2 Hint: Use your bipartite graph from the previous exercise to help you answer this question.

Q3 In a project team there are 5 roles, team leader, facilitator, recorder, timekeeper and team member. The table below shows which roles a group of people are suited to.

	Team leader	Facilitator	Recorder	Timekeeper	Team member
Lamarr		X			X
Marcus	X	X			
Nadia			X	X	X
Oliver			X		X
Pippa	X				

a) Show this information in a bipartite graph.

b) Find a complete matching for the project team so that each person works in one role which they are suited to.

Q4 In Exercise 1.1 Question 4, every chore needs to be completed by one member of the family. Use the bipartite graph from that question to find a complete matching, if possible.

Q5 A row of six beach huts at the seaside are to be repainted in different colours to brighten them up. The owners are allowed to choose two preferences for the colours. Their choices are listed below:

      No. 1 — pink or blue
      No. 2 — yellow or blue
      No. 3 — green or orange
      No. 4 — red or green
      No. 5 — yellow or orange
      No. 6 — pink or red

a) Draw a bipartite graph to represent the possible colours for each beach hut.

The owners of No. 5 have decided they are not willing to be flexible and insist their hut is yellow.

b) Find a complete matching according to the owners' preferences so that every hut is painted a different colour.

> **Q5 Hint:** Even if you draw out the complete matching, it's a good idea to write down the matching as well.

Q6 In Exercise 1.1 Question 3, is it possible to form a complete matching? If yes, show the matching on a bipartite graph.

Q7 A group of workers A-F are to be allocated six tasks 1-6.
The table below shows the tasks each worker is qualified to do:

A	1, 4, 5
B	1
C	2, 3, 4, 5
D	4, 6
E	2
F	1, 3, 5

a) Draw a bipartite graph to illustrate this information.

b) Find a complete matching so that every job is completed by a qualified worker.

Q8 A group of neighbours want to hold a street party and need to share out the jobs. The people at no. 1 can bring drinks or provide decorations, no. 2 can organise the music, provide food or the tables and chairs, no. 3 can organise the music or the tables and chairs, no. 4 can provide food, drinks or decorations and no. 5 can organise either the tables and chairs or the decorations.

a) Draw a bipartite graph to illustrate who can do which jobs for the street party.

The people at no. 5 have a very busy week and decide they don't have time to organise decorations after all.

b) Find a complete matching so that all jobs are done and the street party can go ahead.

2. Maximum Matchings

It can sometimes be hard to find a complete matching, especially if the bipartite graph is really complicated. If your original matching isn't complete, you can often improve it by using the alternating path method.

Alternating paths

To find an alternating path, you start by drawing **any** matching from a bipartite graph. This is the **initial matching** — you're trying to **improve** it.

This is how the alternating path method works:

- An alternating path **starts** at a node on one side of the graph that **isn't included** in the **initial matching** and **finishes** at a node on the **other side** of the graph that also **isn't** in the initial matching.

- To get from the **start node** to the **finishing node**, you have to **alternate** between arcs that are **not in** and **in** the initial matching. So the **first** arc you use (from the **unmatched** starting node) is **not in** the initial matching, the second arc is, the third one isn't and so on until you get to a finish node.

- When you reach a finish node (one not in the initial matching), you can **stop** — you've made a '**breakthrough**'.

- Now use your alternating path to construct an **improved matching**. Take the path and **change** the **status** of the arcs, so any arcs **not in** the initial matching are **in** the new matching, and the arcs that were **in** the initial matching are **not in** the new one. Any arcs in the initial matching that aren't in the alternating path just **stay as they are**.

- The **improved matching** should include **two nodes** that weren't in the initial matching, and have **one extra arc**.

The alternating path **can't change** the **original information** — you can't make people do jobs in the **alternating path** that they weren't doing in the **bipartite graph**. Sometimes an alternating path **won't work** — you end up getting **stuck** somewhere. If this happens, go back to the starting node and try a **different path**.

Learning Objectives:

- Be able to use the alternating path method to improve an initial matching.

- Be able to use the maximum matching algorithm to find a maximum matching.

Tip: If it helps, think of it as making new arcs and 'breaking' existing ones.

Example

Anne, Dick, George, Julian and Timmy are on an adventure holiday. They have a choice of five activities: abseiling, canoeing, diving, mountain biking and rock-climbing

Anne wants to go mountain biking or rock-climbing, Dick wants to go canoeing or diving, George wants to go abseiling or mountain biking, Julian wants to go diving or rock-climbing and Timmy just wants to go abseiling.

Find an alternating path that improves on this initial matching: Anne – mountain biking, Dick – canoeing, George – abseiling, Julian – rock climbing

- Start by drawing a **bipartite graph** so you can see all the preferences: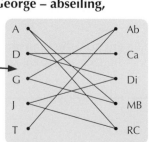

- Then draw the **initial matching**:

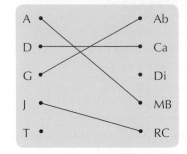

- For the **alternating path**, start at T and find a path that connects it to Di, the other unmatched node (it **won't** be a **direct path**, as Timmy doesn't want to go diving).

  One alternating path goes like this:

  This arc is **not in** the initial matching.

  T - - - Ab —— G - - - MB —— A - - - RC —— J - - - Di

  This arc is **in** the initial matching.

  This is the **breakthrough**

- **Changing the status** of the arcs gives:

  T —— Ab - - - G —— MB - - - A —— RC - - - J —— Di

- Now use this to construct the **improved matching**:

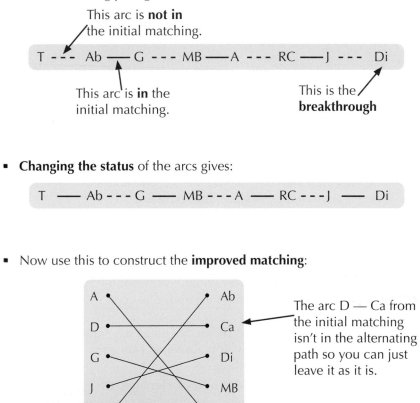

The arc D — Ca from the initial matching isn't in the alternating path so you can just leave it as it is.

A = RC, D = Ca, G = MB, J = Di, T = Ab

There are now the same number of arcs as there are nodes in each set, so this is a **complete matching**.

Q1 A dance teacher must pair up 8 members of the class. She wants to ensure they are suited and makes a list of the members that might match as a couple.

	Paul	Qasim	Richard	Steven
Tina	X	X		
Ursula		X		X
Vanya	X		X	X
Wendy	X		X	

a) Show this information on a bipartite graph.

b) She initially matches up the couples as follows: Tina and Paul, Ursula and Qasim, Vanya and Richard. Find an alternating path that improves on this matching and state the resulting matching.

Q2 Five workers A to E are qualified to do tasks 1 to 5. A bipartite graph representing the tasks the workers are qualified for is shown below. An initial matching for the tasks is A – 2, B – 1, C – 3 and D – 5. Find an alternating path that improves on the initial matching. List the improved matching obtained.

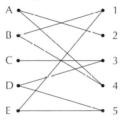

Q3 The students from Exercise 1.1 Question 2 are going to put on a concert. It is decided by the Head of Music that Andrea is not quite good enough to play guitar at a concert and that only one student should play each instrument. An initial matching is Jack – piano, Kate – flute, Andrea – saxophone and Tom – cello.

a) Draw a bipartite graph to represent the initial matching.

b) Find an alternating path that improves on the initial matching and list your new matching.

Q3 Hint: The original information's changed, so you might find it easier to draw a new bipartite graph.

Q4 Alan, Bobby, Charlotte, Dylan and Emily are film critics who are asked to review five films (1 to 5) for a magazine. Due to their busy schedules they are not all free to see all of the films. Their availability is shown in the table:

Alan	3, 4
Bobby	1, 5
Charlotte	2, 4
Dylan	1, 5
Emily	3

a) Draw a bipartite graph to illustrate the information in the table.

The editor of the magazine allocates Alan to film 3, Bobby to film 1, Charlotte to film 4 and Dylan to film 5.

b) Show this initial matching clearly on a bipartite graph.

c) Find an alternating path that improves on this matching and list the improved matching achieved.

Maximum matchings

A **maximum matching** is one that uses the **greatest number** of arcs possible. To find the maximum matching, you need to keep finding **alternating paths** and **improved matchings** — this is the **maximum matching algorithm**.

---

1. Start with **any** initial matching.
2. Try to find an **alternating path** (using the method on p.143). If you find one, use this to form an **improved matching**. If there isn't one, then this is a **maximum matching** — so **stop**.
3. If there are no **unmatched** nodes, **stop** — the matching is **complete**. If there are still unmatched nodes, **repeat step 2)** using the **improved matching** as the new **initial matching**.

Tip: Remember — there might be more than one maximum matching.

In some alternating paths, you have a **choice** between different nodes. You should draw a **tree diagram** to show the possible paths, then pick the route that gets you to a **breakthrough** the **fastest**.

Example

A music school offers tuition in the following instruments: clarinet, flute, piano, saxophone, trumpet and violin. Six children want to start lessons, but the school only takes on one pupil per instrument.
Their preferences are:

Student	First choice	Second choice	Third choice
Chad	Saxophone	Trumpet	—
Elly	Trumpet	Piano	Clarinet
Karen	Flute	Piano	—
Mike	Trumpet	Saxophone	—
Pascal	Clarinet	Violin	Piano
Stuart	Trumpet	Clarinet	—

a) Draw a bipartite graph to show this information.

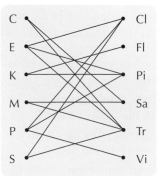

Tip: Take care when drawing your bipartite graph — you're going to use it for the next part of the question so it needs to be accurate.

Initially, Chad, Elly, Karen and Pascal are matched to their first choice.

b) Draw this initial matching, then use the maximum matching algorithm to improve the matching as much as possible.

- The **initial matching** looks like this:

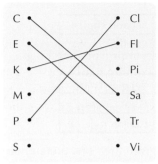

- You can see that there are **4 unmatched nodes** (Mike, Stuart, Piano and Violin), so you can probably find an **improved matching**.

- From the **initial matching**, find an **alternating path** from Mike to an unmatched instrument:

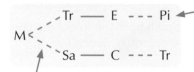

This route reaches a breakthrough first, so use this.

Use a tree diagram to show the possible routes.

Tip: You could have started with Stuart instead of Mike if you wanted.

- This produces the matching:
  Chad = saxophone, Elly = piano, Karen = flute, Mike = trumpet and Pascal = clarinet, which looks like this:

- But there are still **two unmatched nodes**, so you need to look for **another** alternating path.

Tip: Don't forget to change the status of the arcs in the alternating path to form the new matching. You also need to include any arcs from the initial matching that haven't been changed.

- Using this **new matching**, find an alternating path from Stuart to an unmatched instrument:

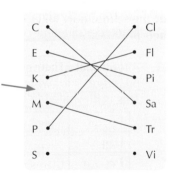

This route reaches a breakthrough first.

- This produces the matching:
  Chad = saxophone, Elly = piano, Karen = flute, Mike = trumpet, Pascal = violin, Stuart = clarinet.

- There are no more unmatched nodes, so this is a **complete matching**.

Q1 Ahmed, Brad, Caleb, Danny and Eric play for a basketball team. There are five positions in basketball: Point Guard, Shooting Guard, Small Forward, Power Forward and Centre. The players have the following preferences for positions:

	First choice	Second choice
Ahmed	Power Forward	Centre
Brad	Point Guard	Power Forward
Caleb	Centre	Small Forward
Danny	Shooting Guard	Point Guard
Eric	Power Forward	Centre

Initially everyone except Eric is given their first preference for position.

a) Draw a bipartite graph to show the preferences of the players and state the initial matching.

b) Use the maximum matching algorithm to find a complete matching, showing your alternating paths clearly.

c) Find another alternating path from the initial matching and hence an alternative complete matching.

Q2 Hint: Remember that the owners of No. 5 insist that their hut is painted yellow.

Q2 In Exercise 1.2, Question 5 starting from the initial matching: no. 1 – pink, no. 2 – yellow, no. 3 – orange, no. 4 – red, use the maximum matching algorithm to ensure every beach hut is painted a different colour. Show your alternating paths clearly.

Q3 After a speed dating night, a group of women write down their preferences for which of the men they would like to see again. This is illustrated in the table below:

	Joe	Raj	Troy	Akil	Chris	George
Lian		X	X			
Eva		X				
Sophie				X		
Kim			X		X	
Betty	X				X	
Maria				X		X

The initial matching of couples is Maria and Akil, Betty and Chris, Kim and Troy and Lian and Raj.

Q3 Hint: For part a), draw the bipartite graph and make the arcs for the initial matching bold or a different colour.

a) Draw a bipartite graph to illustrate the information from the table and show clearly on it the initial matching.

b) Starting from the initial matching use the maximum matching algorithm to find a complete matching where everyone has a date. Show your alternating paths clearly.

Q4 In Exercise 1.2, Question 7 the six workers are allocated to the six tasks with an initial matching of A – 1, C – 2, D – 4 and F – 5. Starting with the initial matching, use the maximum matching algorithm to find a complete matching, showing your alternating paths clearly.

Review Exercise — Chapter 6

Q1   The bipartite graph below shows the languages a group of friends can speak:

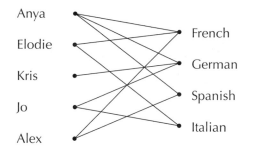

a) Which of the friends can speak French?
b) Who speaks the most languages?
c) What languages can Jo speak?

Q2   Elizabeth, Jane, Kitty, Lydia and Mary are going to an art gallery. Elizabeth likes Renaissance art, portraits and sculptures, Jane likes portraits, sculptures and modern art, Kitty likes the cafe, Lydia likes modern art and the cafe and Mary likes Renaissance art.

a) Draw this information on a bipartite graph.

b) Each girl is going to look at one thing, and they're all going to look at different things. Use your bipartite graph to find a complete matching.

Q3   At a school dance, Alice, Bella, Charlotte, Daisy, Evie and Felicity have to be paired with Gerwyn, Hector, Iago, Jason, Kyle and Liam. The bipartite graph below shows who the girls want to dance with.

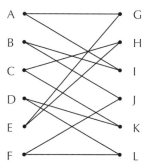

The initial matching pairs Alice with Gerwyn, Bella with Jason, Charlotte with Hector and Daisy with Liam.

a) Draw the initial matching.

b) Using the maximum matching algorithm, find alternating paths so that everyone has someone to dance with and they aren't left sitting by themselves and looking sad.

Q4 Using the bipartite graph from Question 1 of this exercise:
   a) Explain why it is not possible to form a complete matching.
   b) Find a maximum matching so that there is one person speaking each language.

Q5 A travel company wants its members of staff to write reviews of cities they've visited.
    The bipartite graph below shows who has visited which city.

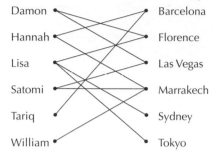

The initial matching has Damon reviewing Las Vegas, Hannah reviewing Marrakech, Lisa reviewing Florence and Tariq reviewing Barcelona.
   a) What would happen if you tried to find an alternating path starting Satomi - - Marrakech?
   b) Use the alternating path method to find a maximum matching.
   c) Explain why a complete matching is not possible.
   Hannah visits Sydney.
   d) Starting with the initial matching, use the alternating path method to find a maximum matching based on this new information. Is this matching complete?

Q6 A group of 4 children, Isabel, Sophie, Charlie and James, want to play dressing up.
    There are five outfits in the dressing up box: fairy, fireman, doctor, princess and monster.
    The table below shows the children's preferences:

	First choice	Second choice	Third choice
Isabel	Fairy	Fireman	—
Sophie	Doctor	Princess	Monster
Charlie	Doctor	Fairy	—
James	Princess	Monster	—

   a) Draw a bipartite graph to illustrate this information.
   b) Find a maximum matching so that every child has an outfit they like to dress up in.
      Is your solution the only possible maximum matching?
   c) Explain why it is not possible to achieve a complete matching in this situation.

   A new child, Harvey, joins the group and as he is new is allowed to have first choice of dressing up outfits. He chooses the fireman.
   d) What effect does this have? Is it now possible to achieve a complete matching, and if so what is it?

   Harvey, Isabel, Sophie and James are allowed to dress up in the first outfit on their list.
   e) Show this initial matching on a bipartite graph.
   f) Find an alternating path that improves on the initial matching and show your improved matching.

Exam-Style Question — Chapter 6

1

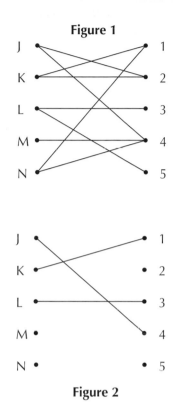

Figure 1

Figure 2

Five tutors, Jamal, Kelly, Lee, Mia and Nick need to be assigned to classes 1 - 5. **Figure 1** shows their preferences and **Figure 2** shows an initial matching.

a) Find an alternating path starting from Mia and ending with class 2. Write out the improved matching that your path gives. *(3 marks)*

b) A complete matching is not possible for this bipartite graph. Explain why. *(1 mark)*

Mia agrees to teach class 3.

c) Starting with the matching found in part (a), use the maximum matching algorithm to find a complete matching. Write out the alternating path and the final matching. *(3 marks)*

Answers

Chapter 1: Algorithms

1. Algorithms

Exercise 1.1 — Algorithms in words

Q1 **a)** Input: radish seeds, water, sunlight, soil;
Output: radishes

b) Input: wool, knitting needles;   Output: scarf

c) Input: flour, sugar, eggs, (any other ingredients);
Output: cake

d) Input: sales figures, costs;   Output: profit

With these questions it's hard to say for definite what the inputs should be, but as long as your answers are sensible then you should be fine.

Q2

	a)	b)	c)	d)
Input	0	20	100	−35
× 9	0	180	900	−315
÷ 5	0	36	180	−63
+ 32	32	68	212	−31
Output	32 °F	68 °F	212 °F	−31 °F

Your trace table might look slightly different — as long as it clearly shows the output and you can understand the working, it should be fine.

Q3

	a)	b)	c)
Step 1	300	460	320
Step 2	0.12	0.09	0.23
Step 3	15	42	22
Step 4	36	41.4	73.6
Step 5	51	83.4	95.6
Step 6	61.2	100.08	114.72
Output	£61.20	£100.08	£114.72

Q4 **a)** $n = 5$

a	b
1	5
5	25
25	125
125	625
625	3125

Stop

b) $n = 10$

a	b
1	10
10	100
100	1000

Stop

c) $n = 3$

a	b
1	3
3	9
9	27
27	81
81	243
243	729
729	2187

Stop

d) $n = 8$

a	b
1	8
8	64
64	512
512	4096

Stop

e) The algorithm generates powers of n until the value is at least 1000.

Q5 **a)**

Input	Working out	Output
18	1 + 8	9

The output is 9, so 18 is divisible by 3.

b)

Input	Working out	Output
239	2 + 3 + 9	14
14	1 + 4	5

The output is 5, so 239 is not divisible by 3.

c)

Input	Working out	Output
928 741	9 + 2 + 8 + 7 + 4 + 1	31
31	3 + 1	4

The output is 4, so 928 741 is not divisible by 3.

d)

Input	Working out	Output
298 218 744	2 + 9 + 8 + 2 + 1 + 8 + 7 + 4 + 4	45
45	4 + 5	9

The output is 9, so 298 218 744 is divisible by 3.

Q6 **a)**

x	y
29	41
~~14~~	~~82~~
7	164
3	328
1	656
Total	1189

b)

x	y
~~102~~	~~87~~
51	174
25	348
~~12~~	~~696~~
~~6~~	~~1392~~
3	2784
1	5568
Total	8874

c)

x	y
57	67
~~28~~	~~134~~
~~14~~	~~268~~
7	536
3	1072
1	2144
Total	3819

Exercise 1.2 — Flow charts

Q1 a) (i)

$a + b$	$c < 0$?	output c	$a =$
10 − 3	no	7	7
7 − 3	no	4	4
4 − 3	no	1	1
1 − 3	yes		

(ii)

$a + b$	$c < 0$?	output c	$a =$
30 − 7	no	23	23
23 − 7	no	16	16
16 − 7	no	9	9
9 − 7	no	2	2
2 − 7	yes		

b) E.g. It outputs all the non-negative terms of an arithmetic sequence with first term $a - b$ and common difference b.

Q2 a) (i)

$a + n$	$b \geq 40$?	output b	$a =$
0 + 6	no	6	6
6 + 6	no	12	12
12 + 6	no	18	18
18 + 6	no	24	24
24 + 6	no	30	30
30 + 6	no	36	36
36 + 6	yes		

(ii)

$a + n$	$b \geq 40$?	output b	$a =$
0 + 13	no	13	13
13 + 13	no	26	26
26 + 13	no	39	39
39 + 13	yes		

b) It finds all the multiples of input number n up to 40.

Q3 a)

C	P	N	$C \leq N$?	A	T
800	7	200	no		
600	7	300	no		
300	7	500	yes	120	£840

The maximum grant available is £840.

b) For Venue A:

C	P	N	$C \leq N$?	A	T
350	6	200	no		
150	6	300	yes	82.5	£495

For Venue B:

C	P	N	$C \leq N$?	A	T
600	4	200	no		
400	4	300	no		
100	4	500	yes	110	£440

Q4 e.g.

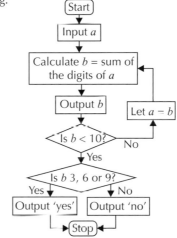

2. Sorting Algorithms

Exercise 2.1 — Bubble sort

Q1 a) The first pass:

<u>5 2</u> 7 6 3 5	swap
2 <u>5 7</u> 6 3 5	no swap
2 5 <u>7 6</u> 3 5	swap
2 5 6 <u>7 3</u> 5	swap
2 5 6 3 <u>7 5</u>	swap
2 5 6 3 5 7	end of first pass

After the second pass, the list is:
2 5 3 5 6 7

After the third pass, the list is:
2 3 5 5 6 7

There are no swaps in the fourth pass, so the list in order is:
2 3 5 5 6 7

b) 4 passes were needed.

Q2 a) The first pass:

<u>3 11</u> 5 0 7 6 4	swap
11 <u>3 5</u> 0 7 6 4	swap
11 5 <u>3 0</u> 7 6 4	no swap
11 5 3 <u>0 7</u> 6 4	swap
11 5 3 7 <u>0 6</u> 4	swap
11 5 3 7 6 <u>0 4</u>	swap
11 5 3 7 6 4 0	end of first pass

After the second pass, the list is:
11 5 7 6 4 3 0

After the third pass, the list is:
11 7 6 5 4 3 0

There are no swaps in the fourth pass,
so the list in descending order is:
11 7 6 5 4 3 0

b) 4 passes were needed.

Q3 a) The first pass:

<u>Z W</u> T S M L K	swap
W <u>Z T</u> S M L K	swap
W T <u>Z S</u> M L K	swap
W T S <u>Z M</u> L K	swap
W T S M <u>Z L</u> K	swap
W T S M L <u>Z K</u>	swap
W T S M L K Z	end of first pass

After the second pass, the list is:
T S M L K W Z

After the third pass, the list is:
S M L K T W Z

After the fourth pass, the list is:
M L K S T W Z

After the fifth pass, the list is:
L K M S T W Z

After the sixth pass, the list is:
K L M S T W Z

There are no changes in the seventh pass,
so the list in alphabetical order is:
K L M S T W Z

b) The maximum number of passes was needed as
the list was in reverse alphabetical order.

Q4 The first pass:

<u>A F</u> B J M B C	swap
F <u>A B</u> J M B C	swap
F B <u>A J</u> M B C	swap
F B J <u>A M</u> B C	swap
F B J M <u>A B</u> C	swap
F B J M B <u>A C</u>	swap
F B J M B C A	end of first pass

After the second pass, the list is:
F J M B C B A

After the third pass, the list is:
J M F C B B A

After the fourth pass, the list is:
M J F C B B A

There are no swaps in the fifth pass,
so the list in reverse alphabetical order is:
M J F C B B A

Q5 a) The maximum number of passes for 5 items is 5.
(4 to sort the list plus 1 to check no more swaps
are possible.)

b) The maximum number of comparisons for 5 items
is $4 + 3 + 2 + 1 = 10$

Q6 a) The maximum number of passes for 8 items is 8.
(7 to sort the list plus 1 to check no more swaps
are possible.)

b) The maximum number of swaps for 8 items is
$\frac{1}{2}(7 \times 8) = 28$.
*If you'd have worked out the maximum number of
comparisons instead, you'd have found it was the same
as the maximum number of swaps.*

Q7 The first pass:

<u>6 7</u> 9 4 5 6 2	no swap
6 <u>7 9</u> 4 5 6 2	no swap
6 7 <u>9 4</u> 5 6 2	swap
6 7 4 <u>9 5</u> 6 2	swap
6 7 4 5 <u>9 6</u> 2	swap
6 7 4 5 6 <u>9 2</u>	swap
6 7 4 5 6 2 9	end of first pass

After the second pass:
6 4 5 6 2 7 9

After the third pass:
4 5 6 2 6 7 9

After the fourth pass:
4 5 2 6 6 7 9

After the fifth pass:
4 2 5 6 6 7 9

After the sixth pass:
2 4 5 6 6 7 9

There are no swaps in the seventh pass,
so the list in ascending order is:
2 4 5 6 6 7 9

Q8 The first pass:

<u>59 39</u> 89 79 69 29 39	no swap
59 <u>39 89</u> 79 69 29 39	swap
59 89 <u>39 79</u> 69 29 39	swap
59 89 79 <u>39 69</u> 29 39	swap
59 89 79 69 <u>39 29</u> 39	no swap
59 89 79 69 39 <u>29 39</u>	swap
59 89 79 69 39 39 29	end of first pass

After the second pass:
89 79 69 59 39 39 29

There are no swaps in the third pass,
so the list in descending order is:
89 79 69 59 39 39 29

Q9 The first pass:

<u>E L</u> E P H A N T	no swap
E <u>L E</u> P H A N T	swap
E E <u>L P</u> H A N T	no swap
E E L <u>P H</u> A N T	swap
E E L H <u>P A</u> N T	swap
E E L H A <u>P N</u> T	swap
E E L H A N <u>P T</u>	no swap
E E L H A N P T	end of first pass

After the second pass:
E E H A L N P T

After the third pass:
E E A H L N P T

After the fourth pass:
E A E H L N P T

After the fifth pass:
A E E H L N P T

There are no swaps in the sixth pass,
so the list in alphabetical order is:
A E E H L N P T

Q10 a) The first pass:

1 <u>5</u> 2 3 11 10 9 3 4 7	no swap
1 <u>5 2</u> 3 11 10 9 3 4 7	swap
1 2 <u>5 3</u> 11 10 9 3 4 7	swap
1 2 3 <u>5 11</u> 10 9 3 4 7	no swap
1 2 3 5 <u>11 10</u> 9 3 4 7	swap
1 2 3 5 10 <u>11 9</u> 3 4 7	swap
1 2 3 5 10 9 <u>11 3</u> 4 7	swap
1 2 3 5 10 9 3 <u>11 4</u> 7	swap
1 2 3 5 10 9 3 4 <u>11 7</u>	swap
1 2 3 5 10 9 3 4 7 11	end of first pass

After the second pass:
1 2 3 5 9 3 4 7 10 11

After the third pass:
1 2 3 5 3 4 7 9 10 11

After the fourth pass:
1 2 3 3 4 5 7 9 10 11

There are no swaps in the fifth pass,
so the list in ascending order is:
1 2 3 3 4 5 7 9 10 11

b) The numbers form the words:
BUBBLE SORT

Exercise 2.2 — Quick sort

Q1 a) 10 is even, so the pivot is the
$\frac{1}{2}(10 + 2)$ = 6th item.

b) 43 is odd, so the pivot is the
$\frac{1}{2}(43 + 1)$ = 22nd item.

c) 52 is even, so for the first pivot use the
$\frac{1}{2}(52 + 2)$ = 27th item

d) 101 is odd, so for the first pivot use the
$\frac{1}{2}(101 + 1)$ = 51st item

Q2 a) There are 7 items, so use the $\frac{1}{2}(7 + 1)$ = 4th
item as the first pivot.

First step:
3, 2, <u>4</u>, 7, 8, 6, 9

Second step:
<u>2</u>, 3, **4**, <u>6</u>, 7, 8, 9

Third step:
2, 3, **4**, **6**, 7, <u>8</u>, 9

All the remaining lists have only 1 item, so the
numbers in ascending order are:
2, 3, 4, 6, 7, 8, 9

*Here the pivot being used was underlined, and any
items whose position was definite were made bold.*

b) 4, 2, 6, 8

Q3 a) There are 7 items, so use the $\frac{1}{2}(7 + 1)$ = 4th item
as the first pivot.

First step:
A, <u>F</u>, M, N, G, H, Q

Second step:
A, **F**, <u>G</u>, M, N, H, Q

Third step:
A, **F**, **G**, <u>H</u>, M, N, Q

Fourth step:
A, **F**, **G**, **H**, M, <u>N</u>, Q

All the remaining lists only have 1 item,
so the letters in alphabetical order are:
A, F, G, H, M, N, Q

b) F, G, H, N

Q4 a) There are 6 items, so use the $\frac{1}{2}(6 + 2)$ = 4th
item as the first pivot.

First step:
101, 96, 103, 107, 98, <u>94</u>

Second step:
107, <u>103</u>, 101, 96, 98, **94**

Third step:
107, **103**, 101, 98, <u>96</u>, **94**

Fourth step:
107, **103**, 101, <u>98</u>, **96**, **94**

All the remaining lists only have 1 item,
so the numbers in descending order are:
107, 103, 101, 98, 96, 94

b) 94, 103, 96, 98

Q5 a) There are 8 items, so use the $\frac{1}{2}(8 + 2)$ = 5th
item as the first pivot.

First step:
3.9, 3.3, 3.7, 3.2, 3.8, <u>4.1</u>, 4.4, 4.2

Second step:
3.3, 3.2, <u>3.7</u>, 3.9, 3.8, **4.1**, <u>4.2</u>, 4.4

Third step:
<u>3.2</u>, 3.3, **3.7**, <u>3.8</u>, 3.9, **4.1**, **4.2**, **4.4**

All the remaining lists only have 1 item,
so the weights in ascending order are:
3.2, 3.3, 3.7, 3.8, 3.9, 4.1, 4.2, 4.4

b) 4.1, 3.7, 4.2, 3.2 and 3.8

Q6 There are 7 items, so use the $\frac{1}{2}(7 + 1)$ = 4th
item as the first pivot.

First step:
<u>T</u>, S, O, R, I, N, G

Second step (using I as the pivot)
T, S, O, R, N, <u>I</u>, G

Third step (using R as the pivot)
T, S, <u>R</u>, O, N, **I**, G

Fourth step (using N as the pivot)
T, **S**, **R**, O, <u>N</u>, **I**, G

All the remaining lists have only 1 item, so the letters
in reverse alphabetical order are:
T, S, R, O, N, I, G

Q7 **a)** There are 7 items, so use the ½(7 + 1) = 4th item as the first pivot.

  b) First step:
11.0, 11.3, 11.7, <u>12.3</u>, 13.1, 12.9, 12.8
Second step:
11.0, <u>11.3</u>, 11.7, **12.3**, 12.8, <u>12.9</u>, 13.1
All the remaining lists only have 1 item, so the times in ascending order are:
11.0 s, 11.3 s, 11.7 s, 12.3 s, 12.8 s, 12.9 s, 13.1 s

  c) 12.3, 11.3 and 12.9

Q8 **a)** There are 6 items, so use the ½(6 + 2) = 4th item as the first pivot.

  b) First step:
14.4, 18.0, 15.4, 23.0, <u>10.6</u>, 7.6
Second step:
18.0, 23.0, <u>15.4</u>, 14.4, **10.6**, **7.6**
Third step:
<u>23.0</u>, 18.0, **15.4**, **14.4**, **10.6**, **7.6**
All the remaining lists only have 1 item, so the weights in descending order are:
23.0 kg, 18.0 kg, 15.4 kg, 14.4 kg, 10.6 kg, 7.6 kg

  c) 10.6, 15.4, 23.0

Q9 **a)** There are 10 items, so use the (10 + 2) ÷ 2 = 6th item as the first pivot.

  b) First step:
Ben, Freda, Babatunde, <u>Ian</u>, Jane, Mary, Pete, Rob, Lorna, Kim
Second step:
Ben, Babatunde, <u>Freda</u>, **Ian**, Jane, Mary, Pete, Lorna, Kim, <u>Rob</u>
Third step:
<u>Babatunde</u>, Ben, **Freda**, **Ian**, Jane, Mary, Lorna, Kim, <u>Pete</u>, **Rob**
Fourth step:
Babatunde, **Ben**, **Freda**, **Ian**, Jane, Kim, <u>Lorna</u>, Mary, **Pete**, **Rob**
Fifth step:
Babatunde, **Ben**, **Freda**, **Ian**, Jane, <u>Kim</u>, **Lorna**, **Mary**, **Pete**, **Rob**
All the remaining lists have only 1 item, so the names in alphabetical order are:
Babatunde, Ben, Freda, Ian, Jane, Kim, Lorna, Mary, Pete, Rob
It's a good idea to code the names (e.g. Be, Ja, Ma etc.) so you don't have to write them out in full each time.

  c) Ian, Freda, Rob, Babatunde, Pete, Lorna, Kim

3. Searching Algorithms
Exercise 3.1 — Binary search

Q1 **a)** There are 7 items, so middle item is the ½(7 + 1) = 4th item (hat).

Hat ≠ scarf and scarf comes after hat, so throw away the first half of the list (including hat). This leaves:
5. Mittens 6. Scarf 7. Socks

The new list has 3 items, so the middle item is the ½(3 + 1) = 2nd item (scarf)

This is the item you're looking for, so the search is complete. Scarf is the 6th item.

  b) Start with the same middle item (hat). Gloves ≠ hat and gloves comes before hat, so throw away the second half of the list (including hat). This leaves:
1. Boots 2. <u>Coat</u> 3. Gloves
The underlined item is the new middle item — it's worked out in the same way as the first one. If you're left with the second half of a list, you can use the formula ½(a + l) to work out the middle item.

Coat ≠ gloves and gloves comes after coat, so throw away the first half of the list (including coat).

This only leaves 1 item — gloves, so gloves is the 3rd item on the list.

  c) Start with the same middle item (hat). Jacket ≠ hat and jacket comes after hat, so throw away the first half of the list (including hat). This leaves:
5. Mittens 6. <u>Scarf</u> 7. Socks

Jacket ≠ scarf, and jacket comes before scarf, so throw away the second half of the list (including scarf).

This only leaves 1 item (mittens), so you know that jacket is not in the list.

Q2 **a)** There are 6 items, so the middle item is the ½(6 + 2) = 4th item (lemonade).

Lemonade ≠ tea and tea comes after lemonade, so throw away the first half of the list (including lemonade). This leaves: 5. Sandwiches 6. <u>Tea</u>

The new middle item is the item you're looking for, so the search is complete. Tea is the 6th item.

  b) Start with the same middle item (lemonade). Coffee ≠ lemonade and coffee comes before lemonade, so throw away the second half (including lemonade):
1. Biscuits 2. <u>Coffee</u> 3. Gateau

The new middle item is the item you're looking for, so the search is complete. Coffee is the 2nd item.

  c) Start with the same middle item (lemonade). Orange juice ≠ lemonade and orange juice comes after lemonade, so throw away the first half (including lemonade): 5. Sandwiches 6. <u>Tea</u>

Tea ≠ orange juice, and orange juice comes before tea, so throw away tea (there are no items after tea to throw away).

There's only 1 item left (sandwiches), so orange juice is not in the list.

Q3 a) There are 8 items, so the middle item is the $\frac{1}{2}(8 + 2) = $ 5th item (grey). Red ≠ grey and red comes after grey, so throw away the first half of the list (including grey). The next middle item is the $\frac{1}{2}(6 + 8) = $ 7th item (red) (using the formula $\frac{1}{2}(a + l)$), so the list looks like this:
6. Orange 7. Red 8. Yellow
It's a good idea to number the items to make it easier to keep track of where you are.

The new middle item is the item you're looking for, so the search is complete. Red is the 7th item.

b) Start with the same middle item (grey). Pink ≠ grey and pink comes after grey, so throw away the first half (including grey). This leaves:
6. Orange 7. Red 8. Yellow

Pink ≠ red and pink comes before red, so throw away the second half of the list (including red)

This only leaves 1 item (orange), so you know that pink is not in the list.

c) Start with the same middle item (grey). Brown ≠ grey and brown comes before grey, so throw away the second half (including grey). This leaves:
1. Black 2. Blue 3. Brown 4. Green

The new middle item is the item you're looking for, so the search is complete. Brown is the 3rd item.

Q4 a) There are 7 items, so the middle item is the $\frac{1}{2}(7 + 1) = $ 4th item (mango). This is the item you're looking for, so the search is complete. Mango is the 4th item.

b) Start with the same middle item (mango). Pineapple ≠ mango and pineapple comes after mango, so throw away the first half of the list (including mango). The next middle item is the $\frac{1}{2}(5 + 7) = $ 6th item (peach) (using the formula $\frac{1}{2}(a + l)$), so the list looks like this:
5. Orange 6. Peach 7. Pineapple

Peach ≠ pineapple and pineapple comes after peach, so throw away the first half of the list (including peach).

This only leaves 1 item (pineapple), so you know that pineapple is the 7th item on the list.

c) Start with the same middle item (mango). Lemon ≠ mango and lemon comes before mango, so throw away the second half of the list (including mango). This leaves:
1. Apple 2. Banana 3. Kiwi

Lemon ≠ Banana and lemon comes after banana, so throw away the first half (including banana).

This only leaves 1 item (kiwi), and lemon ≠ kiwi, so you know that lemon is not in the list.

d) Start with the same middle item (mango). Kiwi ≠ mango and kiwi comes before mango, so throw away the second half (including mango). This leaves:
1. Apple 2. Banana 3. Kiwi

Kiwi ≠ banana and kiwi comes after banana, so throw away the first half (including banana).

This only leaves 1 item (kiwi), so you know that kiwi is the 3rd item on the list.

Q5 a) There are 6 items, so use the $\frac{1}{2}(6 + 2) = $ 4th item on the list as the first pivot (larch).
First step:
Beech Cherry Ash Larch Oak Maple
Second step:
Beech Ash Cherry **Larch** Maple Oak
Third step:
Ash Beech **Cherry** **Larch** **Maple** **Oak**

All remaining lists only have 1 item, so the list in alphabetical order is:
Ash Beech Cherry Larch Maple Oak

b) (i) The new ordered list is 1. Ash 2. Beech 3. Cherry 4. Larch 5. Maple 6. Oak
There are 6 items, so the middle item is the $\frac{1}{2}(6 + 2) = $ 4th item (larch). Maple ≠ larch and maple comes after larch, so throw away the first half of the list (including larch):
5. Maple 6. Oak

Maple ≠ oak. This leaves only 1 item on the list (maple), so you know that maple is the 5th item.

(ii) Start with the same middle item (larch). Cherry ≠ larch and cherry comes before larch, so throw away the second half of the list (including larch). This leaves:
1. Ash 2. Beech 3. Cherry

Cherry ≠ beech and cherry comes after beech, so throw away the first half of the list (including beech).

This leaves only 1 item (cherry), so you know that cherry is the 3rd item on the list.

(iii) Start with the same middle item (larch). Spruce ≠ larch and spruce comes after larch, so throw away the first half of the list (including larch). This leaves:
5. Maple 6. Oak

Spruce ≠ oak and spruce comes after oak, so throw away the first half (including oak).

This doesn't leave any items, so you know that spruce is not on the list.

Q6 a) First pass:
1066 1918 1805 1642 1864 1939
Second pass:
1066 1805 1642 1864 1918 1939
Third pass:
1066 1642 1805 1864 1918 1939
There are no changes on the fourth pass, so the list in order is:
1: 1066   2: 1642   3: 1805
4: 1864   5: 1918   6: 1939

b) (i) There are 6 items, so the middle item is the
½(6 + 2) = 4th item (1864)

1918 ≠ 1864 and 1918 comes after 1864, so
throw away the first half of the list (including
1864). This leaves:
5: 1918 6: <u>1939</u>

1939 ≠ 1918. This only leaves 1 item on the
list (1918), so you know that 1918 is the
5th item.

(ii) Start with the same middle item (1864). This
is the item you're looking for, so the search is
complete. 1864 is the 4th item on the list.

(iii) Start with the same middle item (1864).
1815 ≠ 1864 and 1815 comes before 1864,
so throw away the second half of the list
(including 1864). This leaves:
1: 1066 2: <u>1642</u> 3: 1805

1642 ≠ 1815 and 1815 comes after 1642, so
throw away the first half (including 1642).

This leaves only 1 item (1805) and 1815
≠ 1805, so you know 1815 isn't on the list.

Q7 a) First sort the items into order (using either of the
two sorting algorithms):
1p 2p 5p 10p 20p 50p £1 £2

There are 8 items, so the middle item is the
½(8 + 2) = 5th item (20p)

10p ≠ 20p and 10p comes before 20p, so throw
away the second half of the list (including 20p).
This leaves:
1: 1p 2: 2p 3: <u>5p</u> 4: 10p

5p ≠ 10p and 10p comes after 5p, so throw away
the first half of the list (including 5p).

This only leaves 1 item, so you know that 10p
is the 4th item on the list.

b) Start with the same middle item (20p). £2 ≠ 20p
and £2 comes after 20p, so throw away the first
half of the list (including 20p). This leaves:
6: 50p 7: <u>£1</u> 8: £2

£1 ≠ £2 and £2 comes after £1, so throw away
the first half of the list (including £1).

This only leaves 1 item on the list, so you know
that £2 is the 8th item on the list.

c) Start with the same middle item (20p). 2p ≠ 20p
and 2p comes before 20p, so throw away the
second half of the list (including 20p). This leaves:
1: 1p 2: 2p 3: <u>5p</u> 4: 10p

5p ≠ 2p and 2p comes before 5p, so throw away
the second half (including 5p). This leaves:
1: 1p 2: <u>2p</u>

The new middle item is the item you're looking
for, so the search is complete. 2p is the 2nd item.

4. Bin Packing

Exercise 4.1 — Optimal solutions

Q1 $2.5 + 3 + 1.3 + 3.8 + 2.1 + 2.2 + 0.6 + 1.8 = 17.3$
$17.3 ÷ 4 = 4.325$
So the lower bound is 5 planks.

Q2 $140 + 190 + 65 + 120 + 35 + 70 = 620$
$620 ÷ 200 = 3.1$
So the lower bound is 4 bins.

Q3 To decide whether the solution is optimal,
first calculate the lower bound:

$1000 + 900 + 650 + 400 + 250 + 100 + 150 = 3450$
$3450 ÷ 1200 = 2.875$
So the lower bound is 3 parcels.

Kari used more parcels than the lower bound, so you
can't tell from this if it's an optimal solution.
However, you can see just by looking that you can fit the
items into 3 parcels: [1000, 150], [900, 250] and
[650, 400, 100] — this would be an optimal solution.

Q4 $(13 × 16) + (10 × 6.5) = 273$
$273 ÷ 100 = 2.73$
So the lower bound is 3 lengths of wire.

The electrician ordered more than 3 lengths,
so you can't tell from the lower bound if it's an
optimal solution.
You could find a solution that only uses 3 lengths by
inspection — try it for yourself.

Q5 $2.8 + 3.6 + 5.4 + 7.6 + 1.8 + 2.4 = 23.6$
$23.6 ÷ 9 = 2.62...$
So the lower bound is 3 containers.

Jordan used the smallest possible number of
containers, so his solution was optimal.

Exercise 4.2 — First-fit algorithm

Q1 a)

Box	Blocks (cm)	Space left (cm)
1	60, 35	~~40~~ 5
2	48, 15	~~52~~ 37
3	75	25
4	40	60

b) 4 boxes are needed.

Q2 a)

Container	Crates (kg)	Space left (kg)
1	90 , 10	~~10~~ 0
2	45 , 35	~~55~~ 20
3	60 , 25	~~40~~ 15
4	58	42

b) 4 containers are needed.

Q3 a)

Length	Pieces (m)	length left (m)
1	2.8 , 1.2	~~1.7~~ 0.5
2	3.1 , 0.6	~~1.4~~ 0.8
3	3.4	1.1
4	2.0 , 1.8	~~2.5~~ 0.7

4 lengths of timber are needed.

b) The timber wasted is the sum of the lengths left:
0.5 + 0.8 + 1.1 + 0.7 = 3.1 m

Q4 a)

Bin	Bags (l)	Space left (l)
1	130 , 65 , 30	~~120~~ ~~55~~ 25
2	185 , 65	~~65~~ 0
3	133 , 70	~~117~~ 47

3 bins are needed.

b) Space wasted = 25 + 47 = 72 l.

Q5 a)

Container	Cases (m)	Space (m)
1	2.7 , 3.5 , 1.3	~~6.3~~ ~~2.8~~ 1.5
2	5.6 , 2.5	~~3.4~~ 0.9
3	7.6	1.4
4	5.9	3.1

4 containers are needed.

b) Space wasted = 1.5 + 0.9 + 1.4 + 3.1 = 6.9 m

Q6 a)

Bag	Can (kg)	Space left (kg)
1	1.7, 0.9, 1.1, 0.6	~~2.8~~ ~~1.9~~ ~~0.8~~ 0.2
2	2.5, 1.2, 0.7	~~2~~ ~~0.8~~ 0.1
3	3.4, 1.0	~~1.1~~ 0.1
4	2.3	2.2
5	2.4	2.1

5 bags are needed.

b) Space wasted = 0.2 + 0.1 + 0.1 + 2.2 + 2.1
= 4.7 kg

Q7 a)

Parcel	Item (g)	Space left (g)
1	260, 490, 130	~~640~~ ~~150~~ 20
2	620, 85	~~280~~ 195
3	800	100
4	245, 350	~~655~~ 305

Mary packs 4 parcels.

b) Space wasted = 20 + 195 + 100 + 305 = 620 g

c) The total space wasted is less than the maximum weight of 1 parcel, so it's an optimal solution.
You could also work out the lower bound (= 4) to check if it's optimal.

Q8 a)

Trolley	Box (m)	Space left (m)
1	1.1 , 0.4	~~0.4~~ 0
2	0.6 , 0.9	~~0.9~~ 0
3	1.4	0.1
4	0.8	0.7
5	1.0	0.5
6	1.3	0.2

b) Space wasted = 0.1 + 0.7 + 0.5 + 0.2 = 1.5 m

c) The space wasted is equal to the maximum height of a trolley, so you can't tell for sure if it's an optimal solution. Finding the lower bound would give you the same conclusion.
In fact, this is the optimal solution, as it's not possible to fit these items into fewer trolleys. Trolleys 1 & 2 are full, and you can't fit more than one of the remaining items into a single trolley.

Exercise 4.3 — First-fit decreasing algorithm

Q1 a) First step:
1.6 1.4 <u>1.3</u> 0.9 0.6 0.7 0.8 1.2 0.1
Second step:
1.6 1.4 **1.3** 0.9 1.2 <u>0.8</u> 0.6 0.7 0.1
Third step:
1.6 1.4 1.3 1.2 0.9 **0.8** <u>0.7</u> 0.6 0.1
Fourth step:
1.6 1.4 1.3 1.2 0.9 0.8 0.7 0.6 <u>0.1</u>
The bags in descending order are:
1.6 1.4 1.3 1.2 0.9 0.8 0.7 0.6 0.1

b)

Crate	Bags (t)	Space left (t)
1	1.6, 0.1	~~0.4~~ 0.3
2	1.4, 0.6	~~0.6~~ 0
3	1.3, 0.7	~~0.7~~ 0
4	1.2, 0.8	~~0.8~~ 0
5	0.9	1.1

Q2 First sort the lengths into descending order:
2.3 2.0 1.9 1.6 1.4 0.9 0.7 0.4 0.3

Length	Piece (m)	Length left (m)
1	2.3, 0.9, 0.3	~~1.2~~ ~~0.3~~ 0
2	2.0, 1.4	~~1.5~~ 0.1
3	1.9, 1.6	~~1.6~~ 0
4	0.7, 0.4	~~2.8~~ 2.4

Q3 First sort the lengths into descending order.
2.1 1.5 1.3 1.2 1.1 0.9 0.7 0.6 0.4

Shelf	Boxes (m)	Space left (m)
1	2.1, 0.4	~~0.4~~ 0
2	1.5, 0.9	~~1.0~~ 0.1
3	1.3, 1.2	~~1.2~~ 0
4	1.1, 0.7, 0.6	~~1.4~~ ~~0.7~~ 0.1

Q4 First sort the weights into descending order:
21 17 15 13 12 10 6 6 4 3

Shelf	Crates (kg)	Weight left (kg)
1	21, 4	~~4~~ 0
2	17, 6	~~8~~ 2
3	15, 10	~~10~~ 0
4	13, 12	~~12~~ 0
5	6, 3	~~19~~ 16

Q5 a) First sort the bags into descending order:
35 33 30 27 27 25 23 19 14 12 10 8

Box	Bag	Space left
1	35, 14	~~15~~ 1
2	33, 12	~~17~~ 5
3	30, 19	~~20~~ 1
4	27, 23	~~23~~ 0
5	27, 10, 8	~~23~~ ~~13~~ 5
6	25	25

b) The boxes could hold $1 + 5 + 1 + 5 + 25 = 37$ more coins.

Q6 a) $5.4 + 3.4 + 6.2 + 2.5 + 4.7 + 7.3 + 4.8 + 6.7 = 41$
$41 \div 10 = 4.1$
So the lower bound is 5 rolls.

b) First sort the pieces into descending order:
7.3 6.7 6.2 5.4 4.8 4.7 3.4 2.5

Roll	Lengths (m)	Cloth left (m)
1	7.3, 2.5	~~2.7~~ 0.2
2	6.7	3.3
3	6.2, 3.4	~~3.8~~ 0.4
4	5.4	4.6
5	4.8, 4.7	~~5.2~~ 0.5

c) Cloth wasted $= 0.2 + 3.3 + 0.4 + 4.6 + 0.5$
$= 9$ m

Q7 a) $0.7 + 0.6 + 0.3 + 0.2 + 0.7 + 0.5 + 0.4 + 0.1 + 0.2 = 3.7$
$3.7 \div 1 = 3.7$
So the lower bound is 4 boards

b) First sort the lengths into descending order:
0.7 0.7 0.6 0.5 0.4 0.3 0.2 0.2 0.1

Board	Lengths (m)	Length left (m)
1	0.7 , 0.3	~~0.3~~ 0
2	0.7, 0.2, 0.1	~~0.3~~ ~~0.1~~ 0
3	0.6, 0.4	~~0.4~~ 0
4	0.5, 0.2	~~0.5~~ 0.3

Q8 a) First sort the videos into descending order:
19 18 16 15 13 12 7 6 6 4

DVD	Videos (mins)	Time left (mins)
1	19, 7, 4	~~11~~ ~~4~~ 0
2	18, 12	~~12~~ 0
3	16, 13	~~14~~ 1
4	15, 6, 6	~~15~~ ~~9~~ 3

b) $1 + 3 = 4$ minutes are wasted

c) The amount of minutes wasted is lower than the maximum time of a DVD, so the solution is optimal.

Q9 a) $23 + 10 + 13 + 19 + 21 + 30 + 28 + 17 + 25 + 15 = 201$
$201 \div 50 = 4.02$
So the lower bound is 5 bins

b) First sort the bags into descending order:
30 28 25 23 21 19 17 15 13 10

Bin	Bags (l)	Space left (l)
1	30, 19	~~20~~ 1
2	28, 21	~~22~~ 1
3	25, 23	~~25~~ 2
4	17, 15, 13	~~33~~ ~~18~~ 5
5	10	40

c) The number of bins used is the same as the lower bound, so the solution is optimal.

Q10 a) $230 + 500 + 330 + 140 + 520 + 370 + 610 + 180 + 160 = 3040$
$3040 \div 800 = 3.8$
So the lower bound is 4 bags

b) First sort the items into descending order:
610 520 500 370 330 230 180 160 140

Bag	Items (g)	Weight left (g)
1	610, 180	~~190~~ 10
2	520, 230	~~280~~ 50
3	500, 160, 140	~~300~~ ~~140~~ 0
4	370, 330	~~430~~ 100

c) The solution uses 4 bags, matching the lower bound, so it is optimal.

Exercise 4.4 — Full-bin packing algorithm

For most of the questions in this exercise, there's more than one way of arranging the items into full bins.

Q1 By eye:
E.g. 1.1 and 0.9 fill one shelf
0.8 and 1.2 fill one shelf
1.0, 0.7 and 0.3 fill one shelf

Shelf	Boxes (m)	Space left
1	1.1, 0.9	0
2	1.2, 0.8	0
3	1.0, 0.7, 0.3	0
4	0.6, 0.5, 0.4	~~1.4~~ ~~0.9~~ 0.5

Q2 By eye:
E.g. 350 and 150 fill one container
230, 120 and 150 fill one container
180, 60, 80 and 180 fill one container

Container	Bags (l)	Space left (l)
1	350, 150	0
2	230, 150, 120	0
3	180, 60, 80, 180	0
4	430	70

Q3 All lengths: 20, 20, 25, 25, 15, 15, 30, 30, 22, 22
By eye: E.g. 30, 30, 20 and 20 fill one stick.

Stick	Chopsticks (cm)	Space left (cm)
1	30, 30, 20, 20	0
2	25, 25, 15, 15	~~75~~ ~~50~~ ~~35~~ 20
3	22 22	~~78~~ 56

So 3 sticks are needed.

Q4 **a)** 20 + 55 + 95 + 130 + 70 + 35 + 150 + 50
+ 100 + 30 = 735
735 ÷ 250 = 2.94
So the lower bound is 3 parcels.

b) By eye:
E.g. 150, 70 and 30 fill one parcel
130, 100 and 20 fill one parcel

Parcel	Items (g)	Weight left (g)
1	150, 70, 30	0
2	130, 100, 20	0
3	55, 95, 35, 50	~~195~~ ~~100~~ ~~65~~ 15

So 3 parcels are needed.

Q5 **a)** 2.3 + 1.7 + 1.5 + 1.5 + 2.4 + 3.5 + 0.7 + 2.3
+ 1.8 + 2.2 = 19.9
19.9 ÷ 4 = 4.975
So the lower bound is 5 lengths of worktop.

b) By eye:
E.g. 2.3 and 1.7 fill 1 length
2.2 and 1.8 fill 1 length

Length	Pieces (m)	Length left (m)
1	2.3, 1.7	0
2	2.2, 1.8	0
3	1.5, 1.5 , 0.7	~~2.5~~ ~~1.0~~ 0.3
4	2.4	1.6
5	3.5	0.5
6	2.3	1.7

So 6 lengths of worktop are needed.

Q6 **a)** By eye:
E.g. 5.1, 2.6 and 1.3 fill 1 container
5.0, 2.8 and 1.2 fill 1 container
4.6, 3.4 and 1.0 fill 1 container

Container	Cases (m)	Space left (m)
1	5.1, 2.6, 1.3	0
2	5.0, 2.8, 1.2	0
3	4.6, 3.4, 1.0	0
4	5.5, 1.6, 1.4	~~3.5~~ ~~1.9~~ 0.5

So 4 cases are needed.

b)

Container	Cases (m)	Space left (m)
1	1.3, 5.5, 1.6	~~7.7~~ ~~2.2~~ 0.6
2	3.4, 2.8, 1.2, 1.4	~~5.6~~ ~~2.8~~ ~~1.6~~ 0.2
3	4.6, 2.6, 1.0	~~4.4~~ ~~1.8~~ 0.8
4	5.1	3.9
5	5.0	4.0

c) The solution in a) wastes 0.5 m of space. This is less than the size of a container (9 m), so the solution is optimal. The solution in b) uses more containers than a), so it cannot be optimal.

d) **(i)** Full-bin packing is more likely to provide an optimal solution — they need to buy and move fewer containers.

(ii) First-fit is quicker and easier to use (they don't need to train staff), or they may not want fully packed containers in case they're too heavy.

Q7 **a)** By eye:
E.g. 61, 29 and 10 fill 1 trolley.
75, 17 and 8 fill 1 trolley.
65 and 35 fill 1 trolley.

Trolley	Boxes (kg)	Weight left (kg)
1	61, 29, 10	0
2	75, 17, 8	0
3	65, 35	0
4	26, 48, 19	~~74~~ ~~26~~ 7

b)

Trolley	Boxes (kg)	Weight left (kg)
1	26, 48, 10, 8	~~74~~ ~~26~~ ~~16~~ 8
2	29, 61	~~71~~ 10
3	19, 75	~~81~~ 6
4	35, 17	~~65~~ 48
5	65	35

c) The solution in a) wastes 7 kg of space — this is less than the maximum weight of a trolley (100 kg), so it must be optimal. The solution in b) uses more containers than a), so it can't be optimal.

d) The first-fit algorithm is quicker and easier to use.

Review Exercise — Chapter 1

Q1 **a)** Input: raw ingredients (vegetables, water etc.)
Output: vegetable soup.

b) Input: starting point (Leicester Square)
Output: final destination (the Albert Hall)

c) Input: components (e.g. shelves, screws etc.)
Output: finished TV cabinet

Q2

x	y
17	56
~~8~~	~~112~~
~~4~~	~~224~~
~~2~~	~~448~~
1	896
Total	952

So $17 \times 56 = 952$.

Q3 $a = 16$

n	b	Output	n = a?
1	16	1	No
2	8	2	No
3	$5\frac{1}{3}$		No
4	4	4	No
5	$3\frac{1}{5}$		No
6	$2\frac{2}{3}$		No
7	$2\frac{2}{7}$		No
8	2	8	No
9	$1\frac{7}{9}$		No
10	$1\frac{3}{5}$		No
11	$1\frac{5}{11}$		No
12	$1\frac{1}{3}$		No
13	$1\frac{3}{13}$		No
14	$1\frac{1}{7}$		No
15	$1\frac{1}{15}$		No
16	1	16	Yes

So the factors of 16 are 1, 2, 4, 8 and 16.

Q4

<u>72, 57</u>, 64, 54, 68, 71	swap
57, <u>72, 64</u>, 54, 68, 71	swap
57, 64, <u>72, 54</u>, 68, 71	swap
57, 64, 54, <u>72, 68</u>, 71	swap
57, 64, 54, 68, <u>72, 71</u>	swap
57, 64, 54, 68, 71, 72	end of first pass.

After the second pass, the list is:
57, 54, 64, 68, 71, 72.
After the third pass, the list is:
54, 57, 64, 68, 71, 72.
There are no swaps on the fourth pass, so the list is in order.

Q5 The maximum number of comparisons is $\frac{1}{2} \times 11 \times 12 = 66$.

Q6 **a)** There are 10 items, so the $\frac{1}{2}(10 + 2) = $ 6th item would be the first pivot.

b) 23 29 17 23 24 <u>30</u> 19 252 28 23
252 **<u>30</u>** 23 29 17 23 <u>24</u> 19 28 23
252 **<u>30</u>** 29 28 **<u>24</u>** 23 17 <u>23</u> 19 23
252 **<u>30</u>** 29 **28** **<u>24</u>** 23 <u>23</u> **23** 17 <u>19</u>
252 **<u>30</u>** 29 **28** **<u>24</u>** 23 **23** **23** **19** 17

So the times in order are:
252 30 29 28 24 23 23 23 19 17
In this case, you ended up comparing two items that were the same as the pivot. We put the equal items to the left of the pivot, but you could put them to the right.

c) The list is in descending order, so to sort it into ascending order you would need to make the maximum number of comparisons.

For 10 items, this is $9 + 8 + 7 + 6 + 5 + 4 + 3 + 2 + 1 = 45$ (or $\frac{1}{2}(9 \times 10) = 45$)

Q7 There are 6 numbers in the list, so the pivot is the $\frac{1}{2}(6 + 2) = $ 4th item in the list, which is 108.

Q8 The pivot is the $\frac{1}{2}(7 + 1) = $ 4th item = 0.5, so the list becomes:
0.4, 0.1, <u>0.5</u>, 0.8, 1.2, 0.7, 1.0.

The pivot for the first smaller list is the $\frac{1}{2}(2 + 2)$ = 2nd item = 0.1, and the pivot for the second list is $\frac{1}{2}(4 + 2) = $ 3rd item = 0.7. The list becomes:
<u>0.1</u>, 0.4, **<u>0.5</u>**, <u>0.7</u>, 0.8, 1.2, 1.0.

0.4 is in a list on its own, so it's in the right place. In the other list, the pivot is the $\frac{1}{2}(3 + 1)$ = 2nd item = 1.2, so the list becomes:
0.1, **0.4**, **<u>0.5</u>**, **<u>0.7</u>**, 0.8, 1.0, <u>1.2</u>.

The final list has 2 items, so the pivot is the $\frac{1}{2}(2 + 2)$ = 2nd item = 1.0, so the final (ordered) list is:
0.1, 0.4, 0.5, 0.7, 0.8, 1.0, 1.2.

Q9 The middle item in the list is the $\frac{1}{2}(5 + 1) = $ 3rd item = Manhattan. Brooklyn ≠ Manhattan, and Brooklyn is before Manhattan, so throw away the second half of the list (including Manhattan).

There are 2 items left in the list, so the middle item is the $\frac{1}{2}(2 + 2) = $ 2nd item = Brooklyn. This is the item you're looking for, so the search is complete. Brooklyn is the 2nd item in the list.

Q10 a) onion carrot parsnip leek endive <u>swede</u> turnip

onion carrot leek endive <u>parsnip</u> **swede** turnip

carrot endive <u>leek</u> onion **parsnip swede** turnip

carrot <u>endive</u> **leek onion parsnip swede** turnip

So the list in alphabetical order is:

1. carrot 2. endive 3. leek 4. onion 5. parsnip 6. swede 7. turnip

b) (i) There are 7 items, so the $\frac{1}{2}(7 + 1) = $ 4th item is the middle item (4. onion)

Onion is the item you're looking for, so the search is complete. Onion is the 4th item.

(ii) Start with the same middle item.

Endive ≠ onion, and endive comes before onion, so throw away the second half of the list (including onion).

This leaves 3 items, so the $\frac{1}{2}(3 + 1) = $ 2nd item is the middle item (2. endive)

Endive is the item you're looking for, so the search is complete. Endive is the 2nd item.

(iii) Start with the same middle item.

Parsnip ≠ onion and parsnip comes after onion, so throw away the first half of the list (including onion).

This leaves 3 items, so the $\frac{1}{2}(3 + 1) = $ 2nd item is the middle item (6. swede).

Parsnip ≠ swede, and parsnip comes before swede, so throw away the second half of the list (including swede).

This only leaves 1 item (5. parsnip), so the search is complete. Parsnip is the 5th item.

(iv) Start with the same middle item.

Rhubarb ≠ onion and rhubarb comes after onion, so throw away the first half of the list (including onion).

This leaves 3 items, so the $\frac{1}{2}(3 + 1) = $ 2nd item is the middle item (6. swede)

Rhubarb ≠ swede, and rhubarb comes before swede, so throw away the second half of the list (including swede).

This only leaves 1 item (parsnip) and rhubarb ≠ parsnip, so rhubarb isn't on the list.

Q11 a) Advantage: It's quick and easy to use.
Disadvantage: It's unlikely to find an optimal solution.

b) Advantage: It's more likely to find an optimal solution than the first-fit algorithm.
Disadvantage: It takes more time to use than the first-fit algorithm (and may still find a non-optimal solution).

c) Advantage: It's quite likely to find an optimal solution.
Disadvantage: It's difficult to use (it's easy to make mistakes).

Q12 a) 5 + 11 + 8 + 9 + 12 + 7 = 52.
52 ÷ 15 = 3.467,
so the lower bound is 4 boxes.

b)

Box	Items (kg)	Weight left (kg)
1	5, 8	~~10~~ 2
2	11	4
3	9	6
4	12	3
5	7	8

So the items are packed in 5 boxes, with 2 + 4 + 6 + 3 + 8 = 23 kg wasted space. The lower bound is 4 boxes, so you can't tell if the solution is optimal.

c) First, reorder the numbers in descending order: 12, 11, 9, 8, 7, 5. Then use the first-fit algorithm:

Box	Items (kg)	Weight left (kg)
1	12	3
2	11	4
3	9, 5	~~6~~ 1
4	8, 7	~~7~~ 0

So the items are packed in 4 boxes, with 3 + 4 + 1 + 0 = 8 kg wasted space. The lower bound for this problem is 4, so this solution is optimal (and now we can say for definite that the solution in b) was not optimal).

d) By eye, 8 + 7 = 15, so this fills one box.

Box	Items (kg)	Weight left (kg)
1	8, 7	0
2	5, 9	~~10~~ 1
3	11	4
4	12	3

So the items are packed in 4 boxes, with 0 + 1 + 4 + 3 = 8 kg wasted space. The lower bound is 4, so this solution is also optimal.
This is actually the same as the answer to part c), but in a slightly different order — sometimes different methods produce the same solution.

Q13 a) 300 + 290 + 30 + 160 + 50 + 210 + 320 + 130 + 90 + 40 + 120 = 1740
1740 ÷ 600 = 2.9
So the lower bound is 3 boxes

b) (i) First-fit decreasing algorithm

(ii) First sort the items into decreasing size:
320 300 290 210 160 130 120 90 50 40 30

Box	Items (g)	Weight left (g)
1	320, 210, 50	~~280~~ ~~70~~ 20
2	300, 290	~~300~~ 10
3	160, 130, 120, 90 40, 30	~~440~~ ~~310~~ ~~190~~ ~~100~~ ~~60~~ 30

c) (i) First-fit algorithm

(ii)

Box	Items (g)	Weight left (g)
1	300, 290	~~300~~ 10
2	30, 160, 50, 210	~~570 410~~ 360
	130	~~150~~ 20
3	320, 90, 40, 120	~~280 190 150~~ 30

d) Both solutions use the lower bound of boxes, so both are optimal.

Exam-Style Questions — Chapter 1

Q1 a) There are 10 items in the list, so the pivot is the $\frac{1}{2}(10 + 2)$ = 6th item = 89 *[1 mark]*. The list becomes:

77, 83, 78, 80, <u>89</u>, 96, 105, 112, 98, 94 *[1 mark]*

The first small list has 4 items, so the pivot is the $\frac{1}{2}(4 + 2)$ = 3rd item = 78, and the second list has 5 items, so the pivot is the $\frac{1}{2}(5 + 1)$ = 3rd item = 112. The list becomes:

77, <u>78</u>, 83, 80, **<u>89</u>**, 96, 105, 98, 94, <u>112</u> *[1 mark]*

77 is in a list on its own, so it's in the right place. The second list now has 2 items, so the pivot is the 2nd item = 80, and the third list has 4 items, so the pivot is the 3rd item = 98. The list becomes:

77, <u>78</u>, <u>80</u>, 83, **<u>89</u>**, 96, 94, <u>98</u>, 105, **<u>112</u>** *[1 mark]*

83 and 105 are in lists on their own, so they are in the correct place. The remaining list has 2 items in it, so the pivot is the 2nd item = 94. The list becomes:

77, <u>78</u>, <u>80</u>, 83, **<u>89</u>**, <u>94</u>, 96, **<u>98</u>**, 105, **<u>112</u>** *[1 mark]*

b) (i) After the first pass, the final (6th) number in the list will be in the correct position. *[1 mark]*

(ii) There are 6 items, so the items will all be in order after 5 passes. *[1 mark]*

(iii) The maximum number of swaps is
5 + 4 + 3 + 2 + 1 = 15 *[1 mark]*

Q2 a)

N	C	D	Output	N = A?
1	8	12	1	No
2	4	6	2	No
3	$2\frac{2}{3}$	4		No
4	2	3	4	No
5	$1\frac{3}{5}$	$2\frac{2}{5}$		No
6	$1\frac{1}{3}$	2		No
7	$1\frac{1}{7}$	$1\frac{5}{7}$		No
8	1	$1\frac{1}{2}$		Yes

The results are 1, 2 and 4.
[3 marks available — 1 mark for correct values of C, 1 mark for correct values of D, 1 mark for correct outputs (there should be 3 outputs)]

b) (i) This algorithm produces the common factors of the inputs. *[1 mark]*

(ii) The output would be 1 *[1 mark]*, as 19 and 25 have no common factors except 1 *[1 mark]*.

Q3 a) Calculate the lower bound by adding up all the lengths, dividing by the length of a plank and rounding up.
So 1.2 + 2.3 + 0.6 + 0.8 + 1.5 + 1.0 + 0.9 + 2.5 = 10.8 *[1 mark]*. 10.8 ÷ 3 = 3.6, so the lower bound is 4. *[1 mark]*

b)

Plank	Lengths (m)	Length left (m)
1	1.2, 0.6, 0.8	~~1.8 1.2~~ 0.4
2	2.3	0.7
3	1.5, 1.0	~~1.5~~ 0.5
4	0.9	2.1
5	2.5	0.5

[1 mark]
So 5 planks are used *[1 mark]* and there is 0.4 + 0.7 + 0.5 + 2.1 + 0.5 = 4.2 m wasted wood. *[1 mark]*

c) (i) By eye, 1.2 + 0.8 + 1.0 = 3 and 0.6 + 1.5 + 0.9 = 3 *[1 mark]*, so there are 2 full planks. The rest are placed using the first fit algorithm.

Plank	Lengths (m)	Length left (m)
1	1.2, 0.8, 1.0	0
2	0.6, 1.5, 0.9	0
3	2.3	0.7
4	2.5	0.5

[1 mark]
So 4 planks are used and there is 0.7 + 0.5 = 1.2 m wasted wood *[1 mark]*.

(ii) This solution is optimal as it uses 4 planks and the lower bound is 4 *[1 mark]*.

Q4 a) There are 7 names in the list, so the pivot is the $\frac{1}{2}(7 + 1)$ = 4th name = James *[1 mark]*.
The list becomes:
Adam, Dan, Helen, <u>James</u>, Mark, Stella, Robert *[1 mark]*

There are 3 names in the first list, so the pivot is the 2nd name = Dan. There are 3 names in the second list, so the pivot is the 2nd name = Stella. The list becomes:
Adam, <u>Dan</u>, Helen, **<u>James</u>**, Mark, Robert, <u>Stella</u> *[1 mark]*

Adam and Helen are in a list on their own, so they are in the correct place. The remaining list has 2 names in it, so the pivot is the 2nd name = Robert. The list is:
Adam, <u>Dan</u>, **Helen**, **<u>James</u>**, Mark, <u>Robert</u>, **<u>Stella</u>** *[1 mark]*

There are no more items to choose as a pivot so the list is in order.

b) (i) The list is now: 1. Adam, 2. Dan, 3. Helen, 4. James, 5. Mark, 6. Robert, 7. Stella
From the method above, the middle name is the 4th name = James. Adam ≠ James and Adam comes before James so throw away the second half of the list (including James) *[1 mark]*.

The remaining list is:
1. Adam, 2. Dan, 3. Helen. The middle name is the 2nd name = Dan. Adam ≠ Dan and Adam comes before Dan so throw away the second half of the list (including Dan) *[1 mark]*. This leaves the name Adam, which is the name you're searching for. Adam is the first name in the list *[1 mark]*.

(ii) As above, the middle name is the 4th name = James. Laura ≠ James and Laura comes after James so throw away the first half of the list (including James) *[1 mark]*.

The remaining list is: 5. Mark, 6. Robert, 7. Stella. The middle name is the ½(5 + 7) = 6th name = Robert. Laura ≠ Robert and Laura comes before Robert so throw away the second half of the list (including Robert) *[1 mark]*.

This leaves the name Mark, and Mark ≠ Laura, so Laura is not in the list *[1 mark]*.

Chapter 2: Algorithms on Graphs

1. Graphs

Exercise 1.1 — Graphs

Q1 E.g.

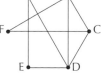

Your graph might look quite different to this — for example, you could have put the vertices in a completely different arrangement. The important thing is that all the connections are right.

Q2 a) E.g.

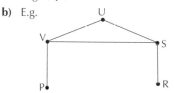

b) 30 km + 70 km = 100 km

Q3 E.g.

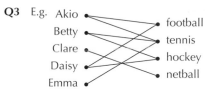

Q4 a) Complete. Every vertex is connected to every other vertex.

b) Not complete. There are no connections for AD, BE, and CF.

Q5 E.g.

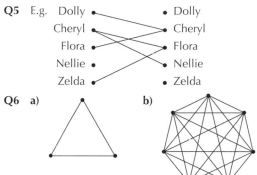

Q6 a)   **b)**

Q7 Each of the 40 vertices is connected by an edge to 39 other vertices, giving 40 × 39 = 1560 — but this counts each edge twice (once at each end), so the actual number of vertices is (40 × 39) ÷ 2 = 1560 ÷ 2 = 780

Q8 a) (ii) is not a subgraph of *G* because it contains an edge (QS) which is not in *G*.

b) E.g.

Exercise 1.2 — Degree of a vertex

Q1 a)

Vertex	A	B	C	D	E	F	G
Degree	1	2	1	1	4	2	3

b)

Vertex	A	B	C	D	E	F	G	H
Degree	1	2	3	3	5	2	4	0

c)

Vertex	H	I	J	K	L
Degree	2	4	4	2	4

d)

Vertex	A	B	C	D	E	F	G	H	I	J	K	L	M
Degree	3	2	6	2	3	3	4	4	2	4	2	1	4

Q2 The sum of the degrees in Aroon's table is 11. This must be wrong, because the sum of the degrees in a graph is always an even number.

Q3 **a)** E.g. **b)** E.g.

c) E.g. **d)** E.g.

Q4 $(3 + 5 + 6 + 2) \div 2 = 16 \div 2 = 8$

Q5 Edges deleted: UV, RT

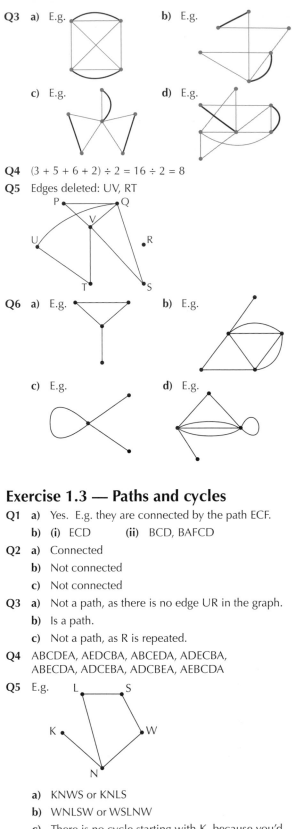

Q6 **a)** E.g. **b)** E.g.

c) E.g. **d)** E.g.

Exercise 1.3 — Paths and cycles

Q1 **a)** Yes. E.g. they are connected by the path ECF.

b) **(i)** ECD **(ii)** BCD, BAFCD

Q2 **a)** Connected

b) Not connected

c) Not connected

Q3 **a)** Not a path, as there is no edge UR in the graph.

b) Is a path.

c) Not a path, as R is repeated.

Q4 ABCDEA, AEDCBA, ABCEDA, ADECBA, ABECDA, ADCEBA, ADCBEA, AEBCDA

Q5 E.g.

a) KNWS or KNLS

b) WNLSW or WSLNW

c) There is no cycle starting with K, because you'd have to pass through N twice to get back to K.
Only Nelly likes Kevin. Poor Kevin.

Q6 **a)** 2 (ACA and ACA (going the other way))

b) 8 — CDEC, CEDC, CDFGC, CGFDC, CEDFGC, CGFDEC, CAC and CAC (going the other way).

c) B

Exercise 1.4 — Trees and spanning trees

Q1 **a)** Tree.

b) Not a tree — not connected.

c) Not a tree — not connected (there is no vertex in the middle).

d) Tree.

e) Not a tree — the graph contains cycles.

Q2 E.g.

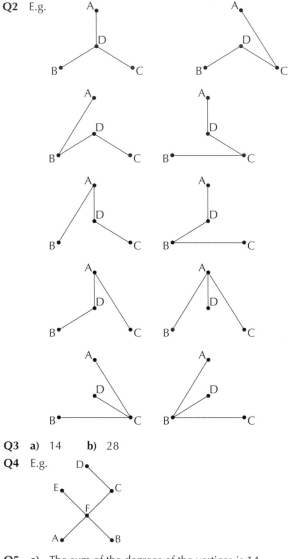

Q3 **a)** 14 **b)** 28

Q4 E.g.

Q5 **a)** The sum of the degrees of the vertices is 14, so the number of edges is $14 \div 2 = 7$.
So Sara's graph has 4 vertices and 7 edges, but a tree with 4 vertices would have only 3 edges.

b) 4

Exercise 1.5 — Adjacency matrices and distance matrices

Q1 a)

	A	B	C	D	E	F
A	0	1	0	0	0	0
B	1	0	1	2	0	1
C	0	1	0	1	0	1
D	0	2	1	0	1	0
E	0	0	0	1	0	2
F	0	1	1	0	2	0

b)

	P	Q	R	S	T
P	0	1	0	0	1
Q	1	0	1	0	1
R	0	1	0	0	0
S	0	0	0	2	1
T	1	1	0	1	2

c)

	A	B	C	D	E	F	G	H	I
A	0	1	0	0	1	0	0	0	0
B	1	0	1	0	2	0	0	0	0
C	0	1	0	2	0	0	0	0	0
D	0	0	2	0	1	0	0	0	0
E	1	2	0	1	0	0	0	0	0
F	0	0	0	0	0	0	1	1	1
G	0	0	0	0	0	1	0	1	0
H	0	0	0	0	0	1	1	0	0
I	0	0	0	0	0	1	0	0	0

d)

	S	T	U	V	W	X	Y	Z
S	0	1	1	0	1	0	0	1
T	1	0	1	1	1	0	0	0
U	1	1	0	1	0	1	0	0
V	0	1	1	0	1	0	1	0
W	1	1	0	1	0	1	0	0
X	0	0	1	0	1	2	0	0
Y	0	0	0	1	0	0	0	3
Z	1	0	0	0	0	0	3	0

This one's pretty tricky — it would be easy to get confused. You just have to take your time and try not to get caught out when the edges cross over each other.

Q2 a) E.g.

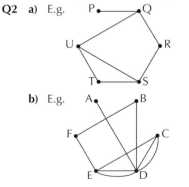

b) E.g.

c) E.g.

d) E.g.

Q3

	W	X	Y	Z
W	0	1	1	1
X	1	0	1	1
Y	1	1	0	1
Z	1	1	1	0

Q4 a)

	A	B	C	D	E	F
A	–	23	12	15	–	–
B	23	–	–	–	34	–
C	12	–	–	10	–	–
D	15	–	10	–	7	21
E	–	34	–	7	–	–
F	–	–	–	21	–	–

b)

	V	W	X	Y	Z
V	–	–	15	–	10
W	–	–	9	22	–
X	15	9	–	17	–
Y	–	22	17	15	12
Z	10	–	–	12	8

c)

	P	Q	R	S
P	–	10	12	15
Q	10	–	14	25
R	–	13	–	–
S	15	25	–	16

d)

	A	B	C	D	E	F
A	–	4	–	–	–	3
B	–	–	–	–	10	–
C	8	–	–	–	–	–
D	–	–	6	–	–	–
E	–	–	8	–	–	–
F	–	–	7	5	–	–

Q5 a) E.g.

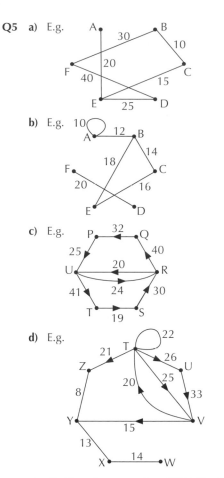

b) E.g.

c) E.g.

d) E.g.

e) (i) There's no route from W, X, Y or Z to T, U and V.

(ii) Reverse the direction of either edge TZ or edge VY (or make one of them undirected).

2. Minimum Spanning Trees

Exercise 2.1 — Kruskal's algorithm

Q1 a) BC (12), EG (13), BG (14), AB (14), CG (15), CE (16), AF (16), FG (17), CD (18), DG (20), AG (21), AC (23), EF (25), DE (26), BF (26)
Arcs with the same weight can be written in either order e.g. AB could come before BG in this list.

b) First choose arc BC (weight 12), then EG (weight 13). The parts of the graphs are not connected at this stage.

Now choose either BG or AB (weight 14). I'll choose BG as that was first in my list.

Next add the other arc of weight 14, AB, to get:

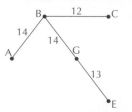

The next choice would be CG (weight 15), but that would create a cycle, so it can't be added.

For the same reason don't choose CE, so next choice is AF (weight 16). Note that you're always trying to add a vertex that is not already attached to the tree, or to join two bits of the tree together.

Finally choose CD (weight 18). All vertices are now connected so the minimum spanning tree is complete.

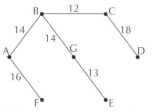

To join seven vertices you need six arcs in the spanning tree — this is a good way to check your answer. For n vertices you'd need (n − 1) arcs.

c) The arcs chosen were BC (12), EG (13), BG (14), AB (14), AF (16) and CD (18).
So the total weight of the spanning tree is
12 + 13 + 14 + 14 + 16 + 18 = 87

Q2 a)

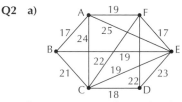

b) E.g. In ascending order, the arcs are:
AB (17), EF (17), CD (18), AF (19), BE (19), CE (19), BC (21), CF (22), DF (22), DE (23), AC (24), AE (25).

Selecting the arcs for the tree, avoiding any cycles, gives the following list:
AB (17), EF (17), CD (18), AF (19), CE(19)

And the minimum spanning tree is:

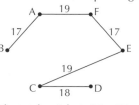

The total weight is 17 + 17 + 18 + 19 + 19 = 90.
The smallest distance needed to join the towns is 90 km.
You might have a slightly different MST that includes arc BE instead of AF.

Q3 Weighted network, e.g.:

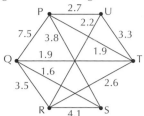

In ascending order, the arcs are:
QS (1.6), PT (1.9), QT (1.9), RU (2.2), RT (2.6), PU (2.7), TU (3.3), QR (3.5), PS (3.8), RS (4.1), PQ (7.5)

Selecting the arcs for the tree, avoiding any cycles, gives the following list:
QS (1.6), PT (1.9), QT (1.9), RU (2.2), RT (2.6)

And the minimum spanning tree is:

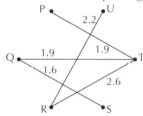

The total weight is 1.6 + 1.9 + 1.9 + 2.2 + 2.6 = 10.2

So 10.2 m of cabling is needed to form a minimum spanning tree for these computers.
You might have put the vertices of your graph in a different position, but the arcs joining them together should be the same as in the diagram above.

Q4 In ascending order, the arcs are:
CG (60), BT (80), CS (100), CR (100), EG (100), CV (130), EC (140), PT (150), SV (160), RS (170), GR (190), BV (200), CP (220)

Selecting arcs to form a minimum connector, avoiding cycles, gives the arcs:
CG (60), BT (80), CS (100), CR (100), EG (100), CV (130), PT (150), BV (200)

And the minimum connector would be:

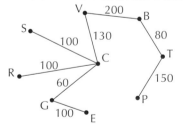

The total weight of the chosen arcs is
60 + 80 + 100 + 100 + 100 + 130 + 150 + 200
= 920 metres

Each metre of pathway costs £175 to lay, so the total cost would be 920 × £175 = £161 000

Q5 **a)** In ascending order, the arcs have lengths:
AB (90), DE (110), BC (120), AC (130), BD (130), BE (140), CE (160), CF (180), EF (180), BF (190)

Selecting arcs to form a minimum spanning tree, without creating cycles, gives:
AB (90), DE (110), BC (120), BD (130), CF (180)

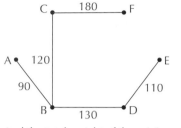

And the total weight of the minimum spanning tree is 90 + 110 + 120 + 130 + 180 = 630 m

b) BF must now be included in the tree. The three arcs BC, CF and BF now form a cycle, which is not allowed in a MST. The most efficient way to modify the tree is to remove arc CF, which has the greatest weight, to give:

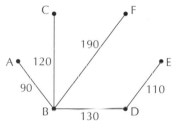

The total weight has therefore increased by 10 m to a total of 640 m.

Q6 In ascending order, the arcs are:
AI (35), BJ (45), EF (45), GH (50), AB (55), AH (65), DJ (65), GJ (70), BI (75), DE (80), CJ (90), GI (90), EJ (95), FG (100), CD (110), EG (120)

Selecting arcs to form a minimum spanning tree, avoiding cycles, gives the arcs:
AI (35), BJ (45), EF (45), GH (50), AB (55), AH (65), DJ (65), DE (80), CJ (90)

And the minimum spanning tree would be:

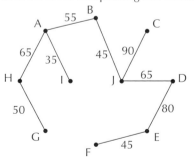

The total weight of the chosen arcs is
35 + 45 + 45 + 50 + 55 + 65 + 65 + 80 + 90
= 530 metres

Exercise 2.2 — Prim's algorithm on graphs

Q1 a) From vertex A there are three choices, AB (9), AF (15) or AG (21). The arc of lowest weight is AB (9) so this starts the tree.

Now look at all arcs joining either vertex A or vertex B to a vertex not yet in the tree. The list of choices is:
AF (15), AG (21), BC (16), BD (26), BF (20), BG (4)

The arc of lowest weight in this list is BG (4), so add this arc to the tree.

Now look for any arc from A, B or G to a vertex not yet in the tree. Choose from:
AF (15), BC (16), BD (26), BF (20), GC (4), GD (18), GE (6), GF (9)

Add the next lowest arc, GC (4). The tree so far looks like this:

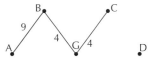

Now you can add any of the following edges:
AF (15), BD (26), BF (20), CD (11), CE (5), GD (18), GE (6), GF (9)

The lowest weight is CE (5) so add this to the tree.

At this stage you only have nodes F and D left to add to the tree. You can use any of:
AF (15), BD (26), BF (20), CD (11), ED (19), EF (12), GD (18), GF (9)

So the next lowest weight arc is GF (9).

Finally, to attach D we can add BD (26), CD (11), ED (19) or GD (18) — the lowest weight is CD (11).

Hence the final minimum spanning tree is:

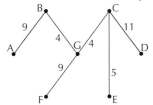

The order the arcs were added was:
AB (9), BG (4), GC (4), CE (5), GF (9), CD (11)

b) The weight of the minimum spanning tree is
$9 + 4 + 4 + 5 + 9 + 11 = 42$

Q2 Starting at node D, the order in which arcs must be chosen is:
DC (80), CB (95), BF (82), FA (81), AE (75), EG (117)

And the minimum connector is:

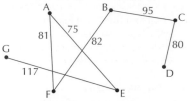

The total weight of the minimum connector is
$80 + 95 + 82 + 81 + 75 + 117 = 530$
so the total cost is $530 \times £100 = £53\ 000$

Q3 Starting at vertex J, the arcs are chosen in the order:
JN (9.5), NL (8), LP (5), PQ (10.5), QO (8.5), QM (12), MK (15)

And the minimum spanning tree is:

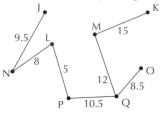

The total weight of the MST, and the total length of power lines needed, is
$9.5 + 8 + 5 + 10.5 + 8.5 + 12 + 15 = 68.5$ km

Q4 Starting at vertex R, the arcs are chosen in the order:
RZ (130), ZW (120), ZS (160), SV (140), ST (180), TU (150), WX(190), XY (190)

And the minimum spanning tree is:

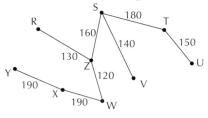

The total weight of the MST, and the total length of cabling needed, is $130 + 120 + 160 + 140 + 180 + 150 + 190 + 190 = 1260$ m
So the total cost of installing the cabling is
$1260 \times 1.25 = £1575$

Q5 a) Starting at G, the arcs are chosen in the order:
GC (13), CB (15), GF (15), GD (18), FE (20), BA (23)

And the minimum spanning tree is:

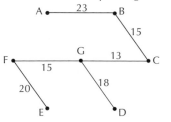

You could have chosen GF first, then CB — remember, if two arcs share the same lowest weight, choose one at random.

b) The total weight of the MST found in part a) is
13 + 15 + 15 + 18 + 20 + 23 = 104 minutes
Veronica's quickest route will take her along each
arc of the MST twice, so the least time it would
take her is 104 × 2 = 208 minutes (or 3 h 28 min)
*Veronica's route would end up being something like
GCBABCGFEFGDG — she travels from G to each of
A, D and E, then back to G each time.*

Q6 a) The minimum spanning tree would be:

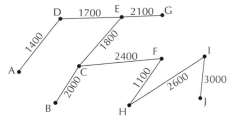

The order the arcs are chosen, starting at J, is:
JI (3000), IH (2600), HF (1100), FC (2400),
CE (1800), ED (1700), DA (1400), CB (2000),
EG (2100), which gives a total weight of 18 100,
which represents a cost of £18 100.

b) If bridge CF is destroyed it splits the minimum
spanning tree into two pieces as shown below:

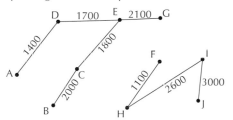

The two parts need to be joined together in the
most economical way possible. The only options
are to join G to F (£3100) or B to H (£4400).

The researchers should build a bridge between
sites F and G, which will cost £3100.

Exercise 2.3 — Prim's algorithm on matrices

Q1 Final labelled matrix:

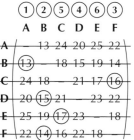

The arcs of the minimum connector were added in
the order AB (13), BF (14), BD (15), FC (16), CE (17).
The weight of the minimum connector is
13 + 14 + 15 + 16 + 17 = 75

Q2 Final labelled matrix:

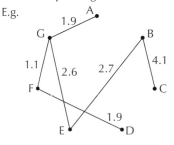

Minimum spanning tree:

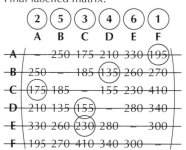

The arcs of the minimum spanning tree were added
in the order CB (4.1), BE (2.7), EG (2.6), GF (1.1),
GA (1.9), FD (1.9).
The total weight of the minimum spanning tree is
4.1 + 2.7 + 2.6 + 1.1 + 1.9 + 1.9 = 14.3 km
*You could have added arc FD before arc GA, as they have
the same weight. This would give slightly different labelling
on the final matrix, but the same minimum spanning tree.
Your minimum spanning trees in this exercise might not look
exactly like the ones given here — it doesn't matter how you
arrange the vertices, as long as the same arcs are chosen.*

Q3 Final labelled matrix:

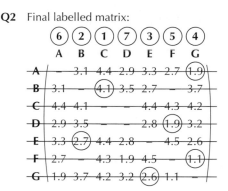

The arcs of the minimum spanning tree were added
in the order FA (195), AC (175), CD (155), DB (135),
CE (230).
The total weight of the minimum spanning tree is
195 + 175 + 155 + 135 + 230 = 890 m
So the total cost of the cabling is 890 × 3 = £2670

Q4 Final labelled matrix:

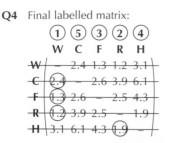

The arcs of the minimum spanning tree were added in the order WR (1.2), WF (1.3), RH (1.9), WC (2.4). The total weight of the minimum spanning tree, and the minimum length of cabling needed, is $1.2 + 1.3 + 1.9 + 2.4 = 6.8$ miles

Q5 Final labelled matrix:

	①	③	④	⑤	⑥	②
	R	**T1**	**T2**	**T3**	**T4**	**T5**
R	—	13	22	15	24	⑨
T1	13	—	16	18	16	⑪
T2	22	16	—	31	26	⑭
T3	⑮	18	31	—	19	17
T4	24	⑯	26	19	—	20
T5	⑨	11	14	17	20	—

Minimum spanning tree:

E.g.

T1 — 16 — T4 (vertical), T1 — 11 — T5, T2 — 14 — T5, T5 — 9 — R, R — 15 — T3

The arcs of the minimum spanning tree were added in the order R-T5 (9), T5-T1 (11), T5-T2 (14), R-T3 (15), T1-T4 (16).
The total weight of the minimum spanning tree, and the minimum length of piping needed, is $9 + 11 + 14 + 15 + 16 = 65$ miles

3. Dijkstra's Algorithm

Exercise 3.1 — Dijkstra's algorithm

Q1 a) First make A vertex 1, with a final value of 0. From A we can reach B in a distance of 4, or E in a distance of 3. Add these as working values.

The smallest working value available is the 3 at vertex E, so make this a final label, and put its 'order of labelling' as 2.

From E we can reach F in a total distance of 5, or D in a total distance of 11, so add these working values.

The new lowest working value available to choose is 4 at B, so put this as a final label and put 'order of labelling' at B as 3. From B we can reach C in a total distance of 9, or D in a total distance of 10. Put these as working values. At D, this means replacing the previous value of 11.

The next lowest working value is 5 at F, so put 'order of labelling' at F as 4, with a final value of 5. From F we can reach D in a new shortest distance of 8, so replace the current working value of 10 with 8. We can also reach G from F in a total distance of 7.

At this point we have a working label of 7 at our final destination of vertex G. None of the other working values are lower than this, so we cannot possibly find a route that would reach G in a distance less than 7. Label G with a final label of 7, and an 'order of labelling' of 5, since it was the fifth vertex to be chosen. Notice that vertices C and D have not been chosen.

This gives a completed diagram as follows:

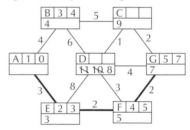

b) Working backwards from G, the distance FG = 2 and the difference between their final labels is 2, so this is on the shortest route.

From F, the distance EF = 2 and this is the difference between the final labels at E and F, so EF is on the shortest route.

Finally, the distance AE = 3 is the difference between the final labels at A and E, so AE is on the shortest route.

The shortest route is A–E–F–G with total length 7. This is shown in bold on the diagram.

Q2 The final diagram, showing all the working values, final values and order of labelling is:

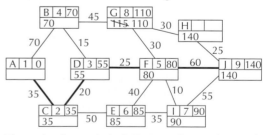

The optimal route is A–C–D–F–J with a total time of 140 minutes. This is shown above in bold.

Q3 The final diagram is:

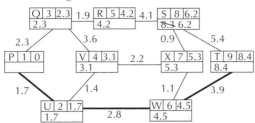

The optimal route for the newspaper boy (shown in bold) is P–U–W–T with a total time of 8.4 mins, meaning he would reach house T at approximately 6.38 am. Therefore the owner of house T will get his newspaper before he leaves for work.

Q4 The final diagram is:

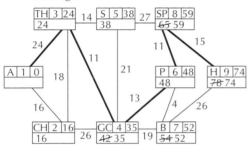

The optimal route is A–TH–GC–P–SP–H, giving a total walking time for the pilot of 74 mins.
The optimal route is shown in bold on the diagram.

Q5 If we start from the warehouse and apply the algorithm working from right to left, the nearest depot can be identified without having to apply the algorithm twice.

Working right to left gives the diagram below:

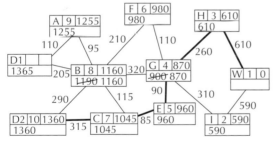

The first depot to be given a final label is D2. This means depot 2 is closest to the warehouse and we stop at this point. Working backwards through the diagram produces the route D2–C–E–G–H–W (shown in bold), with a total distance of 1360 m.
Be careful with this one — when you're working backwards, the distances need to be getting shorter. So CB is not on the route, even though it looks like it should be.

Q6 The final diagram is:

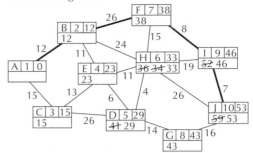

The optimal route is A–B–F–I–J which has a total duration of 53 mins. The latest time David could leave his Hall of Residence is 8:07 am if he is to be on time for the 9 am lecture.

Q7 **a)** The shortest route from A to I is indicated in the diagram below. The route is A–B–F–E–D–I and has a total cost of 555 pence (i.e. £5.55).

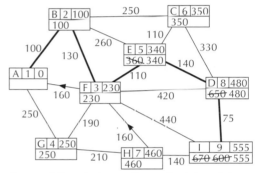

Beware of directed edges — if you missed those little arrows and treated AF and FH as two-way routes, you'd have got this question all wrong.

b) The new route means that C could be reached with a minimal cost of 200 pence.
Possible routes from A to I via C could be A–C–D–I or A–C–E–D–I.
A–C–D–I costs 200 + 330 + 75 = 605p
A–C–E–D–I costs 200 + 110 + 140 + 75 = 525p

So the new bus makes A–C–E–D–I the new cheapest route for Ammar.

Q8 Starting at node B, the optimal route to G is shown in the diagram below.

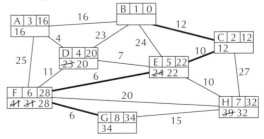

The optimal route is B–C–E–F–G, with a total length of 34.

Q9 The shortest route from B to K is 120 km, travelling along the route B–C–F–G–H–K.

E.g.

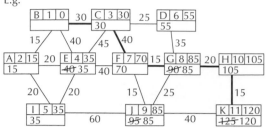

At a maximum speed of 20 km/h, the shortest possible time needed to transport the piece of equipment to the site is 120 ÷ 20 = 6 hours.

You might have labelled your vertices in a different order, because there are two points where there was a tie for the lowest working value — either of E and I could have been randomly chosen first, and either of G and J.

Q10 The optimal route from E to L is shown below. The route is E–D–J–K–L and has a total cost of £380.

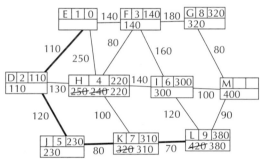

When booking the journey, Ambreen might also wish to take into account factors such as

- the number of flight changes;
- the flight times and availability;
- any booking fees;
- the airline operating on each route;
- baggage weight restrictions;
- other possible modes of transport, e.g. train

For example, flying E–F–I–L costs £420 but involves only three flights, rather than the four flights needed on the optimal route. Ambreen might prefer this as it would be more convenient.

Q11 The final diagram is:

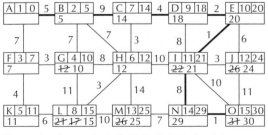

The optimal route is A–B–C–D–E–I–N–O, giving a journey time of 30 minutes.

When carrying out these calculations, it's assumed that there are no delays on any of the sections of the journey and that there is a train waiting in the station at each changeover (i.e. there is no 'waiting time' to take into account).

It's also assumed that no time is required to walk between platforms at each station, and that the times given are precise and not rounded to the nearest minute.

Review Exercise — Chapter 2

Q1 **a)** A graph which has a number associated with each edge.

b) A graph in which one or more of the edges have a direction associated with them.

c) A connected graph with no cycles.

d) A subgraph which contains all the vertices of the original graph and is also a tree.

Q2 **a)** E.g.

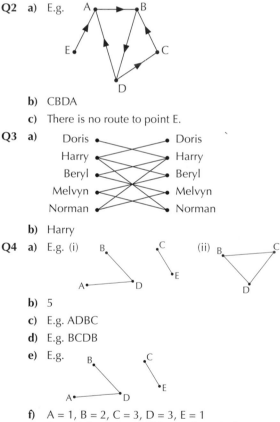

b) CBDA

c) There is no route to point E.

Q3 **a)** Doris, Harry, Beryl, Melvyn, Norman (bipartite matching diagram)

b) Harry

Q4 **a)** E.g. (i) B, C, A, D, E (ii) B, C, D

b) 5

c) E.g. ADBC

d) E.g. BCDB

e) E.g. B, C, A, D, E

f) A = 1, B = 2, C = 3, D = 3, E = 1
Sum of degrees = double number of edges

Q5 **a)** E.g. PQRT or PSRT

b) E.g. QRSPQ or QPSRQ

c) 4 (add R row)

d) 9 (sum of degrees then divide by 2)

Q6 In ascending order the arcs are: AG (5), DH (5), EG (7.5), CH (8), BG (9.5), AB (10), CD (10), DE (10), AF (11), EF (11), FH (12), BC (13), CG (15)

Selecting arcs for the tree, avoiding any cycles, gives the following list: AG (5), DH (5), EG (7.5), CH (8), BG (9.5), DE (10), AF (11)

And the minimum spanning tree is:

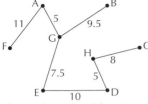

The total weight of the minimum spanning tree is
5 + 5 + 7.5 + 8 + 9.5 + 10 + 11 = 56

So the lowest cost of providing the sewerage system is 56 × £100 = £5600.

You might have chosen EF as your final arc instead of AF, as they have the same weight. You'd have ended up with a slightly different-looking MST to the one above, but with the same total weight.

Q7 a) E.g. Prim's algorithm forms a connected tree at each stage of the process, whereas Kruskal's algorithm can produce a non-connected graph as it is formed.

In Kruskal's algorithm, the shortest arc is added next, whereas in Prim's algorithm, the nearest unattached node is attached next at each stage.

You do not need to check for cycles using Prim's algorithm, but you do with Kruskal's algorithm.

b) (i) Starting at A, the order of adding arcs is AB (8), AF (9), BE (9), ED (9), BC (12).
AF and BE could have been selected in the opposite order, but one of them would always be the second choice if starting at A. If BE was selected second, you could then select ED third and AF fourth.

This produces the following minimum spanning tree, with total weight 47:

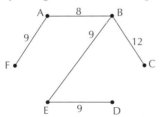

(ii) Starting at D, the order of adding arcs is DE (9), EB (9), BA (8), AF (9), BC (12) which produces the following minimum spanning tree, with total weight 47:

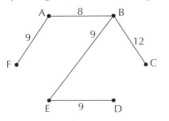

The trees are exactly the same in both cases.
In general, you might get a slightly different minimum spanning tree depending on which vertex you start from, but the overall weight of the tree will always be the same. In this question, whichever node we start at, the MST will have total weight 47.

Q8 There are two possible answers to this question.
Final labelled matrix:

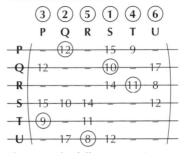

This gives the following minimum spanning tree:

E.g.

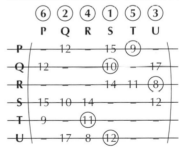

The order of choosing the arcs is
SQ (10), QP (12), PT (9), TR (11), RU (8)

Alternatively, we can select SU instead of QP as the second arc. The matrix would then look like this:

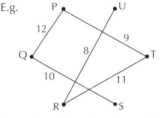

The minimum spanning tree would then be:

E.g.

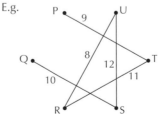

The order of choosing the arcs in this case is
SQ (10), SU (12), UR (8), RT (11), TP (9)

Both MSTs have a total weight of 50.

Q9 Final labelled matrix:

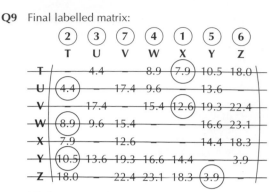

Minimum spanning tree:

E.g.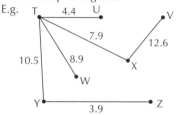

The order of choosing the arcs is XT (7.9), TU (4.4), TW (8.9), TY (10.5), YZ (3.9), XV (12.6) giving a total weight of 48.2 km.

Q10 a) The final diagram is:

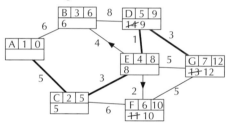

The optimal route is A–C–E–D–G, with a total weight of 12.

b) The final diagram is now:

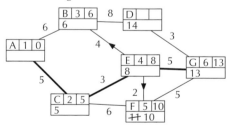

The optimal route is A–C–E–G, with a total weight of 13.

Q11 The final diagram is:

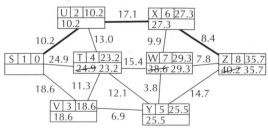

The optimal route for the cable is S–U–X–Z, with a total length of 35.7 m. So the cost of cabling needed is 35.7 × 2.5 = £89.25.

Exam-Style Questions — Chapter 2

Q1 a) DG (22) – add; EF (24) – add; BE (25) – add; DE (25) – add; EG (26) – don't add; AB (26) – add; BD (27) – don't add; BF (28) – don't add; FH (28) – add; CF (30) – add; AC (32) – don't add; GH (33) – don't add. Edges of equal length can be considered in either order.

[3 marks available — 1 mark for edges in correct order, 2 marks for all added edges correct. Lose 1 mark for each error.]

b) 22 + 24 + 25 + 25 + 26 + 28 + 30 = £180
[1 mark]

c)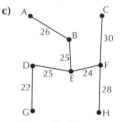

[2 marks for correct edges. Lose 1 mark for each error.]

d) FC / CF.
Order edges added: EF, EB, ED, DG (or ED, DG, EB), BA, FH, FC.

[2 marks available. 1 mark for correct edge, 1 mark for evidence that Prim's algorithm has been applied.]

e) E.g. Prim's algorithm can be applied to data in matrix form; you don't have to check for cycles using Prim's; the tree grows in a connected way using Prim's. *[2 marks — 1 mark for each.]*

Q2 a)

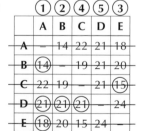

Order arcs added: AB, AE, EC, AD/BD/CD (Arcs AD, BD and CD are interchangeable.)

[3 marks available — 2 marks for arcs in correct order (1 mark if one error). 1 mark for correct use of matrix.]

Each time you circle a number, write down which arc it represents by reading the row and column labels — don't leave it until the end.

b) E.g.

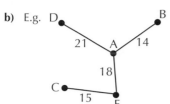

D may be connected to B or C instead of A
[1 mark].
weight = 68 *[1 mark]*.

c) 2 (using any of the alternatives AD, BD and CD)
[1 mark].

Q3 a) Bipartite graph *[1 mark]*

b) 3 (A2, B1, B3) *[1 mark]*

c) 1 (e.g. AD) *[1 mark]*

d) 8 (2 × number of edges) *[1 mark]*

e) The sum of the orders is double the number of edges, so is always even *[1 mark]*. There are 5 vertices, and the sum of 5 odd numbers is always odd *[1 mark]*.

Q4 a) 8 (no. of vertices − 1) *[1 mark]*

b)

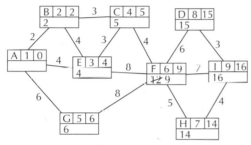

Fastest route = ABCFI, 16 minutes

[6 marks available — 1 mark for route, 1 mark for 16 minutes, 4 marks for all vertices correctly completed in diagram, lose 1 mark for each error.]

Find the fastest route by tracing back from the final destination. You know an edge is on the route if its weight is the difference between the final values at either end of it.

c) $6 + x + 4 < 16$, $x < 6$
Fastest route from A to G is 6. Fastest route from H to I is 4.
Total route AGHI must be less than 16 minutes.
[2 marks available — 1 mark for 6 + x + 4 as new route length, 1 mark for solving inequality for x.]

Chapter 3: The Route Inspection Problem

1. Eulerian Graphs

Exercise 1.1 — Eulerian and semi-Eulerian graphs

Q1 a) Eulerian

b) Semi-Eulerian

c) Eulerian

d) Neither

e) Semi-Eulerian

f) Semi-Eulerian

Q2 e.g. A B C D A B C D A (once around the circle and once around the square).
This is just an example — there are lots of different routes.

Q3 e.g. A B E A C B D E D C

Q4 e.g. A B C D E F G D H I J K L I C M A

2. Route Inspection Problems

Exercise 2.1 — Eulerian graphs

Q1 a) e.g. C D F G H A B E D B C
Route length:
$2 + 3 + 6 + 5 + 4 + 4 + 2 + 3 + 2 + 1 = 32$

b) e.g. C D F B A H G F D B C
$2 + 3 + 2 + 4 + 4 + 5 + 6 + 3 + 2 + 1 = 32$

Q2 e.g. E F A B C D A D F
$3 + 4 + 4 + 3 + 4 + 7 + 12 + 4 = 41$

Q3 e.g. A B C D A E D F E A
$1 + 6 + 3 + 5 + 9 + 2 + 14 + 6 + 10 = 56$
So the length is 5600 m or 5.6 km.

Q4 e.g. A B I C D E F G D H I J A
$2 + 2 + 3 + 5 + 2 + 2 + 2 + 2 + 4 + 7 + 2 + 2 = 35$
So the length is 350 m.

Exercise 2.2 — Semi-Eulerian graphs

Q1 a) The two odd vertices are A and D, and the shortest route from A to D is A B C D (9)

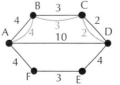

The repeated route is shown in grey.

b) e.g. A B C D A B C D E F A
The repeated route has been underlined.

c) Weight of network
$= 4 + 3 + 2 + 10 + 4 + 3 + 4 = 30$
Weight of route $= 30 + 4 + 3 + 2 = 39$

Q2 a) The two odd vertices are B and D, and the shortest route from B to D is B C D (4).

b) e.g. B C D B C D A B A D C B

c) Weight of network = 2 + 2 + 7 + 5 + 6 + 2 + 3 + 4 + 5 = 36; weight of route = 36 + 2 + 2 = 40

Q3 a) E and G

b) E B G and E F G, both have weight 6.

c) e.g. E B G A B C D E F <u>G F E</u>

d) Weight of network = 3 + 3 + 5 + 4 + 3 + 5 + 4 + 2 + 4 = 33
Weight of route = 33 + 4 + 2 = 39

Q4 a) Odd vertices are A and D, and the shortest route between them is A D (4*t*), so that should be the repeated section.

b) Length of complete circuit = total weight of network + weight of shortest path
= 4*t* + 4*t* + 3*t* + 5*t* + *t* + *t* + (*t* + 3) + *t* + *t* + (*t* + 2) + (*t* + 1) + 4*t* = 27*t* + 6
So for the race to last an hour,
27*t* + 6 = 60 ⇒ 27*t* = 54 ⇒ *t* = 2 minutes

c) e.g. A B C D A I E F G H E <u>D A</u>

Q5 a) B and D

b) B C D (3)

c) e.g. A B C D E <u>B A</u> H G F D
For this one, treat it like a normal semi-Eulerian question, where you start at one odd vertex and end at the other, and find a route from B to D — you won't have to repeat any edges. Then add on to the start the shortest route from A to the nearest odd vertex (B), so you end up repeating AB.

d) Weight of network = 1 + 2 + 3 + 2 + 2 + 4 + 5 + 6 + 3 = 28; weight of route = 28 + 2 = 30
So the length is 3000 m or 3 km.

Exercise 2.3 — Other graphs

Q1 a) The odd vertices are B, C, E and F.

b) BC + EF, weight = 2 + 2 = 4
BE + CF, weight = 8 + 8 = 16
BF + CE, weight = 6 + 8 = 14
The route B A F is shorter than the direct route BF.

c) BC and EF is the pairing with the smallest total path length, so repeat those paths.
e.g. A B C D E F <u>B C E F</u> A
Path length = 37 + 4 = 41

Q2 a) The odd vertices are A, B, C and E.

b) AB + CE, weight = 4 + 4 = 8
AC + BE, weight = 6 + 8 = 14
AE + BC, weight = 4 + 4 = 8
For AC the path taken was A F G D C.

c) Either AB and CE or AE and BC would work as the repeated paths (using AB and CE here).
e.g. G D F A B C D E F G <u>E D C</u><u>A B</u> G
Path length = 49 + 8 = 57

Q3 a) The network is not Eulerian (there are 4 odd vertices), so it isn't traversable — she'll have to repeat paths and pass some stalls more than once.

b) The odd vertices are C, D, F and H.
Pairing up the odd vertices:
CD + FH, weight = 10 + 2 = 12
CF + DH, weight = 16 + 8 = 24
CH + DF, weight = 18 + 6 = 24
CD and FH is the pair that adds the least total weight if repeated, so she'd have to pass 12 stalls more than once.

c) e.g. A B C A D C F <u>D C</u> E B G E F H G I <u>H F</u> D A

Q4 Start by finding all the possible pairs of odd vertices and calculating the shortest total paths between them: A, B, C and D are the odd vertices.
AB + CD, weight = 250 + 210 = 460
AC + BD, weight = 100 + 250 = 350
AD + BC, weight = 180 + 350 = 530
The shortest total length of pairings is 350 m, so if he repeats those paths the distance he has to travel is 2890 + 350 = 3240 m.

Q5 The odd vertices are C, I, J, K
All possible pairs not involving K are:
CI, weight 6   CJ, weight 5   IJ, weight 5
The shortest of these are CJ and IJ, both with weight 5, so repeat either. The total length of the inspection route is therefore 71 + 5 = 76 km.

Q6 a) The odd vertices are B, C, E, J
All possible pairs are:
BC, weight 60   BE, weight 35   BJ, weight 125
CE, weight 70   CJ, weight 95   EJ, weight 90
The shortest of these is BE with weight 35, so that's the path to repeat. Start and end at either C or J.
e.g. C I C B E D A A B E H G J F D F G H I J
Total length = 765 + 35 = 800 m

b) The network would become Eulerian, so the length would be 765 × 2 = 1530 m.

Review Exercise — Chapter 3

Q1 a) Eulerian   **b)** semi-Eulerian

c) semi-Eulerian   **d)** neither

Q2 The odd vertices are A, B, F, J. The possible pairings are: AB and FJ, AF and BJ, AJ and BF

Q3 a) It's Eulerian, so length = weight of network = 36.

b) It's semi-Eulerian where the two odd vertices are A and B, so length = 31 (weight of network) + 4 (distance AB) = 35.

c) 4 odd vertices: A, B, D, F. Possible pairings:
AB + DF, weight = 7 + 8 = 15
AD + BF, weight = 5 + 3 = 8 (minimum)
AF + BD, weight = 4 + 7 = 11
Length = 42 (weight of network) + 8 = 50

Q4 a) 36, any vertex.

b) 31, start and end at A and B.

c) BF is shortest distance between odd vertices, so start and end at A and D. Length = 42 + 3 = 45.

Q5 a) Odd vertices are G and J, and the shortest route between them is G D C I J (4).

b) Length of route = weight of network +length of repeated path = 25 + 4 = 29.

Q6 a) B, C, F, J

b) BC + FJ, weight = 11 + 7 = 18
The route BC is B I J K C, not the direct one

BF + CJ, weight = 8 + 7 = 15
BJ + CF, weight = 4 + 14 = 18

c) Repeating BF and CJ:
Length of route = weight of network + length of repeated paths = 120 + 15 = 135.

Q7 a) The odd vertices are A, C, D and F.

AC + DF = 9 + 9 = 18 (= 180 m)
AD + CF = 10 + 10 = 20 (= 200 m)
AF + CD = 1 + 2 = 3 (= 30 m)

Repeating AF and CD, length = 56 + 2 + 1 = 59.
So the shortest path is 590 m.

b) e.g. E B C D E G <u>D C</u> G B A G F <u>A F</u> E

c) Walking down each path twice makes the network Eulerian, so distance = 560 × 2 = 1120 m.

Exam-Style Questions — Chapter 3

Q1 a) Logo A = semi-Eulerian *[1 mark]*
Logo B = neither *[1 mark]*

b) (i) Logo A = 0 *[1 mark]*; Logo B = once *[1 mark]*

(ii) B or D *[1 mark]*

c) Logo A = 1 *[1 mark]*; Logo B = 2 *[1 mark]*

Q2 a) There are odd vertices *[1 mark]*
So it's not Eulerian. And there are four odd vertices, so it's not even semi-Eulerian.

b) Odd vertices are A, D, I, J
Possible pairings are AD + IJ, AI + DJ and AJ + ID *[1 mark]*
Weights: AD + IJ = 180 + 100 = 280 *[1 mark]*
AI + DJ = 440 + 310 = 750 *[1 mark]*
AJ + ID = 490 + 340 = 830 *[1 mark]*
minimum pairing = AD + IJ
route length = 2740 + 280 *[1 mark]*
= 3020 m *[1 mark]*
The question says that you must start and end at K — but as you've made the graph effectively Eulerian, it doesn't actually matter where you start and finish.

c) (i) IJ is minimum distance between odd vertices. *[1 mark]*
Length of route = 2740 + 100 = 2840 m *[1 mark]*

(ii) A or D *[1 mark]*

Q3 a) Odd vertices are B, G, M, L
Possible pairings are BL + GM, BG + LM and BM + GL *[1 mark]*
Weights: BL + GM = 41 + 26 = 67 *[1 mark]*
BG + LM = 30 + 29 = 59 *[1 mark]*
BM + GL = 30 + 28 = 58 *[1 mark]*
minimum pairing = BM + GL
route time = 336 + 58 *[1 mark]*
= 394 mins *[1 mark]*

b) (i) GM is minimum *[1 mark]* so end at L *[1 mark]*

(ii) 336 + 26 = 362 minutes *[1 mark]*

Q4 a) Odd vertices are A, D, E, F
Possible pairings are AD + EF, AE + DF and AF + DE *[1 mark]*
Weights: AD + EF = 12 + 15 = 27 *[1 mark]*
AE + DF = 12 + 21 = 33 *[1 mark]*
AF + DE = 18 + 6 = 24 *[1 mark]*
minimum pairing = AF + DE
route length = 106 + 24 *[1 mark]*
= 130 miles *[1 mark]*

b) Example route = ABFG<u>E</u>FBA<u>C</u>B<u>E</u>D<u>EC</u>DA
[1 mark] so 5 times *[1 mark]*.

Alternatively, you could say that C has four edges connected to it, so must be passed through twice. E has six edges connected to it (including the extra pass along DE) so must be passed through three times *[1 mark]*, so 2 + 3 = 5 times past an ice-cream shop *[1 mark]*.

c) 106 × 2 *[1 mark]* = 212 miles *[1 mark]*
You've effectively doubled the edges and made the graph Eulerian. You have to traverse it twice, so the distance is just double the network's weight.

Chapter 4: Critical Path Analysis

1. Activity Networks

Exercise 1.1 — Precedence tables

Q1

Activity	Immediately preceding activities
A	—
B	—
C	B
D	A
E	C, D

Remember, you don't need to write A and B in the last row because they're already covered by C and D.

Q2

Activity	Immediately preceding activities
A	—
B	—
C	A, B
D	C
E	C
F	D, E

Q3 E.g.

Activity	Immediately preceding activities
A	—
B	—
C	B
D	A, C
E	A, C
F	A, C
G	D, E, F
H	G

Your table might have looked slightly different — you might have had C relying on B and A, then D, E and F would just rely on C.

Exercise 1.2 — Activity networks

Q1 E.g.

Q2 E.g.
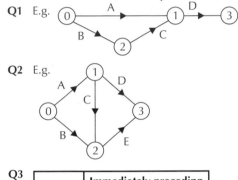

Q3

Activity	Immediately preceding activities
A	—
B	—
C	B
D	C
E	A, D
F	E
G	F

You don't need to make a precedence table first, but it will help with drawing the activity network if you do.

E.g.
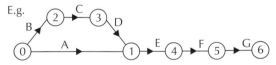

Q4

Activity	Immediately preceding activities
A	—
B	A
C	—
D	—
E	D
F	B, C, E
G	B, C, E
H	F
I	G

Exercise 1.3 — Dummies

Q1 E.g.
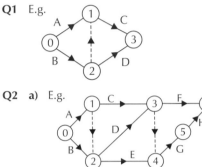

Q2 a) E.g.

b) The first dummy is needed because C only depends on A, but D and E depend on both A and B. The second dummy is needed because F only depends on C and D but G depends on C, D and E.

Q3 a)

Activity	Immediately preceding activities
A	—
B	—
C	A
D	A
E	A, B
F	C
G	D, E, F
H	C
I	C
J	G, H

b)

Activity	Immediately preceding activities
A	—
B	—
C	—
D	C
E	C
F	A
G	A, B, E
H	A, B, E
I	D, F, G, H

2. Critical Paths

Exercise 2.1 — Early and late event times

Q1

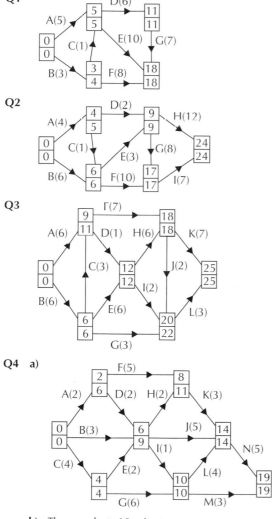

Q2

Q3

Q4 a)

b) The scan lasts 19 minutes.

Q5 a)

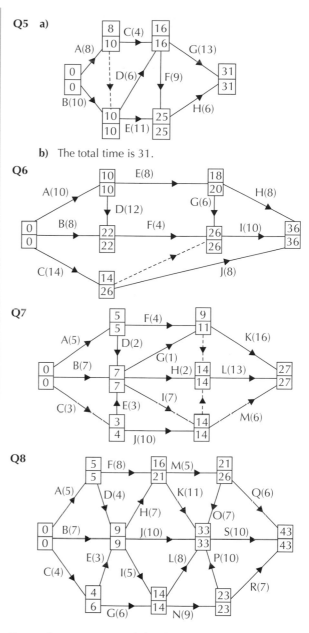

b) The total time is 31.

Q6

Q7

Q8

Exercise 2.2 — Critical paths

Q1 $5 \neq 7 - 0$, so A is not a critical activity.
$4 = 4 - 0$, so B is a critical activity.
$3 = 7 - 4$, so C is a critical activity.
$5 = 12 - 7$, so D is a critical activity.
$7 \neq 12 - 4$, so E is not a critical activity.

Q2 $6 = 6 - 0$, so B is a critical activity.
$3 = 9 - 6$, so E is a critical activity.
$10 \neq 17 - 6$, so F is not a critical activity.
$8 = 17 - 9$, so G is a critical activity.
$12 \neq 24 - 9$, so H is not a critical activity.
$7 = 24 - 17$, so I is a critical activity.
So the critical path is B, E, G, I.
Remember you don't have to check activities touching nodes that don't have matching early and late event times.

Q3 The critical activities are A, B, D, I, L, so the critical paths are B I L and A D I L.

Q4 **a)** For x, the options are $8 + 6 = 14$, or $12 + 0 = 12$. 14 is the largest, so use that.
For y, the options are $3 + 7 = 10$, $17 + 5 = 22$ and $11 + 10 = 21$. 22 is the largest, so use that.
For z, the options are $12 - 8 = 4$, $8 - 4 = 4$ and $22 - 7 = 15$. 4 is the smallest, so use that.

b) The critical activities are A, G, J and N, so the critical path is A G J N.

Exercise 2.3 — Floats

Q1 **a)** **(i)** Float $= 8 - 5 - 0 = 3$

(ii) Float $= 14 - 3 - 4 = 7$

(iii) Float $= 8 - 4 - 3 = 1$

(iv) Float $= 10 - 3 - 7 = 0$
As part (iv) has zero float, it's a critical activity.

b) E is a critical activity, so x must be 4, and the total float must be zero.
$z - 6 - 4 = 0 \Rightarrow z = 10$
As $z = 10$, y must also $= 10$.

Q2 Float for A $= 5 - 5 - 0 = 0$
Float for B $= 4 - 3 - 0 = 1$
Float for C $= 5 - 1 - 3 = 1$
Float for D $= 11 - 6 - 5 = 0$
Float for E $= 18 - 10 - 5 = 3$
Float for F $= 18 - 8 - 3 = 7$
Float for G $= 18 - 7 - 11 = 0$
Remember the activities with float of 0 are the critical activities.

Q3 **a)** Float for A $= 5 - 4 - 0 = 1$
Float for B $= 6 - 6 - 0 = 0$
Float for C $= 6 - 1 - 4 = 1$
Float for D $= 9 - 2 - 4 = 3$
Float for E $= 9 - 3 - 6 = 0$
Float for F $= 17 - 10 - 6 = 1$
Float for G $= 17 - 8 - 9 = 0$
Float for H $= 24 - 12 - 9 = 3$
Float for I $= 24 - 7 - 17 = 0$

b) The critical activities are B, E, G and I.

Q4 First find the early and late event times:

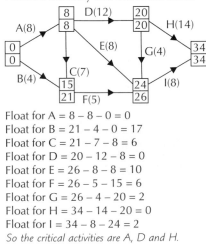

Float for A $= 8 - 8 - 0 = 0$
Float for B $= 21 - 4 - 0 = 17$
Float for C $= 21 - 7 - 8 = 6$
Float for D $= 20 - 12 - 8 = 0$
Float for E $= 26 - 8 - 8 = 10$
Float for F $= 26 - 5 - 15 = 6$
Float for G $= 26 - 4 - 20 = 2$
Float for H $= 34 - 14 - 20 = 0$
Float for I $= 34 - 8 - 24 = 2$
So the critical activities are A, D and H.

Q5 **a)** First find the early and late event times:

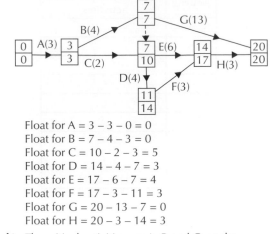

Float for A $= 3 - 3 - 0 = 0$
Float for B $= 7 - 4 - 3 = 0$
Float for C $= 10 - 2 - 3 = 5$
Float for D $= 14 - 4 - 7 = 3$
Float for E $= 17 - 6 - 7 = 4$
Float for F $= 17 - 3 - 11 = 3$
Float for G $= 20 - 13 - 7 = 0$
Float for H $= 20 - 3 - 14 = 3$

b) The critical activities are A, B and G, so the critical path is A B G.

3. Scheduling

Exercise 3.1 — Gantt charts

Q1 **a)** A, E and F have a float of 0.
B and C have a float of 3.
D has a float of 4.

b) The critical activities are those with zero float: A, E and F.
You can see this from the top row of the Gantt chart.

Q2 **a)** Activities A, B, C and D will definitely be happening in the first 3 hours.
F can start within the first 3 hours, but it won't definitely happen as it can have a float that lets it start after 3 hours.

b) Activities D and E might be happening, and activities A and F will definitely be happening.

c) Activities F and G will definitely be happening after 10 hours.

Q3 **a)** The total length of the project is 10 weeks.

b) Activities E and B will definitely be taking place during week 4.
Remember, during week 4 means between 3 and 4 on the timeline — 4 on the timeline means 4 full weeks have passed.

Q4 **a)** The critical path is A D G I.

b)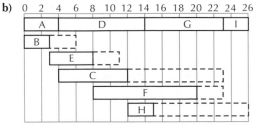

c) Activities D and F will definitely be taking place.

Q5 a) The critical paths are B F J and B F K

b)

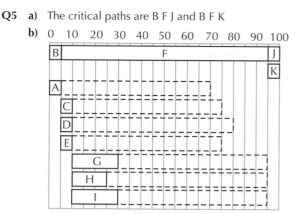

Remember critical activities always come before the non-critical activities.

c) G and I could be started after 75 minutes, and H could be started after 80 minutes.

Q6 a)

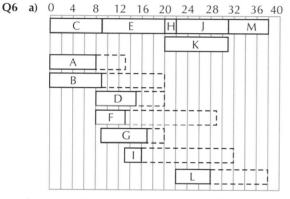

b) In the first week of month 14, activities E, D and G must be taking place. In the first week of month 25, activities J and K must be taking place.

Exercise 3.2 — Scheduling

Q1 E.g.

	0 1 2 3 4 5 6 7 8 9 10 11 12 13
Worker 1	A ⋯ E
Worker 2	C ⋯ D ⋯ G
Worker 3	B ⋯ F

3 workers are needed.
At first it looks like it doesn't matter if you assign B or D first, but if you start with D then you end up needing an extra worker.

Q2 E.g.

	0 2 4 6 8 10 12 14 16 18
Worker 1	C ⋯ E ⋯ H
Worker 2	B D A ⋯ G
Worker 3	F ⋯ I ⋯ J
Worker 4	K

4 workers are needed.

Q3 a)

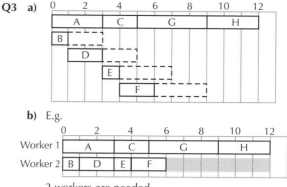

b) E.g.

	0 2 4 6 8 10 12
Worker 1	A ⋯ C ⋯ G ⋯ H
Worker 2	B D E F

2 workers are needed.

c) The project wouldn't be delayed — E and F have enough float that both can be delayed by 2 hours without holding up the project.

Q4 a)

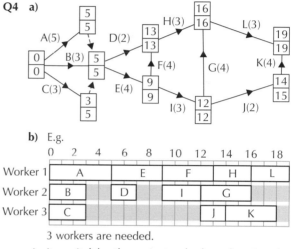

b) E.g.

	0 2 4 6 8 10 12 14 16 18
Worker 1	A ⋯ E ⋯ F ⋯ H ⋯ L
Worker 2	B ⋯ D ⋯ I ⋯ G
Worker 3	C ⋯ J ⋯ K

3 workers are needed.

c) It won't delay the project — both workers 2 and 3 have 2 (or more) spare days before their second activity, and there's enough float on B and C for them to be delayed without affecting E or D.

Exercise 3.3 — Lower bounds

Q1 a) $\dfrac{\text{Sum of activity durations}}{\text{critical time of project}} = \dfrac{56}{8} = 7$
⇒ lower bound = 7

b) $\dfrac{37}{13} = 2.84... \Rightarrow$ lower bound = 3

c) $\dfrac{90}{18} = 5 \Rightarrow$ lower bound = 5

d) $\dfrac{193}{56} = 3.44... \Rightarrow$ lower bound = 4

Q2 Critical time = 100
Sum of activity durations = 2 + 3 + 3 + 4 + 5 + 90 + 20 + 15 + 20 + 7 + 4 = 173
$\dfrac{173}{100} = 1.73 \Rightarrow$ lower bound = 2

Q3 a) Critical time = 44
Sum of durations = 5 + 7 + 2 + 14 + 6 + 8 + 20 + 10 + 8 + 3 + 9 = 92
$\dfrac{92}{44} = 2.09... \Rightarrow$ lower bound = 3

b) E.g.

	0	4	8	12	16	20	24	28	32	36	40	44
Worker 1	A		D			F		I			K	
Worker 2	B	C	E		G						J	
Worker 3							H					

The number of workers required is 3.

Careful here — activity J can't start immediately after G as it can't start till H has been finished (think about the immediately preceding activities).

c) Yes — the solution matches the lower bound.

d) The new schedule would become e.g:

	0	4	8	12	16	20	24	28	32	36	40	44	48
Worker 1	A		D			F		I		H			J
Worker 2	B	C	E		G					K			

The project will take 48 hours to complete.

Q4 a) Critical time = 33

Sum of durations $= 5 + 7 + 2 + 10 + 6 + 8 + 10 + 23 + 8 + 3 = 82$

$\frac{82}{33} = 2.48... \Rightarrow$ lower bound = 3

b) E.g.

	0	4	8	12	16	20	24	28	32
Worker 1	A		D		G			I	
Worker 2	B	C	E		F		J		
Worker 3			H						

c) E.g.

	0	4	8	12	16	20	24	28	32	36	40
Worker 1	A		D		H						J
Worker 2	B	C	E		F		G			I	

It this case, you don't actually schedule the activity that finishes first immediately after A — if you'd put C after A, it would have taken 44 days, not 41.

Review Exercise — Chapter 4

Q1 a)

Activity	Immediately preceding activities
A	—
B	—
C	A
D	B
E	C, D

b) E.g.

Q2 E.g.

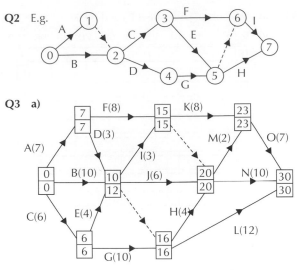

Q3 a)

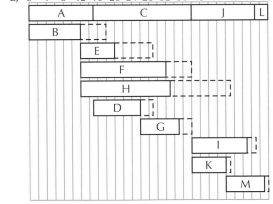

b) The critical paths are A F K O and C G H N.

Q4 Float for A $= 3 - 3 - 0 = 0$
Float for B $= 7 - 1 - 0 = 6$
Float for C $= 7 - 4 - 3 = 0$
Float for D $= 11 - 2 - 3 = 6$
Float for E $= 18 - 1 - 9 = 8$
Float for F $= 14 - 7 - 7 = 0$
Float for G $= 11 - 2 - 7 = 2$
Float for H $= 14 - 3 - 9 = 2$
Float for I $= 18 - 3 - 14 = 1$
Float for J $= 22 - 4 - 17 = 1$
Float for K $= 22 - 8 - 14 = 0$

Q5 a)

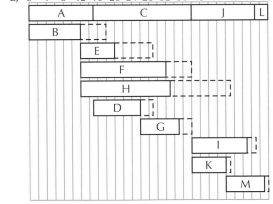

b) (i) On day 16 only activity C will definitely be happening.

(ii) On day 31 activities C, F, H and G will definitely be happening.

c) E.g.

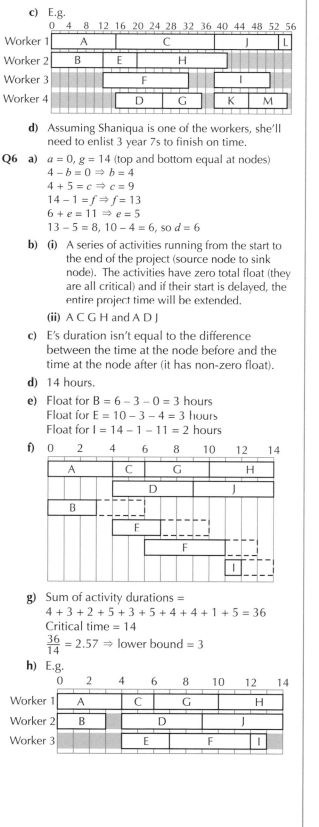

d) Assuming Shaniqua is one of the workers, she'll need to enlist 3 year 7s to finish on time.

Q6 a) $a = 0$, $g = 14$ (top and bottom equal at nodes)
$4 - b = 0 \Rightarrow b = 4$
$4 + 5 = c \Rightarrow c = 9$
$14 - 1 = f \Rightarrow f = 13$
$6 + e = 11 \Rightarrow e = 5$
$13 - 5 = 8$, $10 - 4 = 6$, so $d = 6$

b) (i) A series of activities running from the start to the end of the project (source node to sink node). The activities have zero total float (they are all critical) and if their start is delayed, the entire project time will be extended.

(ii) A C G H and A D J

c) E's duration isn't equal to the difference between the time at the node before and the time at the node after (it has non-zero float).

d) 14 hours.

e) Float for B = $6 - 3 - 0 = 3$ hours
Float for E = $10 - 3 - 4 = 3$ hours
Float for I = $14 - 1 - 11 = 2$ hours

f)

g) Sum of activity durations =
$4 + 3 + 2 + 5 + 3 + 5 + 4 + 4 + 1 + 5 = 36$
Critical time = 14
$\frac{36}{14} = 2.57 \Rightarrow$ lower bound = 3

h) E.g.

Exam-Style Questions — Chapter 4

Q1 a)

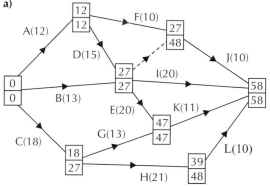

[4 marks available — 1 mark for each 4 correct numbers.]

b) Critical activities: ADEK *[1 mark]*
Length of critical path = 58 days *[1 mark]*

c) Total float on F = $48 - 10 - 12 = 26$ days
Total float on G = $47 - 13 - 18 = 16$ days
[3 marks available — 1 mark for each total float and 1 mark for showing correct working.]

d)

[4 marks available — 1 mark for every 3 correctly plotted activities]

e) $\frac{173}{58} = 2.98$. Rounding up, the lower bound is 3.

[2 marks available — 1 mark for method, 1 mark for rounded answer].

f) E.g.

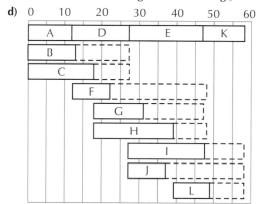

[3 marks available — 1 for every 4 activities scheduled correctly].

g) It seems that it isn't possible to complete the project in 58 days with the lower bound number of workers. / An extra worker is likely to be needed. *[1 mark]*

The lower bound often isn't enough workers to get the project done, so watch out for questions about this.

Q2 a) E.g.

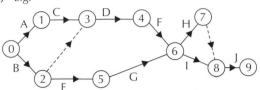

[5 marks available — 1 mark for 9 numbered nodes, 1 mark for each correctly placed dummy (2 dummies), 2 marks for other correct precedences. Lose 1 mark for each error.]

b) The dummy between nodes 2 and 3 is needed to show dependency (that D depends on B and C, but E depends on B only). *[1 mark]*

The dummy between nodes 7 and 8 is needed so that all activities are uniquely represented in terms of their events. *[1 mark]*

Q3 a)

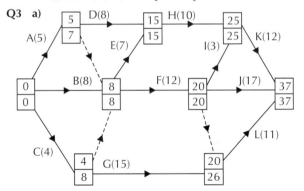

[3 marks available — 1 mark for every 2 correct numbers.]

b) BEHK *[1 mark]*, BFJ *[1 mark]*.

c) $\frac{112}{37} = 3.03$ *[1 mark]*, so rounding up, the lower bound is 4 *[1 mark]*.

d) H (critical activity between day 15 and day 25) *[1 mark]*
I (takes 3 days, and must start on day 21, 22 or 23) *[1 mark]*
J (critical activity between day 20 and day 37) *[1 mark]*

e) From c) you know you need a minimum of 4 workers. E.g.

	0	4	8	12	16	20	24	28	32	36
Worker 1	B		E		H		K			
Worker 2	A		F			J				
Worker 3	C		D		I					
Worker 4		G			L					

[3 marks available — 1 mark for every 4 correctly scheduled activities.]

f) No. *[1 mark]*
D won't be finished until day 22. Critical activity H must start after 15 days, and depends on D being completed. *[1 mark]*

Chapter 5: Linear Programming

1. Linear Programs

Exercise 1.1 — Definitions

Q1 a) The decision variables are x and y.
The objective function is $P = 5x + 7y$, which is to be maximised.
The constraints are the inequalities that x and y are subject to ($5x + 2y < 4$, $x + y \geq 1$, $x, y \geq 0$).

b) The decision variables are h and a.
The objective function is $C = 200h + 250a$, which is to be minimised.
The constraints are the inequalities that h and a are subject to ($50h + 20a \leq 1200$, $h + a \leq 30$, $h, a \geq 0$).

c) The decision variables are x, y and z.
The objective function is $W = 2x + 3y + 4z$, which is to be maximised.
The constraints are the inequalities that x, y and z are subject to ($x, y, z > 0$, $3x - y + z \leq 0$, $2x \geq y$).

Q2 Non-negativity constraints mean that a decision variable must be equal to or greater than zero, and are needed when it's impossible for one of the decision variables to be negative. For example, if you're producing toys, you can't have a negative number of stuffed monkeys.

Q3 a) The decision variables are x (number of home shirts) and y (number of away shirts).

b) The objective function is profit, £P (where $P = 2x + 1.5y$), which will be maximised.

c) The problem does need non-negativity constraints, as you can't produce a negative number of football shirts: $x, y \geq 0$.

d) The total number of shirts produced can't be more than 900 (i.e. $x + y \leq 900$).
They must make at least twice as many home shirts (x) as away shirts (y) (i.e. $x \geq 2y$).

Exercise 1.2 — Setting up linear programming problems

Q1 The objective function is £C (cost) which is to be minimised, where heating elements (x) cost £2 and frothing motors (y) cost £3. This is subject to the constraints:
They must buy at least 5 of each component (from $x, y \geq 5$).
The total number of components they buy can't be more than 20 (from $x + y \leq 20$).

The number of heating elements added to twice the number of motors they buy can't exceed 30 (from $x + 2y \leq 30$).

They cannot buy more than 5 motors for every 3 heating elements (from $3y \leq 5x$) OR they must buy at least 3 heating elements for every 5 motors.

Q2 a)

MP3 Player Size	Software	Q–control	Profit (£)
16GB	5	2	40
32GB	3	3	30
Total minutes	180	150	

b) £P = 40x + 30y

You want the profit, so you need to look at how much money each makes to form the objective function, not how long they take to make.

c) $5x + 3y \leq 180$
$2x + 3y \leq 150$
$x, y \geq 0$

Remember to include non-negativity constraints even if they're not mentioned in the question (as long as it makes sense to have them).

Q3 The shop will want to spend as little as possible on buying fireworks, so the objective function is cost: £C = 3x + 6y, which is to be minimised.

Minimise   £C = 3x + 6y
Subject to $x + y \geq 90$
                $x \geq 2y$
                $0 < x \leq 120$
                $0 < y \leq 80$

The $x \geq 2y$ comes from the fact that they'll sell at least twice as many small boxes (x) as big boxes (y). This means if you double the number of big boxes (i.e. 2y) it will still be smaller than or equal to the number of big boxes (x).
$0 < x \leq 120$ means x is between 0 and 120, but be careful with the signs — the shop will sell some of each box and so x can't be 0, so use < instead of ≤.

2. Solving Linear Programming Problems

Exercise 2.1 — Feasible regions

Q1 a), b)

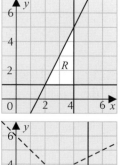

Q2 a), b)

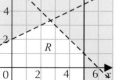

Q3 $x \leq 4$ $y \leq x + 2$ $y > 4 - x$ $(x, y \geq 0)$

Q4 $y < 4$ $2y \leq 12 - x$ (or $y \leq 6 - \frac{x}{2}$) $(x, y \geq 0)$

Q5 a), b)

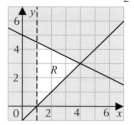

Q6 a) $2d \geq 3c$ $3c + 2d \leq 120$ $c, d \geq 0$
In $y = mx + c$ form, the inequalities become $d \geq 1.5c$ and $d \leq -1.5c + 60$

b)

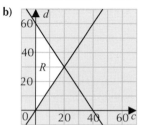

Q7 a) $y \leq x + 40$ $2y + x < 170$ (gradient = $-\frac{1}{2}$, y-intercept = 85)

b)

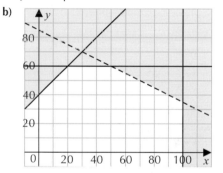

c) The two non-negativity constraints: $x, y \geq 0$

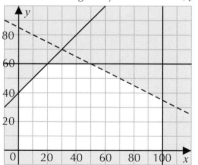

Q8 $x, y \geq 0$; $y \leq 100$; $5y + 4x \leq 800$

(gradient $= \frac{160}{-200} = -\frac{4}{5}$, y-intercept $= 160$);

$2y + 5x < 700$ (gradient $= \frac{0 - 100}{140 - 100} = -\frac{5}{2}$; using

$y = mx + c$ to find c: $0 = -2.5(140) + c \Rightarrow c = 350$);

$y < 2x - 20$ (gradient $= \frac{100 - 20}{60 - 20} = 2$,

y-intercept $= -20$)

Even though you can't see that $x \geq 0$ from the graph, the context shows you need non-negativity constraints.

You could also write some of the inequalities in different forms — e.g. $5y + 4x \leq 800$ could be $y \leq 160 - \frac{4}{5}x$.

Exercise 2.2 — Optimal solutions — the objective line method

Q1 a)

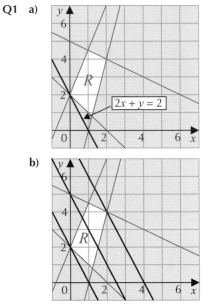

b)

Q2 a) Starting with objective line $6 = 2x + 3y$

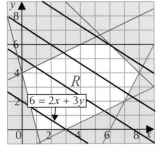

The last point within the feasible region that the lines touch is (6, 6), so the highest value Z can take is $(2 \times 6) + (3 \times 6) = 30$.

b) Starting with objective line $6 = 3x + 2y$

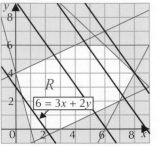

The last point within the feasible region that the lines touch is (8, 4), so the highest value Z can take is $(3 \times 8) + (2 \times 4) = 32$.

c) Starting with objective line $0 = 3x - 2y$

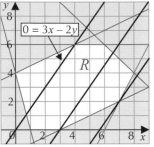

The last point within the feasible region that the lines touch is (7, 2), so the highest value Z can take is $(3 \times 7) - (2 \times 2) = 17$.

Q3 a) Starting with objective line $24 = 4x + 3y$

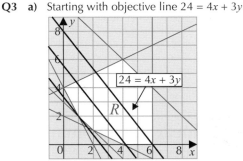

The last point within the feasible region that the lines touch is (1, 2), so the lowest value Z can take is $(4 \times 1) + (3 \times 2) = 10$.

b) Starting with objective line $20 = 2x + 5y$

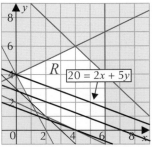

The last point within the feasible region that the lines touch is (4, 0), so the lowest value Z can take is $(2 \times 4) + (5 \times 0) = 8$.

c) Starting with the objective line $6 = 3x + y$

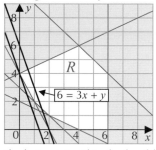

The last point within the feasible region that the lines touch is $(0, 4)$, so the lowest value Z can take is $(3 \times 0) + 4 = 4$.

Q4 a)

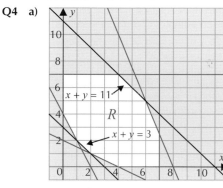

b) Starting with the objective line $6 = 3x + 2y$

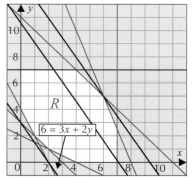

The last point within the feasible region that the lines touch is $(6, 5)$, so the highest value T can take is $(3 \times 6) + (2 \times 5) = 28$. So the maximum takings are £28, when $x = 6$ and $y = 5$.

c) Starting with the objective line $12 = x + 4y$

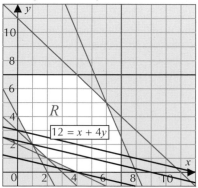

The last point within the feasible region that the lines touch is $(4, 0)$, so the lowest value C can take is $4 + (4 \times 0) = 4$. So the minimum cost is £4, when $x = 4$ and $y = 0$.

Q5 a)

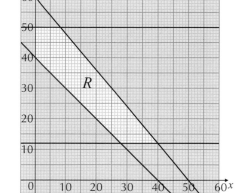

b) Starting with the objective line $60 = 0.8x + 1.2y$

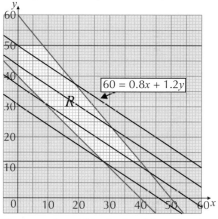

The last point within the feasible region that the lines touch is $(28, 12)$, so the lowest value C can take is $(0.8 \times 28) + (1.2 \times 12) = 36.8$

Q6 a) The objective function is $£P = 2x + 5y$, which is to be maximised.

b) The insecticide constraint is $2x + 8y \leq 1000$. Simplifying, this becomes $x + 4y \leq 500$.

c) $4x + 5y \leq 1000$ (water constraint)
$x + 2y \leq 300$ (land constraint)
$x, y \geq 0$ (non-negativity constraint)

d)

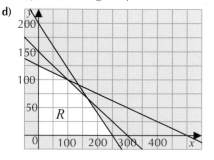

e) Starting with the objective line $500 = 2x + 5y$

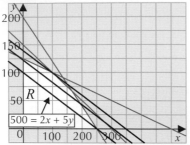

The last point within the feasible region that the lines touch is (100, 100), so the highest value £P can take is $(2 \times 100) + (5 \times 100) = £700$. This can be achieved by planting 100 indoor trees and 100 outdoor trees.

Exercise 2.3 — Optimal solutions — the vertex method

Q1 a) $y = 2x - 3$ (1) and $y = 6 - x$ (2)
Sub (2) into (1): $6 - x = 2x - 3 \Rightarrow x = 3$
Sub into (2): $y = 6 - 3 \Rightarrow y = 3$

b) $x + 4y = 14$ (1) and $9x - 2y + 26 = 0$ (2)
Rearrange (1): $x = 14 - 4y$
Sub into (2): $9(14 - 4y) - 2y + 26 = 0 \Rightarrow y = 4$
Sub into (1): $x + 16 = 14 \Rightarrow x = -2$

c) $2y = 4x - 19$ (1) and $6x + 2y - 23 = 0$ (2)
Sub (1) into (2): $6x + 4x - 19 - 23 = 0 \Rightarrow x = 4.2$
Sub into (1) $2y = 16.8 - 19 \Rightarrow y = -1.1$

Q2 At vertex A (0, 4), $P = (2 \times 0) + (3 \times 4) = 12$
At vertex B (5, 2), $P = (2 \times 5) + (3 \times 2) = 16$
At vertex C (3, 1), $P = (2 \times 3) + (3 \times 1) = 9$
So B would maximise P and C would minimise P.

Q3 a)

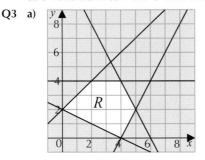

b) At (0, 2), $Z = 0 + (5 \times 2) = 10$
At (2, 4), $Z = 2 + (5 \times 4) = 22$
At (4, 4), $Z = 4 + (5 \times 4) = 24$
At (5, 2), $Z = 5 + (5 \times 2) = 15$
At (4, 0), $Z = 4 + 0 = 4$
So the maximum value of Z is 24 at (4, 4).

Q4 a)

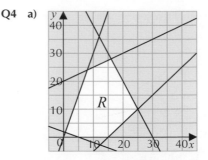

b) The (25, 10) coordinate is at the intersection between $x - y = 15$ (1) and $2x + y = 60$ (2)
Rearrange (1): $x = 15 + y$
Sub into (2): $30 + 2y + y = 60 \Rightarrow y = 10$
Sub into (1): $x - 10 = 15 \Rightarrow x = 25$
So the coordinates of the vertex are (25, 10)

The (16, 28) coordinate is at the intersection between $x - 2y + 40 = 0$ (1) and $2x + y = 60$ (2)
Rearrange (1): $x = 2y - 40$
Sub into (2): $4y - 80 + y = 60 \Rightarrow y = 28$
Sub into (1): $x - 56 + 40 = 0 \Rightarrow x = 16$
So the coordinates of the vertex are (16, 28)

c) At (25, 10), $P = (3 \times 25) + (7 \times 10) = 145$
At (16, 28), $P = (3 \times 16) + (7 \times 28) = 244$
So (16, 28) gives the optimal solution.

Q5 a)

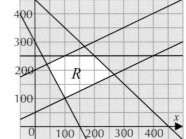

b) At (100, 250), $C = (3 \times 100) + 250 = 550$
At (200, 250), $C = (3 \times 200) + 250 = 850$
Use simultaneous equations to find the coordinates of the other vertices:
At (40, 220), $C = (3 \times 40) + 220 = 340$
At (100, 100), $C = (3 \times 100) + 100 = 400$
At $(\frac{800}{3}, \frac{550}{3})$, $C = (3 \times \frac{800}{3}) + \frac{550}{3} = 983\frac{1}{3}$
So the optimal solution is at (40, 220), where $C = 340$.

Q6 a) Let x be the number of steam trains and y be the number of electric trains:

Maximise $\quad £P = 32x + 20y$
Subject to $\quad x, y \geq 0$
$\qquad\qquad\qquad x + y \leq 60$
$\qquad\qquad\qquad 2x + y \leq 100$
$\qquad\qquad\qquad x + 4y \leq 180$

b) First plot the constraints on a graph:

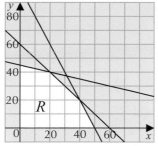

At $(0, 0)$, $P = 0$
At $(0, 45)$, $£P = 0 + (20 \times 45) = £900$
At $(20, 40)$, $£P = (32 \times 20) + (20 \times 40) = £1440$
At $(40, 20)$, $£P = (32 \times 40) + (20 \times 20) = £1680$
At $(50, 0)$, $£P = (32 \times 50) + 0 = £1600$

So 40 steam trains and 20 electric trains should be made, making £1680 profit.

Q7 a) Minimise $£C = 2x + 4y$
Subject to $x, y \geq 0$
$x + y \geq 30$
$x + y \leq 70$
$5y \geq 2x$
$y \leq 2x - 20$

b)

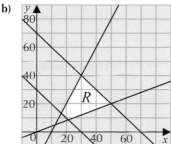

At $(30, 40)$, $£C = (2 \times 30) + (4 \times 40) = £220$
At $(50, 20)$, $£C = (2 \times 50) + (4 \times 20) = £180$
Use simultaneous equations to find the coordinates of the other two vertices.
At $(\frac{50}{3}, \frac{40}{3})$, $£C = £86.67$
At $(\frac{150}{7}, \frac{60}{7})$, $£C = £77.14$

So the optimal solution is at $(\frac{150}{7}, \frac{60}{7})$, costing a total of £77.14.

c) This solution isn't very realistic as the company would not be able to make a fraction of an ornament.
If the optimal solution is a decimal or fraction and you need a whole number, you need to find the optimal integer solution — there's more on this in the next section.

Exercise 2.4 — Optimal integer solutions

Q1 a) $2y + 3x \leq 12$ and $6y + 5x \leq 30$

b) Find the coordinates by solving simultaneous equations $2y + 3x = 12$ (1) and $6y + 5x = 30$ (2).
Rearrange (1): $2y = 12 - 3x \Rightarrow 6y = 36 - 9x$
Sub into (2): $36 - 9x + 5x = 30 \Rightarrow x = \frac{3}{2}$
Sub into (1): $2y + \frac{9}{2} = 12 \Rightarrow y = \frac{15}{4}$
so the coordinates of the vertex are $(\frac{3}{2}, \frac{15}{4})$ $= (1.5, 3.75)$

c) $Z = (4 \times \frac{3}{2}) + (3 \times \frac{15}{4}) = \frac{69}{4}$

d) At $(1, 3)$, $Z = (4 \times 1) + (3 \times 3) = 13$
At $(1, 4)$, $Z = (4 \times 1) + (3 \times 4) = 16$
$(2, 4)$ is outside the feasible region.
At $(2, 3)$, $Z = (4 \times 2) + (3 \times 3) = 17$

e) The optimal integer solution is at $(2, 3)$, where $Z = 17$.

Q2 a) The constraints are: $3y + x \leq 15$
$6y + 5x \leq 36$
$y + 5x \leq 26$

Use simultaneous equations to find coordinates of A: $3y + x = 15$ (1) and $6y + 5x = 36$ (2)
Rearrange (1): $x = 15 - 3y$
Sub into (2): $6y + 75 - 15y = 36 \Rightarrow y = \frac{13}{3}$
Sub into (1): $13 + x = 15 \Rightarrow x = 2$
So the coordinates of A are $(2, \frac{13}{3})$ $(= (2, 4.33))$.
For B use $6y + 5x = 36$ (1) and $y + 5x = 26$ (2)
Subtract (2) from (1): $5y = 10 \Rightarrow y = 2$
Sub into (2): $2 + 5x = 26 \Rightarrow x = \frac{24}{5} = (4.8)$
So the coordinates of B are $(\frac{24}{5}, 2)$.

b) At A, $Z = (3 \times 2) + (5 \times \frac{13}{3}) - \frac{83}{3}$ $(= 27.6...)$
At B, $Z = (3 \times \frac{24}{5}) + (5 \times 2) = \frac{122}{5}$ $(= 24.4)$
So the optimal solution is at A.

c) So to find the optimal integer solution, look at the integer solutions around A.
At $(2, 4)$, $Z = (3 \times 2) + (5 \times 4) = 26$
$(2, 5)$ isn't within the feasible region
So the optimal integer solution is at $(2, 4)$, where $Z = 26$.

Q3 a)

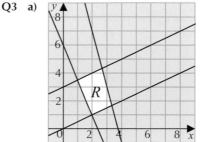

b) First find the coordinates of the points of intersection using simultaneous equations.

At $(2, 1)$, $Z = 2 + (5 \times 1) = 7$

At $(1, \frac{7}{2})$, $Z = 1 + (5 \times \frac{7}{2}) = \frac{37}{2}$ $(= 18.5)$

At $(\frac{8}{3}, \frac{13}{3})$, $Z = \frac{8}{3} + (5 \times \frac{13}{3}) = \frac{73}{3}$ $(24.3...)$

At $(\frac{10}{3}, \frac{5}{3})$, $Z = \frac{10}{3} + (5 \times \frac{5}{3}) = \frac{35}{3}$ $(= 11.6...)$

So the optimal solution is at $(\frac{8}{3}, \frac{13}{3})$

$(= (2.67, 4.33))$, where $Z = \frac{73}{3}$

You could have used the objective line method here — it would actually have been quicker, as you'd only have to solve one pair of simultaneous equations.

c) At $(2, 4)$, $Z = 2 + (5 \times 4) = 22$
$(2, 5)$ isn't within the feasible region.
$(3, 4)$ isn't within the feasible region.
$(3, 5)$ isn't within the feasible region.

So the optimal integer solution is at $(2, 4)$.

Q4 a)

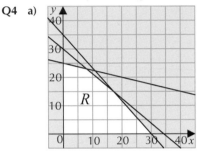

b) At $(0, 0)$, $Z = 0$
At $(0, 25)$, $Z = 0 + (8 \times 25) = 200$
At $(30, 0)$, $Z = (9 \times 30) + 0 = 270$

Use simultaneous equations to find the coordinates of the other two vertices $((8, 23)$ and $(\frac{120}{7}, 15))$.

At $(8, 23)$, $Z = (9 \times 8) + (8 \times 23) = 256$

At $(\frac{120}{7}, 15)$, $Z = (9 \times \frac{120}{7}) + (8 \times 15) = 274.2...$

So the optimal solution is at $(\frac{120}{7}, 15)$.

To find the optimal integer solution, look at points around this vertex with integer values:

At $(17, 15)$, $Z = (9 \times 17) + (8 \times 15) = 273$
$(18, 15)$ is not within the feasible region

So the optimal integer solution is at $(17, 15)$, where $Z = 273$.

Q5 a)

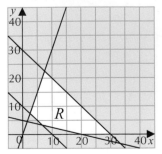

b) Using the objective line method, with starting line $75 = 3x + 5y$

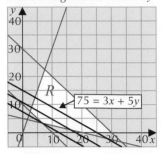

The optimal solution is at the intersection point between the lines $x + 4y = 20$ and $10 = x + y$ $(\frac{20}{3}, \frac{10}{3})$. To find the optimal integer solution, look at points around the vertex with integer values.

$(6, 3)$ isn't inside the feasible region.
At $(6, 4)$, $C = (3 \times 6) + (5 \times 4) = 38$
$(7, 3)$ isn't inside the feasible region.
At $(7, 4)$, $C = (3 \times 7) + (5 \times 4) = 41$

So the optimal integer solution is at $(6, 4)$.
You could have used the vertex method instead here — but the objective line method meant you had to solve fewer simultaneous equations.

Q6 a) Let x be the number of basic calculators and y be the number of scientific calculators.

Maximise $£P = 2.8x + 4.6y$
Subject to $x + y \leq 70$
$x + 3y \leq 135$
$4x + y \leq 240$
$x, y \geq 0$

b)

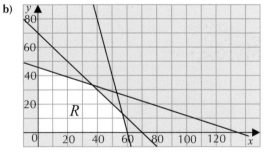

c) At $(0, 0)$, $£P = £0$
At $(60, 0)$, $£P = (2.8 \times 60) + 0 = £168$
At $(0, 45)$, $£P = 0 + (4.6 \times 45) = £207$
Use simultaneous equations to find the coordinates of the other vertices.

At $(\frac{75}{2}, \frac{65}{2})$, $£P = (2.8 \times \frac{75}{2}) + (4.6 \times \frac{65}{2})$
$= £254.50$

At $(\frac{170}{3}, \frac{40}{3})$, $£P = (2.8 \times \frac{170}{3}) + (4.6 \times \frac{40}{3})$
$= £220$

So the optimal solution is at $(\frac{75}{2}, \frac{65}{2})$
$(= (37.5, 32.5))$

To find the optimal integer solution, look at points around the vertex with integer values.

At (37, 32), $£P = £250.80$
(37, 33) is not in the feasible region
At (38, 32), $£P = £253.60$
(38, 33) is not in the feasible region

So the optimal integer solution is at (38, 32). The maximum profit of £253.60 is achieved by manufacturing 38 basic and 32 scientific calculators.

Q7 a) Minimise $£C = 6000x + 3000y$
Subject to $4 \le x + y \le 14$
$\qquad\qquad 3y \le 5x$
$\qquad\qquad x, y \ge 0$

b)

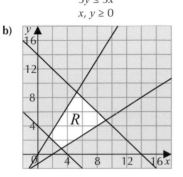

Use simultaneous equations to find the coordinates of the vertices.

At $(\frac{3}{2}, \frac{5}{2})$, $£C = (6000 \times \frac{3}{2}) + (3000 \times \frac{5}{2}) = £16\ 500$

At $(\frac{21}{4}, \frac{35}{4})$, $£C = (6000 \times \frac{21}{4}) + (3000 \times \frac{35}{4})$
$\qquad\qquad\qquad = £57\ 750$

At $(\frac{16}{5}, \frac{4}{5})$, $£C = (6000 \times \frac{16}{5}) + (3000 \times \frac{4}{5})$
$\qquad\qquad\qquad = £21\ 600$

At $(\frac{46}{5}, \frac{24}{5})$, $£C = (6000 \times \frac{46}{5}) + (3000 \times \frac{24}{5})$
$\qquad\qquad\qquad = £69\ 600$

So the optimal solution is at $(\frac{3}{2}, \frac{5}{2})$ (= (1.5, 2.5)).
To find the optimal integer solution, look at points around the vertex with integer values.

(1, 2) is not in the feasible region.
(1, 3) is not in the feasible region.
At (2, 2), $£C = (6000 \times 2) + (3000 \times 2) = £18\ 000$.
At (2, 3), $£C = (6000 \times 2) + (3000 \times 3) = £21\ 000$.

So the optimal integer solution is to manufacture 2 offroaders and 2 hatchbacks per production run.

Review Exercise — Chapter 5

Q1 Minimise $\qquad £C = 300x + 200y$
Subject to the constraints $\qquad x \ge 5$
$\qquad\qquad\qquad\qquad\qquad\qquad y \ge 10$
$\qquad\qquad\qquad\qquad\qquad\qquad x + y \ge 20$
$\qquad\qquad\qquad\qquad\qquad\qquad 5x + 2y > 60$

Q2 $x, y \ge 0$
$\quad y \le 4$
$\quad x + 2y \le 14$
$\quad 3y - 2x < 2$

Q3 a) They must produce at least 100 packs of each variety every day.
They can't produce more than 500 packs in total.
For every 2 jumbo packs they want to make at least 1 standard pack.
They don't want to make more than 3 standard packs for every jumbo pack.

b)

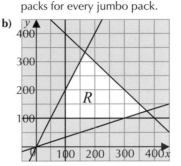

Q4 a) Starting with the objective line $1 = x + y$

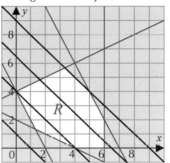

The last point within the feasible region that the lines touch is a line segment, so the optimal solution can be any point along this line segment — e.g (4, 5) or (5, 4).
So the largest value Z can take is $4 + 5 = 9$.

b) Starting with the objective line $10 = 2x + 5y$

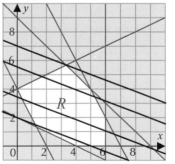

The last point within the feasible region that the lines touch is the crossing point between the lines $x + y = 9$ (1) and $2y - x = 8$ (2), so use simultaneous equations to find its coordinates:
Rearrange (1): $x = 9 - y$
Sub into (2): $2y - 9 + y = 8 \Rightarrow y = \frac{17}{3}$
Sub into (1): $x + \frac{17}{3} = 9 \Rightarrow x = \frac{10}{3}$
So the coordinates of the optimal solution are $(\frac{10}{3}, \frac{17}{3})$, and the highest value Z can take is
$(2 \times \frac{10}{3}) + (5 \times \frac{17}{3}) = 35$.

c) Starting with the objective line $4 = 4x + y$

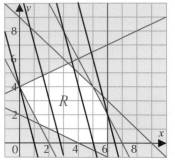

The last point within the feasible region that the objective lines touch is $(6, 2)$, so the highest value Z can take is $(4 \times 6) + 2 = 26$.

Q5 a)

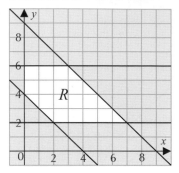

b) Starting with the objective line $6 = 3x + 2y$

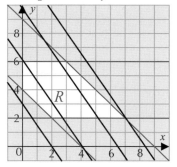

The last point within the feasible region that the lines touch is $(7, 2)$, so the largest value Z can take is $(3 \times 7) + (2 \times 2) = 25$

Q6 a) Let x be the number of square screen models and y be the number of widescreen models produced.
Maximise $£P = 40x + 32y$
Subject to $x + y \leq 25$
$0 \leq y \leq 10$; $x \geq 0$
$x + 2y \leq 30$

b)

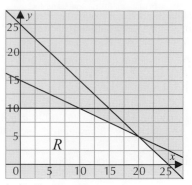

At $(0, 0)$, $£P = £0$
At $(0, 10)$, $£P = 0 + (32 \times 10) = £320$
At $(10, 10)$, $£P = (40 \times 10) + (32 \times 10) = £720$
At $(20, 5)$, $£P = (40 \times 20) + (32 \times 5) = £960$
At $(25, 0)$, $£P = (40 \times 25) + 0 = £1000$

So the optimal solution is at $(25, 0)$ — the company should make only square screen models.
Here you can see that linear programming doesn't always give a realistic solution — the company would probably still want to make some widescreen models. We'd need more constraints to get a more realistic model.

Q7 a)

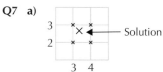

b) Not all points would necessarily need to be tested as some may not lie inside the feasible region.

Q8 a) Let x = number of large posters and y = number of small posters.
Maximise profit, $P = 6x + 3.5y$,
subject to the constraints:
$10x + 5y \leq 250 \Rightarrow 2x + y \leq 50$
$6x + 4y \leq 200 \Rightarrow 3x + 2y \leq 100$
$x \geq y, y \geq 10$ and $x, y \geq 0$.
You could use x for the number of small posters and y for the number of large posters instead — so x and y in each inequality would just swap round.

b)

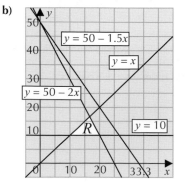

c) E.g. starting with the objective line for $P = 42$ (which goes through (0, 12) and (7, 0)) and moving it towards R gives:

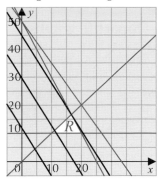

So the final point in the feasible region touched by the objective line is the point of intersection of the lines $y = x$ and $y = 50 - 2x$. Solving these simultaneous equations gives the point of intersection as $(\frac{50}{3}, \frac{50}{3})$. Putting these values into the objective function gives a maximum profit of £158.33.

You can choose any value of P as a starting value — 42 makes it easy to draw the line. This answer uses the objective line method, but you could have used the vertex method instead.

d) From part c) above, the maximum profit is found at $(\frac{50}{3}, \frac{50}{3})$. However, you can't have fractions of a poster, so an integer solution is required. The points with integer coordinates nearby are (16,16), (16,17), (17, 17) and (17, 16). (16, 17) doesn't satisfy the constraint $x \geq y$ and (17, 17) doesn't satisfy the constraint $y \leq 50 - 2x$. The value of the objective function at (16, 16) is £152 and at (17, 16) it's £158, so (17, 16) gives the maximum solution.

Exam-Style Questions — Chapter 5

Q1 The objective function is cost, $C = 0.75x + 0.6y$ in £ (or $C = 75x + 60y$ in pence) *[1 mark]* which is to be minimised *[1 mark]* (where x is the number of red roses and y is the number of white roses), subject to the constraints:

$x, y > 0$ *[1 mark]* (from the statement that she will sell both red and white roses — x and y can't be 0).

$x > y$ *[1 mark]* (from the statement that she will sell more red roses than white roses).

$x + y \geq 100$ *[1 mark]* (from the statement that she will sell a total of at least 100 flowers).

$x \leq 300$ *[1 mark]* and $y \leq 200$ *[1 mark]* (from the statement that the wholesaler has 300 red roses and 200 white roses).

Don't waste time trying to solve these inequalities — the question doesn't ask for a solution. Just write them down.

Q2 a) The solid line that passes through (0, 6) and (3, 0) has equation $y = 6 - 2x$, and as the area below the line is shaded, the inequality is $2x + y \geq 6$. The dotted line that passes through (2, 0) has equation $y = x - 2$, and as the area below the line is shaded, the inequality is $x - y < 2$. The horizontal solid line that passes through (0, 4) has the equation $y = 4$, and as the area above the line is shaded, the inequality is $y \leq 4$.
[4 marks available — 1 mark for each line equation and 1 mark for all inequality signs correct]

b) The coordinates of the vertices of R are (1, 4) (the intersection of the lines $y = 4$ and $y = 6 - 2x$) *[1 mark]*, (6, 4) (the intersection of the lines $y = 4$ and $y = x - 2$) *[1 mark]* and $(\frac{8}{3}, \frac{2}{3})$ *[1 mark]* (the intersection of the lines $y = 6 - 2x$ and $y = x - 2$) *[1 mark for solving the simultaneous equations]*.

c) The value of C at (1, 4) is 8, the value of C at (6, 4) is 28 and the value of C at $(\frac{8}{3}, \frac{2}{3})$ is $\frac{34}{3} = 11\frac{1}{3}$ *[1 mark for use of a correct method]*. Hence the minimum value of C is 8 *[1 mark]*, which occurs at the point (1, 4) *[1 mark]*.
This answer uses the vertex method, but you could also have used the objective line method to answer this question — pick whichever method you prefer.

Q3 a) There are 6 sheets of foil in a gold pack, so in x gold packs there will be $6x$ sheets of foil. There are 2 sheets of foil in a silver pack, so in y silver packs there will be $2y$ sheets of foil. There is 1 sheet of foil in a bronze pack, so in z bronze packs there will be z sheets of foil. There are 30 sheets of foil available, so the inequality is $6x + 2y + z \leq 30$
[2 marks — 1 mark for LHS, 1 mark for correct inequality sign and RHS].

Using the same method for sugar paper produces the inequality $15x + 9y + 6z \leq 120$ *[1 mark]*, which simplifies to give $5x + 3y + 2z \leq 40$ *[1 mark]*. For tissue paper, the inequality is $15x + 4y + z \leq 60$ *[2 marks — 1 mark for LHS, 1 mark for correct inequality sign and RHS]*. Finally, the amount of foil used is $6x + 2y + z$, and the amount of sugar paper used is $15x + 9y + 6z$. The amount of sugar paper used needs to be at least three times the amount of foil, so the inequality for this constraint is $15x + 9y + 6z \geq 3(6x + 2y + z)$ *[1 mark]*
$15x + 9y + 6z \geq 18x + 6y + 3z$
$3y + 3z \geq 3x$
$y + z \geq x$ *[1 mark]*

b) (i) If the number of silver packs sold is equal to the number of bronze packs, then $y = z$. Substituting this into the inequalities from part **a)** gives:

$6x + 2y + y \leq 30 \Rightarrow 6x + 3y \leq 30 \Rightarrow 2x + y \leq 10$

$5x + 3y + 2y \leq 40 \Rightarrow 5x + 5y \leq 40 \Rightarrow x + y \leq 8$

$15x + 4y + y \leq 60 \Rightarrow 15x + 5y \leq 60$
$\Rightarrow 3x + y \leq 12$

$y + y \geq x \Rightarrow 2y \geq x$

[3 marks available — 1 mark for making the correct substitution, 1 mark for correctly forming the inequalities and 1 mark for simplifying the inequalities.]

(ii)

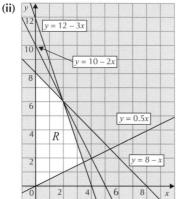

[5 marks available — 1 mark for each of the four inequality lines (with equations as shown on the graph) and 1 mark for correct feasible region]

(iii) Using the vertex method, the feasible region has vertices (0, 0) (the origin), (0, 8) (intersection of the y-axis and $y = 8 - x$), (2, 6) (intersection of $y = 8 - x$ and $y = 10 - 2x$) and $(\frac{24}{7}, \frac{12}{7})$ (intersection of $y = \frac{1}{2}x$ and $y = 12 - 3x$) *[1 mark]*. The number of packs made on Monday is $x + y + z = x + 2y$, so the numbers made at each vertex are 0, 16, 14 and $\frac{48}{7} = 6.857$, so the maximum number of packs made that day is 16 = 8 silver and 8 bronze *[1 mark]*.

You could have used the objective line method instead, using the line $Z = x + y + z = x + 2y$ to find the maximum.

(iv) The objective function is
$P = 3.5x + 2y + z = 3.5x + 2y + y = 3.5x + 3y$, which needs to be maximised. The value of P for each of the vertices found in part (iii) is £0, £24, £25 and £17.14 *[1 mark]*. The maximum value is £25 *[1 mark]*, which occurs at (2, 6), so the company needs to sell 2 gold packs, 6 silver packs and 6 bronze packs (as the number of bronze packs is equal to the number of silver packs) *[1 mark]*.

Chapter 6: Matchings

1. Matchings

Exercise 1.1 — Bipartite graphs

For all these questions, you can put the nodes in each set in any order, as long as the arcs still link the right ones.

Q1

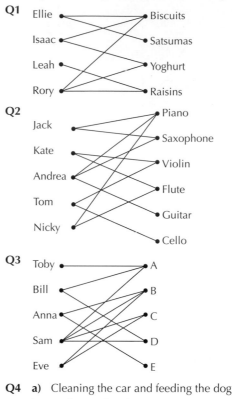

Q2

Q3

Q4 a) Cleaning the car and feeding the dog
  b) Dad, David and Karen
  c) Karen

Exercise 1.2 — Matchings

Q1 a)

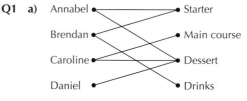

  b) Annabel = starter, Brendan = drinks, Caroline = main course, Daniel = dessert.
  Remember — you don't always have to draw the matching. Here, it's just been written out.

Q2 E.g.

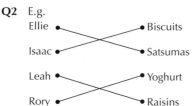

You might have ended up with a slightly different matching — Ellie = satsumas, Isaac = yoghurt, Leah = raisins and Rory = biscuits.

Q3 **a)**

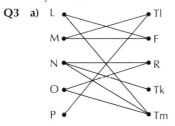

b) Lamarr = team member, Marcus = facilitator, Nadia = timekeeper, Oliver = recorder, Pippa – team leader

Q4

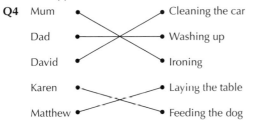

So the complete matching is Mum = ironing, Dad = washing up, David = cleaning the car, Karen = feeding the dog, Matthew = laying the table

Q5 **a)**

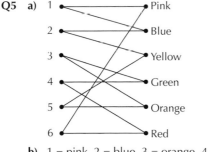

b) 1 = pink, 2 = blue, 3 = orange, 4 = green, 5 = yellow, 6 = red

Q6 Yes — e.g.

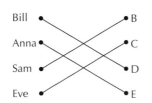

Sam and Eve could swap round and still produce a complete matching.

Q7 **a)**

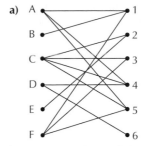

b) e.g. A = 4, B = 1, C = 3, D = 6, E = 2, F = 5
There are a few different complete matchings you could make here — but B, D and E can't change.

Q8 **a)**

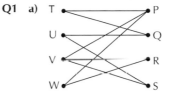

b) E.g. 1 = drink, 2 = food, 3 = music, 4 = decorations, 5 = tables/chairs
Again, there's more than one complete matching for this one.

2. Maximum Matchings
Exercise 2.1 — Alternating paths

Q1 **a)** T ●————● P
U ●————● Q
V ●————● R
W ●————● S

b) Initial matching: T — P, U — Q, V — R.
E.g. Alternating path: W - - R — V - - S (where — = in and - - = not in). Changing the status of the arcs: W — R - - V — S. So the new matching is T = P, U = Q, W = R, V = S.
If you'd started off with W - - P, you'd have ended up with a different alternating path and new matching.

Q2 Alternating path: E - - 1 — B - - 4. Changing the status of the arcs: E — 1 - - B — 4. So the improved matching is A = 2, B = 4, C = 3, D = 5, E = 1.

Q3 **a)**

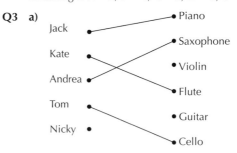

b) Alternating path: Nicky - - flute — Kate - - violin. Changing the status of the arcs: Nicky — flute - - Kate — violin. Improved matching: Jack = piano, Kate = violin, Andrea = saxophone, Tom = cello, Nicky = flute.

Q4 a)

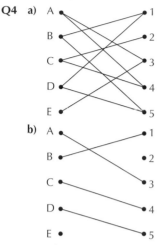

b)

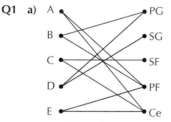

c) Alternating path: E - - 3 — A - - 4 — C - - 2. Changing the status of the arcs:
E —3 - - A — 4 - - C — 2.
So the improved matching is Alan = 4, Bobby = 1, Charlotte = 2, Dylan = 5 and Emily = 3.

Exercise 2.2 — Maximum matchings

Q1 a) A

B

C

D

E

PG

SG

SF

PF

Ce

Initial matching: A = PF, B = PG, C = Ce, D = SG.

b) Alternating path: E - - Ce — C - - SF. Changing the status of the arcs: E — Ce - - C — SF. So the improved matching is A = PF, B = PG, C = SF, D = SG, E = Ce. There are no more unmatched nodes so this is a maximum (and complete) matching.
This alternating path reaches a breakthrough the quickest — the other one takes longer, as you'll see below.

c) Alternating path: E - - PF — A - - Ce — C - - SF. Changing the status of the arcs: E — PF - - A — Ce - - C — SF. So the improved matching is A = Ce, B = PG, C = SF, D = SG, E = PF. There are no more unmatched nodes so this is a maximum (and complete) matching.

Q2 Initial matching 1 = pink, 2 = yellow, 3 = orange, 4 = red. Alternating path: 5 - - yellow — 2 - - blue. Changing the status of the arcs: 5 — yellow - - 2 — blue. So the new matching is 1 = pink, 2 = blue, 3 = orange, 4 = red, 5 = yellow. There are still 2 unmatched nodes (6 and green) so you need another alternating path:

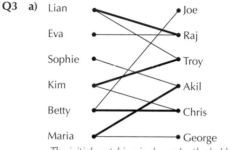

pink — 1 - - blue

6

red — 4 - - green   Breakthrough

Changing the status of the arcs: 6 — red - - 4 — green.
So the improved matching is 1 = pink, 2 = blue, 3 = orange, 4 = green, 5 = yellow, 6 = red. There are no more unmatched nodes, so this is a maximum (and complete) matching.
You could have found the alternating path from 6 first, then the one from 5. If you'd followed through the alternating path starting 6 - - pink, you'd have found that it failed when it got to 5, as 5 can only be yellow.

Q3 a) Lian

Eva

Sophie

Kim

Betty

Maria

Joe

Raj

Troy

Akil

Chris

George

The initial matching is shown by the bold arcs on the bipartite graph.

b) E.g. Alternating path: Eva - - Raj — Lian - - Troy — Kim - - Chris — Betty - - Joe. Changing the status of the arcs: Eva — Raj - - Lian — Troy - - Kim — Chris - - Betty — Joe. So the improved matching is Lian = Troy, Eva = Raj, Kim = Chris, Betty = Joe, Maria = Akil.
There are still two unmatched nodes, so find another alternating path: Sophie - - Akil — Maria - - George. Changing the status of the arcs: Sophie — Akil - - Maria — George. So the improved matching is Lian = Troy, Eva = Raj, Sophie = Akil, Kim = Chris, Betty = Joe, Maria = George. There are no more unmatched nodes, so this is a maximum (and complete) matching.

Q4 E.g. Alternating path: B - - 1 — A - - 4 — D - - 6. Changing the status of the arcs: B — 1 - - A — 4 - - D — 6. So the improved matching is A = 4, B = 1, C = 2, D = 6, F = 5. There are still two unmatched nodes, so find another alternating path from E: E - - 2 — C - - 3. Changing the status of the arcs: E — 2 - - C — 3. The improved matching is A = 4, B = 1, C = 3, D = 6, E = 2, F = 5. There are no more unmatched nodes, so this is a maximum (and complete) matching.

Review Exercise — Chapter 6

Q1 **a)** Anya, Elodie and Alex

b) Anya

c) German and Italian

Q2 **a)**

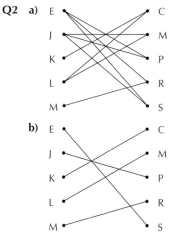

b)

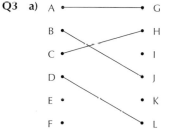

So E = S, J = P, K = C, L = M, M = R.
An alternative complete matching would start with E = P and J = S. Kitty, Lydia and Mary can't change.

These are both complete matchings — it shows that you can have more than one.

Q3 **a)**

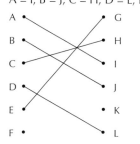

b) Find an alternating path starting from E:
E - - G — A - - I (where - - = not in, — = in).
(You could have done E - - H — C - - K instead — it reaches a breakthrough just as quickly.)
Changing the status of the arcs gives:
E — G - - A — I
Construct the improved matching:
A = I, B = J, C = H, D = L, E = G

A •⟍⟋• G
B •⟋⟍• H
C •⟋ • I
D •⟍ • J
E • • K
F • • L

Now try and find an alternating path from F to K:

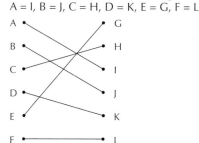

.•L — D - - K   Breakthrough
F⟨
⟩•J — B - - I

The path F - - L — D - - K reaches a breakthrough first, so use this one (if you found a path from E to K in your first alternating path, the second path would be F - - J — B - - I).
Changing the status of the arcs: F — L - - D — K
Construct the improved matching:
A = I, B = J, C = H, D = K, E = G, F = L

A • • G
B • • H
C • • I
D • • J
E • • K
F •————————• L

There are no more unmatched nodes, so this is a complete matching.
An alternative complete matching would be A = G, B = I, C = K, D = L, E = H, F = J if you'd used the alternating paths in brackets.

Q4 **a)** There are more people than languages so a complete matching is not possible.

b) e.g.

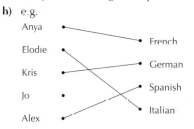

Anya •
Elodie •
Kris •
Jo •
Alex •
• French
• German
• Spanish
• Italian

Q5 **a)** The alternating path Satomi - - Marrakech — Hannah - - Barcelona — Tariq gets stuck at Tariq, as he has only visited Barcelona.

b) E.g. alternating path: Satomi - - Las Vegas — Damon - - Florence — Lisa - - Sydney. Changing the status of the arcs: Satomi — Las Vegas - - Damon — Florence - - Lisa — Sydney. So the improved matching is: Damon = Florence, Hannah = Marrakech, Lisa = Sydney, Satomi = Las Vegas, Tariq = Barcelona. There are still two unmatched nodes, so look for another alternating path: William - - Marrakech — Hannah - - Barcelona — Tariq. This path fails, and there is no alternating path that matches William to an unmatched node. This means that a complete matching is not possible, so the improved matching above is a maximum matching.

c) Lisa is the only person to have visited Sydney and Tokyo, so a complete matching is not possible.

d) e.g. alternating path:

Las Vegas — Damon - - Florence

Satomi
Marrakech — Hannah - - Sydney Breakthrough

Changing the status of the arcs: Satomi — Marrakech - - Hannah — Sydney, so the improved matching is: Damon = Las Vegas, Hannah = Sydney, Lisa = Florence, Satomi = Marrakech, Tariq = Barcelona. There are still two unmatched nodes, so find another alternating path: William - - Marrakech — Satomi - - Las Vegas — Damon - - Florence — Lisa - - Tokyo. Changing the status of the arcs: William — Marrakech - - Satomi — Las Vegas - - Damon — Florence - - Lisa — Tokyo. The improved matching is now: Damon = Florence, Hannah = Sydney, Lisa = Tokyo, Satomi = Las Vegas, Tariq = Barcelona, William = Marrakech. There are no more unmatched nodes, so this is a complete matching.

Q6 a)

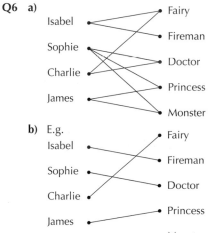

b) E.g.

This isn't the only possible matching.

You weren't actually asked to draw the matching here (you could have just written it out), but it'll come in handy for the rest of this question.

c) There are more costumes than children so a complete matching isn't possible.

d) There are now the same number of children as costumes, and a complete matching is now possible: E.g. Harvey = fireman, Isabel = fairy, Sophie = monster, Charlie = doctor, James = princess.

e)

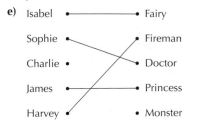

f) Alternating path:

Doctor — Sophie - - Monster Breakthrough

Charlie
Fairy — Isabel - - Fireman

Changing the status of the arcs: Charlie — doctor - - Sophie — monster. So the improved matching is: Isabel = fairy, Sophie = monster, Charlie = doctor, James = princess, Harvey = fireman. There are no more unmatched nodes, so this is a complete matching.

Exam-Style Question — Chapter 6

Q1 a) Alternating path is M - - 4 — J - - 2 (where - - = not in, — = in) *[1 mark]*.
Change the status of the arcs: M — 4 - - J — 2 *[1 mark]*
So in the new matching, Mia will teach class 4 and Jamal will teach class 2. Lee and Kelly are unchanged.
Construct the improved matching:
J = 2, K = 1, L = 3, M = 4 *[1 mark]*

b) Lee is the only person who can teach class 3 and the only person who can teach class 5, so both classes cannot be taught at the same time *[1 mark]*.

c) The improved matching from part a) is:

J • ╲ ╱ • 1
K • ╱ ╲ • 2
L • ———— • 3
M • ———— • 4
N •   • 5

Finding a new alternating path from N:

4 — M - - 3 — L - - 5 Breakthrough

N
1 — K - - 2 — J - - 4

The path N - - 4 — M - - 3 — L - - 5 reaches a breakthrough quicker, so use this one *[1 mark]*.
Change the status of the arcs: N — 4 - - M — 3 - - L — 5 *[1 mark]*.
Construct the improved matching:
Jamal = 2, Kelly = 1, Lee = 5, Mia = 3 and Nick = 4 *[1 mark]*

J • ╲ ╱ • 1
K • ╱ ╲ • 2
L • ╲ • 3
M • ╲ • 4
N • ╱ • 5

There are no more unmatched nodes, so this is a complete matching.

Glossary

A

Activity network
A **network** that shows the order in which activities must be completed. Activities are shown by **arcs** and their completion is shown by **nodes**.

Adjacency matrix
A matrix (number grid) that shows the number of links between each pair of **vertices** in a **graph**.

Algorithm
A set of instructions for solving a problem.

Alternating path
A way of improving an **initial matching**.

Arc
The line connecting two **vertices** of a **graph**. Also called an **edge**.

B

Binary search
A searching **algorithm** used to find items in an ordered list.

Bipartite graph
A graph with two sets of **nodes**, joined by **arcs**. The arcs only join nodes from one set to nodes in the other.

Breakthrough
Reaching an unmatched **node** using the **alternating path** method.

Bubble sort
An **algorithm** that sorts a list into order by systematically swapping terms.

C

Chinese postman problem
Another name for the **route inspection problem**.

Complete graph
A **graph** where every **vertex** has a direct connection to every other vertex.

Complete matching
A **matching** with the same number of **arcs** as there are **nodes** in each set.

Connected graph
A graph where every **vertex** is connected to every other vertex by a **path** (not necessarily a direct arc).

Constraint
A limiting factor in a **linear programming** problem. Usually written as an inequality in terms of the **decision variables**.

Critical activity
An activity in an **activity network** that must be started as soon as possible or the entire project will be delayed.

Critical path
A set of **critical activities** that run from **source node** to the **sink node**.

Cycle
A closed **path** through a **graph** that brings you back to your starting point. Also called a circuit.

D

Decision variable
An item that's being produced, bought, sold etc. in a **linear programming** problem.

Degree
The number of **edges** connected to a **vertex**.

Digraph
A **graph** in which some **edges** have a direction (known as directed **edges**).

Dijkstra's algorithm
A method for finding the shortest **path** between two **vertices** of a **network**.

Distance matrix
A matrix (number grid) that shows the distance (or **weight**) between each pair of **vertices** in a **graph**.

Dummy
A dummy shows precedence in an **activity network** without adding any activities to the project.

E

Early event time
The earliest an activity within a project can possibly be started.

Edge
The line connecting two **vertices** of a **graph**. Also called an **arc**.

Eulerian graph
A **graph** in which every **vertex** is even.

Even vertex
A **vertex** with an even **degree**.

F

Feasible region
An area on a graph in which all points are **feasible solutions** to a **linear programming** problem.

Feasible solution
A set of values that satisfies all the **constraints** in a **linear programming** problem.

First-fit algorithm.
An **algorithm** used to pack items into bins.

First-fit decreasing algorithm
A bin-packing **algorithm** similar to the **first-fit algorithm**, but used on an ordered list.

Float
The amount of time you can delay an activity for without delaying the project it's part of.

Flow chart
A way of visually representing an **algorithm**.

G

Gantt chart
A diagram that shows the time intervals in which activities can take place. Used for scheduling activities.

Graph
A diagram made up of points (called **vertices** or **nodes**) joined by lines (called **edges** or **arcs**).

Improved matching
A **matching** with more **arcs** than the **initial matching**, improved using an **alternating path**.

Initial matching
Any **matching** on a **bipartite graph**.

Inspection route
The shortest possible route through a **network** that crosses each **edge** at least once.

Kruskal's algorithm
A way of finding **minimum spanning trees** by adding **arcs** in order of **weight**.

Late event time
The latest an activity within a project can be started without delaying it.

Linear programming
A way of finding an **optimal solution** to a problem subject to **constraints**.

Lower bound (bin packing)
A minimum for the number of bins that items can be packed into. Items can't necessarily be packed into this number of bins though.

Lower bound (scheduling)
A minimum for the number of workers needed to complete a project within the critical time. The activities can't necessarily be done by this number of workers though.

Matching
A solution that assigns nodes on one side of a **bipartite graph** to nodes on the other side. Each node can have at most one arc coming from it.

Maximum matching
A **matching** that uses the greatest number of **arcs** possible.

Minimum spanning tree
A **spanning tree** of a graph with the smallest possible total **weight**. Also called a minimum connector.

Network
Another name for a **weighted graph**.

Node
The name given to the points on a **graph** (also called **vertices**).

Objective function
A function given in terms of the **decision variables** in a **linear programming** problem that you're trying to minimise or maximise, usually profit or cost.

Objective line method
A way of finding **optimal solutions** in **linear programming** problems by drawing lines on a graph.

Odd vertex
A **vertex** with an odd **degree**.

Optimal solution (bin packing)
A solution that uses the smallest number of bins possible.

Optimal solution (linear programming)
A solution that maximises or minimises the **objective function**.

Path
A route in a **graph** that doesn't go through a **vertex** more than once.

Pivot
An item chosen in sorting and searching algorithms, usually the 'middle item' of a list.

Precedence table
A table showing the immediately preceding activities of each activity.

Prim's algorithm
A way to find **minimum spanning trees** by adding the smallest adjacent arcs.

Quick sort
An **algorithm** that sorts a list into order by arranging the items around **pivots**.

Semi-Eulerian graph
A **graph** with exactly 2 odd vertices.

Sink node
The final node in an **activity network**. It marks the completion of a project.

Source node
The first node in an **activity network**. It marks the start of a project.

Spanning tree
A **subgraph** that includes all the **vertices** of the original **graph** and is a **tree**.

Subgraph
A **graph** where all the **vertices** and **edges** are from a larger **graph**.

Trace table
A table used to keep track of an **algorithm**.

Tree
A **connected graph** with no **cycles**.

V

Vertex/Vertices
The name given to the points on a **graph** (also called **nodes**).

Vertex method
A way of finding **optimal solutions** in a **linear programming** problem by testing every **vertex** of the **feasible region**.

W

Weight
The number associated with an **edge** of a weighted graph (or **network**), often relating to a distance.

Index

A

activity networks 85-108
adjacency matrices 41, 42
algorithms 1-26, 46-58, 146
   Dijkstra's 56-58
   Kruskal's 46, 47
   matching 146
   packing 18-26
   Prim's 49-54
   searching 16, 17
   sorting 10-14, 23
alternating paths 143-147
apple pie 83-85
arcs (or edges) 32-58, 66-76,
   85-101, 138-147

B

bin packing 18-26
binary search 16, 17
bipartite graphs 32, 34, 138-147
breakthrough 143-147
bubble sort 10, 11

C

cascade charts 99
Chinese postman problem 70
comparisons 10, 11
complete graphs 34
complete matchings 140-147
connected graphs 38, 39
constraints 114-131
critical path analysis 83-113
   critical activities 94-104
   critical events 94, 95
   critical nodes 94, 95
   critical paths 94-104
   critical time 91, 94, 105,
      107, 108
cycles 37, 39, 46, 47

D

decision variables 114-131
degree of a vertex 35, 66-68,
   72, 74
digraphs 33, 85-108
Dijkstra's algorithm 56-58
directed edges 33, 43, 44, 57
distance matrices 43, 44, 53, 54
dummies 87-89

E

early and late event times 90-99,
   104, 108
edges — see 'arcs'
Eulerian graphs 66-70

F

feasible regions 114, 119-131
feasible solutions 114, 119-131
first-fit algorithm 20-26
first-fit decreasing algorithm
   23, 24
floats 97-104
flow charts 5-7
full-bin packing algorithm 26

G

Gantt charts 99-107
graphs 32-40, 138
   bipartite graphs 32, 34,
      138-147
   complete graphs 34
   digraphs 33, 85-108
   subgraphs 33, 40
greedy algorithm 46

I

immediately preceding activities
   83-89
inequalities 114-131
initial matchings 143-147
inputs 1-7
instructions 1
integer solutions 130, 131

K

Königsberg bridges 68
Kruskal's algorithm 46, 47

L

linear programming 114-131
loops 5, 6, 35
lower bounds 19, 21, 24, 26,
   107, 108

M

matchings 138-147
matrices
   adjacency 41, 42
   distance 43, 44, 53, 54
   Prim's algorithm 53, 54
maximum matching algorithm
   146, 147
maximum matchings 140-147
middle items 13, 16, 17
minimum spanning trees 46-54

N

networks — see 'weighted graphs'
nodes 32-58, 66-76, 85-95,
   138-147
non-Eulerian graphs 68, 74-76
non-negativity constraints 114,
   117, 119, 120

O

objective functions 114-131
objective line method 123, 124, 130, 131
optimal integer solutions 130, 131
optimal solutions 18-26, 114, 123-131
ordered lists 10-14, 16, 23
outputs 1-7

P

packing algorithms 18-26
passes 10, 11
paths 37
pivots 13, 14
precedence tables 83-89
Prim's algorithm 49-54

Q

quick sort 13, 14

R

route inspection problems 70-76
ruler method 123
Russian Peasant Algorithm 3, 5

S

scheduling 99-108
searching algorithms 16, 17
semi-Eulerian graphs 67, 72
shortest paths 56-58
shortest routes 70-76
simultaneous equations 124, 127, 128
sink nodes 85-95
sorting algorithms 10-14, 23
source nodes 85-95
spanning trees 40, 46-54
speed dating 148
stopping conditions 1, 7
subgraphs 33, 40

T

trace tables 2, 3, 6, 7
traversable graphs 66
tree diagrams 146, 147
trees 39-54

U

undirected edges 44

V

valency 35
vertex method 127-131
vertices 32-58, 66-76, 127-131, 138-147

W

weighted graphs (or networks) 33, 43-58, 70-76
working values 56-58

MED1T51